No. 515
$7.95

Small Appliance Repair Guide

By Wayne Lemons & Glen Montgomery

 TAB BOOKS

BLUE RIDGE SUMMIT, PA. 17214

FIRST EDITION

FIRST PRINTING — FEBRUARY 1970

Copyright © 1970 by TAB BOOKS

Printed in the United States
of America

Library of Congress Card Number: 76-105971

CONTENTS

PREFACE

Electrical appliance repair is a field in itself, related certainly to the manufacturer or the original assembly of the item but certainly subject to its own special problems. There is one thing, though, that is most helpful to any repairman. It can change him from a "fix-it" man into a specialist. It comes natural to some; it is learned through brute-force experience by others, while still others actively seek the necessary information. This "thing" is an insight into the overall operation of the unit as seen by the original designer. In other words, if you know what the designer was trying to do, repair methods will suggest themselves as you go along, and reassembly—correct reassembly—will be a good deal easier.

Of course this takes time, but if you are sincere about service of any sort, the only real way you can stay ahead of the game (as in anything else) is to know what's going on and leave the haphazard approach to the handyman who sometimes— almost by accident—makes a brilliant repair but more often than not just stumbles onto the obvious troubles, replaces parts unnecessarily when the trouble isn't obvious, and never develops a systematic approach required by any one seriously concerned in improving his native ability.

The question must be: What do you want to be? If you want to be a good technician, dig out all the information you can, from books like this, from manufacturers service manuals; make notes as you disassemble and reassemble unfamiliar pieces of equipment; try to determine what the original designer had in mind—just what did he set out to do and how did he do it?

Today, more than at any previous time, the service and repair field is crying for good technicians. All forecasts point to a constantly increasing need for good technicians as more and more appliances with progressively sophisticated designs hit the market and eventually need repair. Sure, there is and will be a number of "throwaway" items on which any major repair would be impractical or too expensive. You have to develop judgment on what should and what should not be repaired. For example, it's not good sense to run up a repair bill of say $7.50 on a $9.95 appliance. Try to become expert on the more expensive units since these will normally be the ones the customer can feel wise to have repaired rather than lay out considerable cash for a new one.

Develop good work habits, a systematic approach, keep up with new developments, and you can't help but find small appliance repair a rewarding business.

The authors wish to thank the following people who aided in various ways to make this book possible. Mr. John Fenton and Mr. Ernie Boyd, appliance servicemen, Empire District Electric Co., Joplin Mo. Mr. Keith Kendall who took many of the pictures or prepared the prints. Mr. Keith Cully, whose cooperation resulted in the new appliance photographs. Mr. C. B. Boeckman, Mar-Beck Appliance, Kansas City. Lowell Kahler, manager of Kahler Electric Co., Buffalo, Mo., where some of the pictures were taken. Mr. John McDermott, Kansas City, Secretary. National Appliance Service Association. Ed Florence of Waage Manufacturing Co., Chicago, and to many others too numerous to mention who contributed in various ways to the preparation of this material.

Wayne Lemons and Glen Montgomery

CHAPTER 1

General Troubleshooting Procedures

There are a number of shortcuts to better appliance service, but also a number of precautions that apply to most all small appliances. It seems to go without saying that most readers will also be in the business to make money, though some may do appliance service mostly as a retirement job or even as a hobby. Whatever your aim, you should profit by the following hints.

CHECK OBVIOUS FAULTS FIRST

Never assume that a customer knows how to make even simple repairs. Chances are they don't, or else don't have time. This means that a good portion of the appliances brought in for repair may be suffering no more serious trouble than a broken power cord. Cords break most often at just two places—the attachment cap (plug that goes into the wall receptacle) or at the strain relief or grommet. Fig. 1-1 shows the weak points where you're most apt to find a broken wire.

TESTING THE CORD

To find cord troubles, plug the appliance into the series test plug on the appliance tester (see Chapter 11) and switch in the 40-watt lamp. Turn the appliance on. If the lamp does not light, check for breaks in the cord by gently pulling and tugging at the weak points indicated in Fig. 1-1. Quite often you will be able to move the cord around so that at least an intermittent connection is made if indeed the trouble is in the cord.

If you are not able to get the lamp lit in this manner, the trouble can still be in the cord. Find the points where the cord connects to the appliance. Take a clip-clip jumper (#2

POINTS WHERE
CORDS MOST
OFTEN BREAK

Fig. 1-1. Wires usually break at the points shown because of normal bending of the line cord. Point 1 in this case is most susceptible.

in Fig. 1-2) and connect it across the input terminals of the appliance, see Fig. 1-3. If the lamp lights now, the cord is OK (bend and twist it to make sure that there are no loose connections) and the trouble is in the appliance itself. Precaution: Notice that this jumper is a short circuit across the cord, so do not leave it connected should you plug the cord into the tester wattage receptacle or into a regular AC outlet.

If the lamp still doesn't light with the jumper across the appliance terminals, the problem is the cord, so replace it.

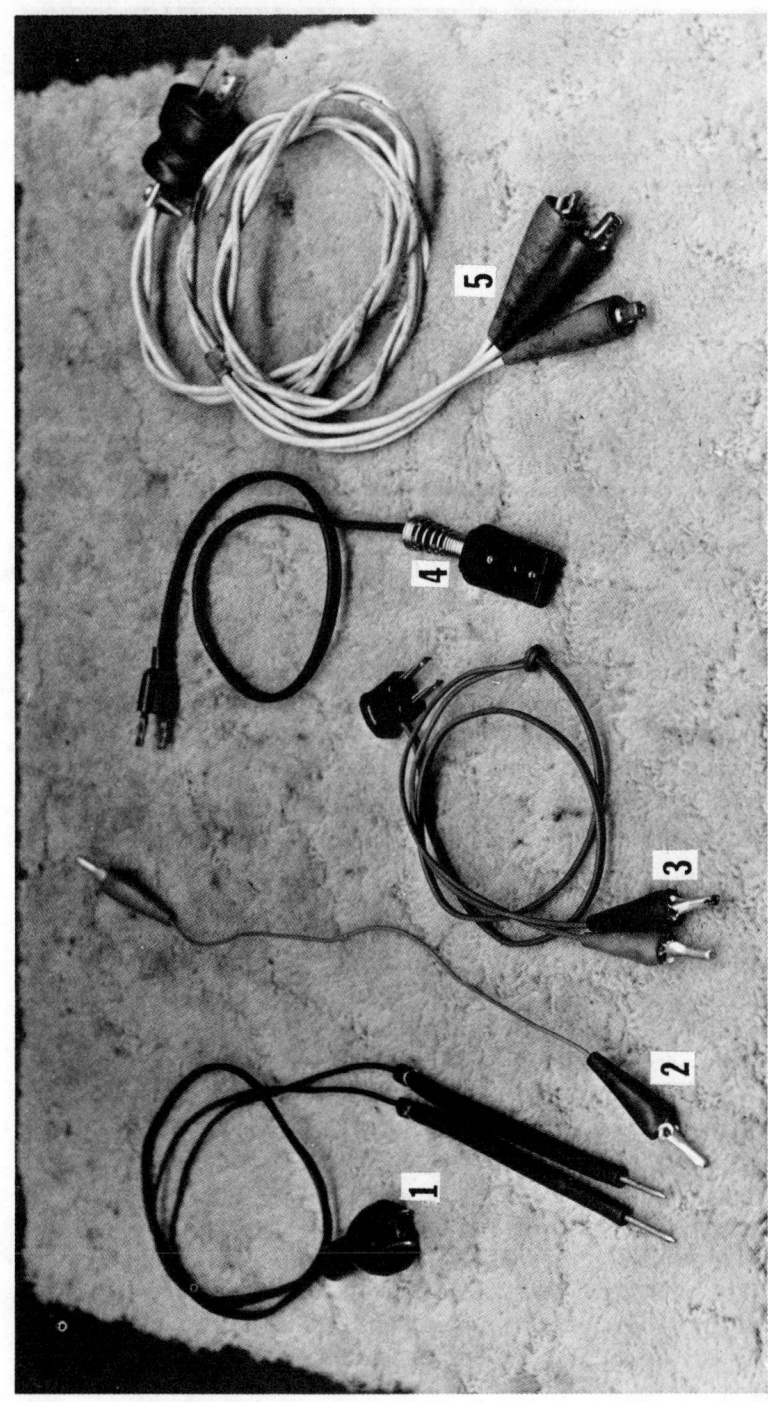

Fig. 1-2. Various test cables used in appliance servicing. 1. Plug and test probes. 2. Clip-clip jumper. 3. AC cord with clip connectors. 4. Test appliance cord. 5. 240v test cord.

9

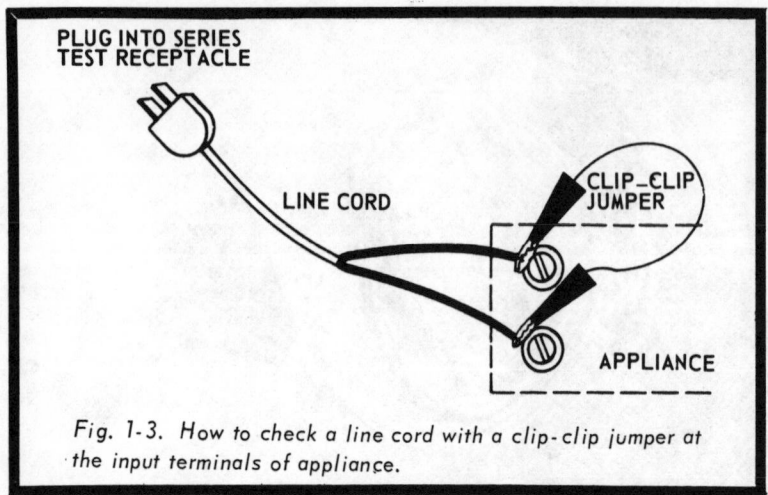

Fig. 1-3. How to check a line cord with a clip-clip jumper at the input terminals of appliance.

Replacing a cord is generally not good practice, though, if only the attachment cap end is defective. Simply replace the cap (plug) with one suitable for the job. If it is broken at the strain relief or grommet, the cord is probably old enough that you should replace it regardless. Old cords, especially cords used on heating appliances, lose resilience, and the insulation tends to crack, while the resistance of the wires increases as they age. A bad cord can cause an electrical fire, too, so don't take chances!

CONTINUITY TESTING

The oldest and most respected appliance test is a <u>continuity</u> check. Continuity simply means that the circuit is continuous and has no breaks in it. The idea of continuity testing is covered to some extent in Chapter 11, but we feel it should be covered in a little more detail here.

The oldest and perhaps best form of continuity testing is the AC test lamp. Most repairmen have more than one test lamp, and a portable one is always a handy thing to have around. Fig. 1-4A and B is a picture and wiring diagram of this device. A unit of this sort can be built, however; the price at most parts houses is less than about $3.00.

The idea of continuity testing is to make the suspected component a part of the test circuit. If the part you are testing has continuity, it will complete the test circuit and light the lamp.

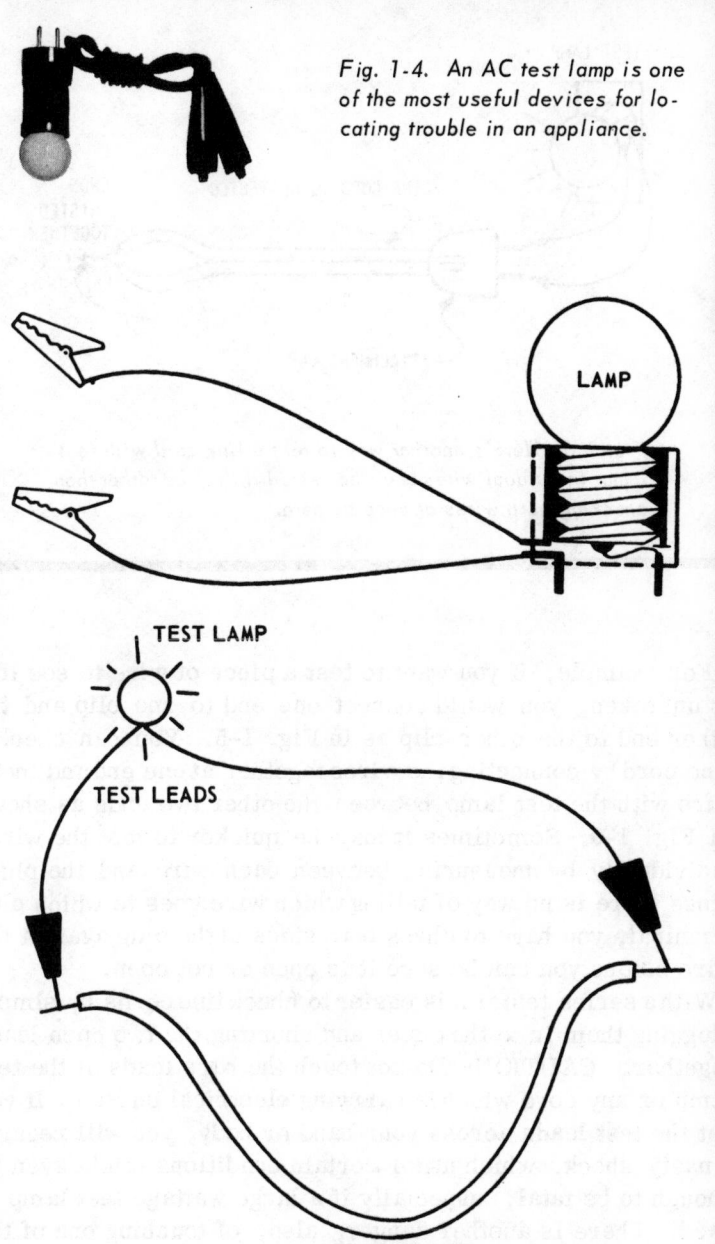

Fig. 1-4. An AC test lamp is one of the most useful devices for locating trouble in an appliance.

LAMP

TEST LAMP

TEST LEADS

PIECE OF WIRE

Fig. 1-5. Sketch showing a continuity test of a line cord, using a test lamp.

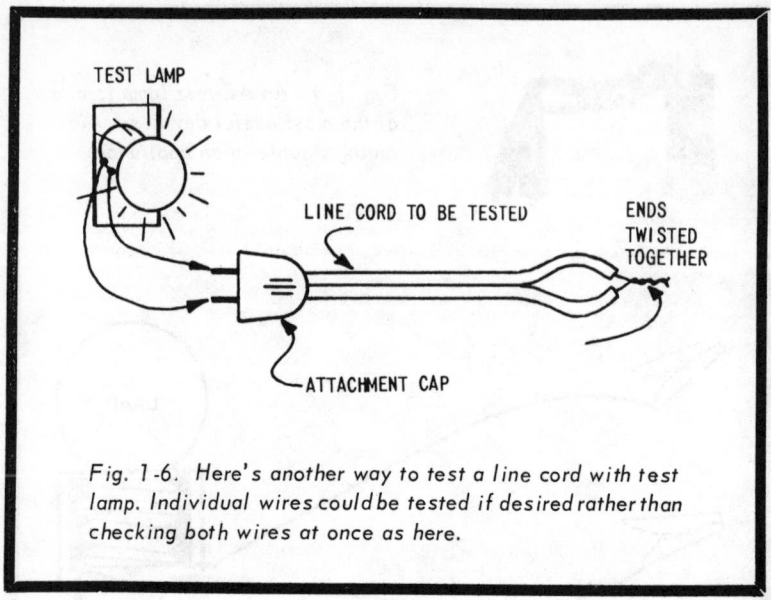

TEST LAMP

LINE CORD TO BE TESTED

ENDS
TWISTED
TOGETHER

ATTACHMENT CAP

Fig. 1-6. Here's another way to test a line cord with test lamp. Individual wires could be tested if desired rather than checking both wires at once as here.

For example, if you want to test a piece of wire to see if it is unbroken, you would connect one end to one clip and the other end to the other clip as in Fig. 1-5. You can check a line cord by connecting the wires together at one end and measure with the test lamp between the other two ends as shown in Fig. 1-6. Sometimes it may be quicker to test the wires individually by measuring between each wire and the plug. Since there is no way of telling which wire goes to which plug terminal, you have to check both sides of the plug against the wire before you can be sure it is open or not open.

With a series tester it is easier to check line cords by simply plugging them in to the tester and shorting the two open leads together. CAUTION: Do not touch the bare leads of the test lamp or any cord which is carrying electrical current. If you get the test leads across your hand or body, you will receive a nasty shock, which under certain conditions might even be enough to be fatal, especially if a large wattage test lamp is used. There is another danger, also, of touching one of the leads while standing against some grounded piece of machinery, a water pipe, damp concrete floor, etc. Play it SAFETY FIRST. TAKE CARE NOT TO BECOME A PART OF A LIVE ELECTRICAL CIRCUIT.

THE OHMMETER

Radio and TV technicians use an ohmmeter for continuity testing because a test lamp draws so much current that it can easily damage delicate electronic parts. The ohmmeter uses internal battery power and so is always safe to use. But in small appliance testing it draws such a small current that it may indicate continuity in a circuit that is not actually continuous when a larger current tries to flow through. Also, the resistances of many heating elements are so low that the ohmmeter may not be able to give you too much information as to its condition.

However, an ohmmeter does offer the distinct advantage that the actual resistance of a circuit can be measured if the resistance is above a few tenths of an ohm. This is particularly important for making comparisons; for example, the field coils of a motor should have almost identical resistances, and the meter can show whether or not they do. The meter also is ideal for checking blankets, heat pads, and other low-current appliances.

Fig. 1-7 is a picture of an ohmmeter used for appliance testing. In the R x 1 switch position the meter scale is used as is. In the R x 10 position, each reading is multiplied by 10 (add a 0; for example, a reading of three on the scale is actually 30). This particular meter will read very high resistances, too, which is helpful when checking for leakage between the internal electrical circuit and the case of an appliance, but this is not always a satisfactory test as explained later.

Often a better choice, though there are more meter scales to contend with, is a VOM (volt-ohm-milliammeter). A VOM has AC and DC voltage scales and DC milliammeter scales, and a switch selects the desired function. A meter of this type is shown in Fig. 1-8.

SNAP-ON AMMETERS

An ammeter is used to measure the actual current flow in an electrical circuit. With a conventional ammeter it is necessary to place the meter in series with the circuit to measure current, which means breaking the circuit and inserting the meter. The snap-on meter, Fig. 1-9, measures current by

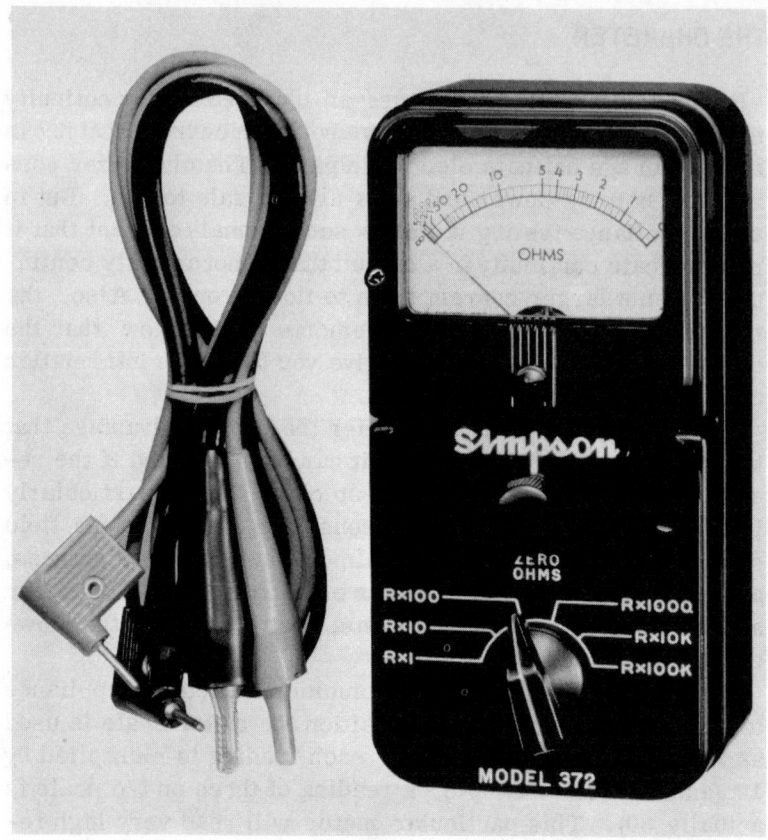

Fig. 1-7. A typical ohmmeter.

inductance and so needs only to be snapped around <u>one</u> of the conductors going to the appliance. A special device, designed to separate the conductors when inserted in series with the appliance cord (Fig. 1-10), can be used or the test cord can be split apart as in Fig. 1-11.

Most snap-on ammeters also have test lead jacks so that voltage can be measured, too. The sensitivity of the ammeter can be increased by looping the conductor one or more times around the jaw of the ammeter, Fig. 1-12. For example, if you loop the conductor around once, the meter will read twice as much; twice it will read three times as much, etc. The device shown in Fig. 1-13 has built-in provisions to increase the sensitivity 5 to 10 times.

HIGH POTENTIAL (HI-POT) LEAKAGE CHECKING

By switching ranges, ohmmeters can measure circuit resistance from about 1 ohm to above 1 million ohms with good accuracy. The high-resistance scale is often used to check for leakage between the electrical circuit and an appliance case or housing. Unfortunately, this is not always a good method since the low voltage of the ohmmeter may not be

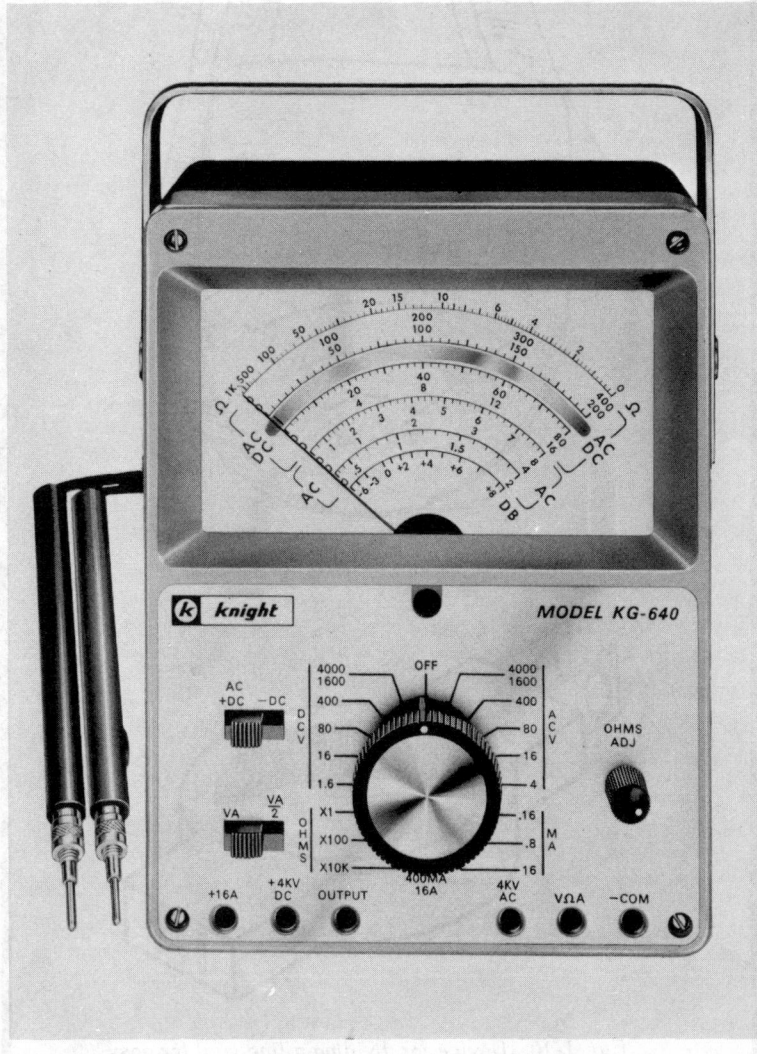

Fig. 1-8. A vom, such as this one, offers more test functions than an ohmmeter.

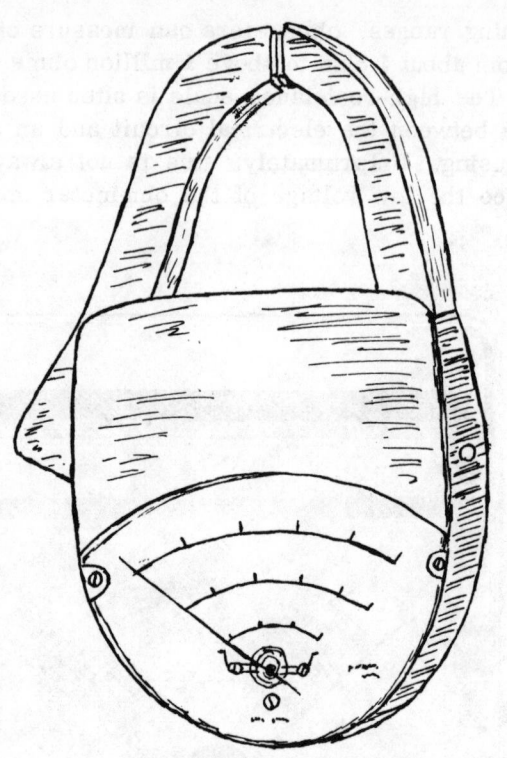

Fig. 1-9. Sketch of a snap-on ammeter.

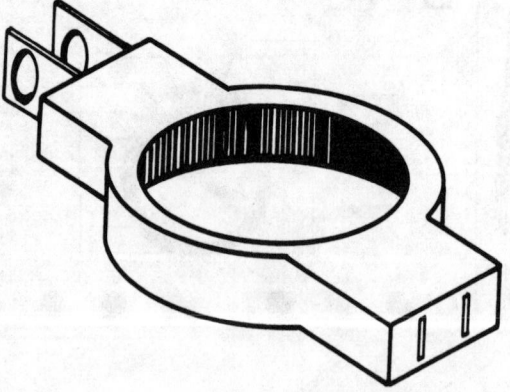

Fig. 1-10. Device for dividing a line cord for easy
use of a snap-on ammeter.

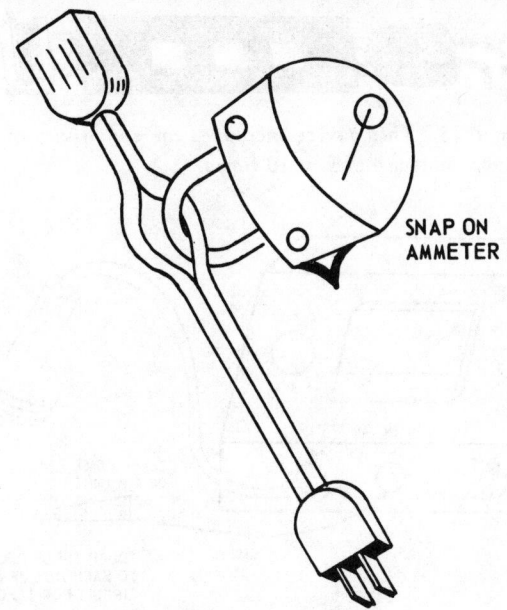

SNAP ON
AMMETER

Fig. 1-11. A split cord makes it easy
to use a snap-on ammeter.

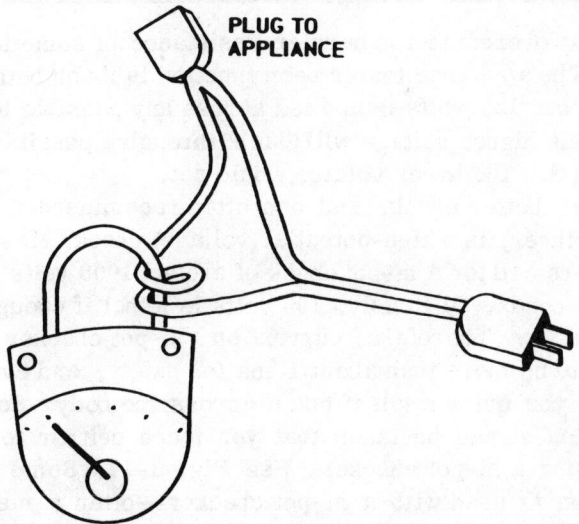

PLUG TO
APPLIANCE

Fig. 1-12. Wrapping the wire around the jaw of a snap-on
ammeter increases meter sensitivity for reading lower current values.

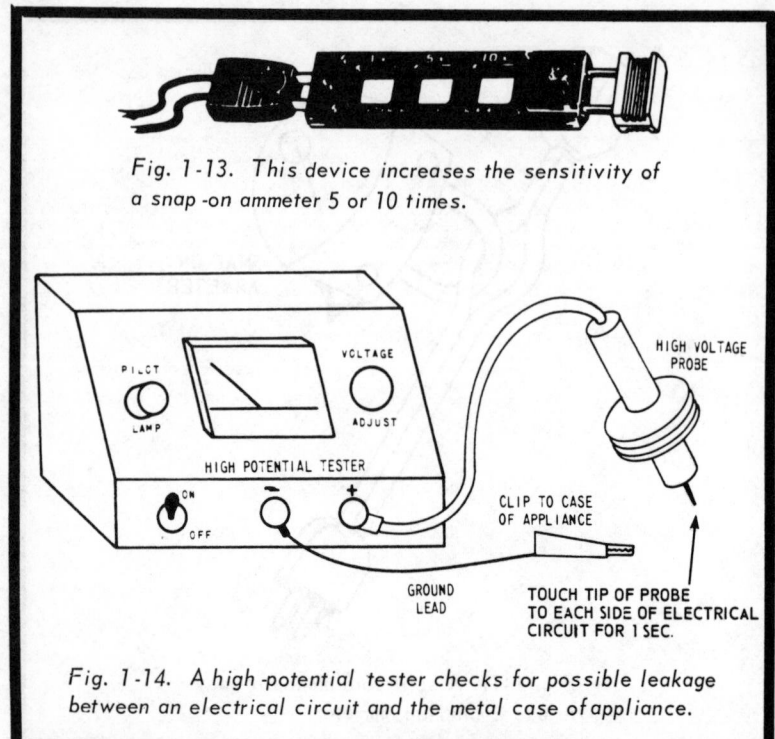

Fig. 1-13. This device increases the sensitivity of a snap-on ammeter 5 or 10 times.

HIGH VOLTAGE PROBE

PILOT LAMP

VOLTAGE

ADJUST

HIGH POTENTIAL TESTER

ON OFF

CLIP TO CASE OF APPLIANCE

GROUND LEAD

TOUCH TIP OF PROBE TO EACH SIDE OF ELECTRICAL CIRCUIT FOR 1 SEC.

Fig. 1-14. A high-potential tester checks for possible leakage between an electrical circuit and the metal case of appliance.

enough to overcome the barrier resistance of some leakage paths. The appliance tester neon function is much better because about 120 volts is applied across any possible leakage path. This higher voltage will "stab" through a possible leakage path that the lower voltage would not.

An even better check, and one often recommended by the manufacturer, is a high-potential (voltage) check. Most manufacturers call for a hi-pot check of around 1000 volts for one to two seconds. Obviously, 100 volts is lethal if enough current can flow. Therefore, current on a hi-pot checker should be held to no more than about 1 ma for safety, and even this can give you quite a jolt if taken across the body. So every precaution should be taken that you touch neither terminal when using a hi-pot checker. See Fig. 1-14. Some sort of indication is used with a hi-pot checker—often a meter, a neon lamp, an "eye" tube, or sometimes an audible signal.

Although many small shops do not feel that the hi-pot checker is a necessity, it will on occasion show up a potential danger point that you won't find with either the test lamp or neon. The added voltage will break across a weak point and expose a dangerous situation before it actually occurs.

Some repairmen build their own hi-pot tester from an old TV power transformer, many of which often have an output of up to 800 or 900 volts. Fig. 1-15 shows how you might rig one up, but be sure you take all the precautions emphasized here to prevent or greatly reduce the possibility of a lethal shock. Notice that the circuit in Fig. 1-15 has a spring-return on-off switch. Two clips are used so that the high-voltage leads need not be handled while the instrument is in use.

The silicon diodes may be replacement types with a peak inverse voltage rating of at least 600 or higher. The diodes change the AC into DC voltage, filtered by the 0.1-mfd capacitor. Using DC in the tester prevents the neon from glowing due to capacity effects when measuring such things as cords; however, any other leakage will show up. (Capacity leakage is normal and should be disregarded in all leakage tests. It is caused by an actual charging and discharging that occurs between two separated conductors when AC voltage is applied between them. The current leakage due to capacity is extremely tiny and never lethal, but there is enough current to cause a neon tube to glow lightly under certain circumstances.)

TOOLS

Fig. 1-16 shows most of the common tools needed in appliance repair. You will find use for all of them at one time or another on a number of different types of appliances. You

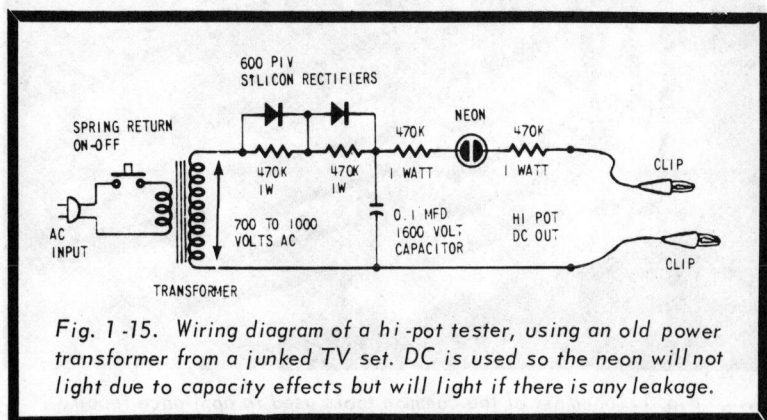

Fig. 1-15. Wiring diagram of a hi-pot tester, using an old power transformer from a junked TV set. DC is used so the neon will not light due to capacity effects but will light if there is any leakage.

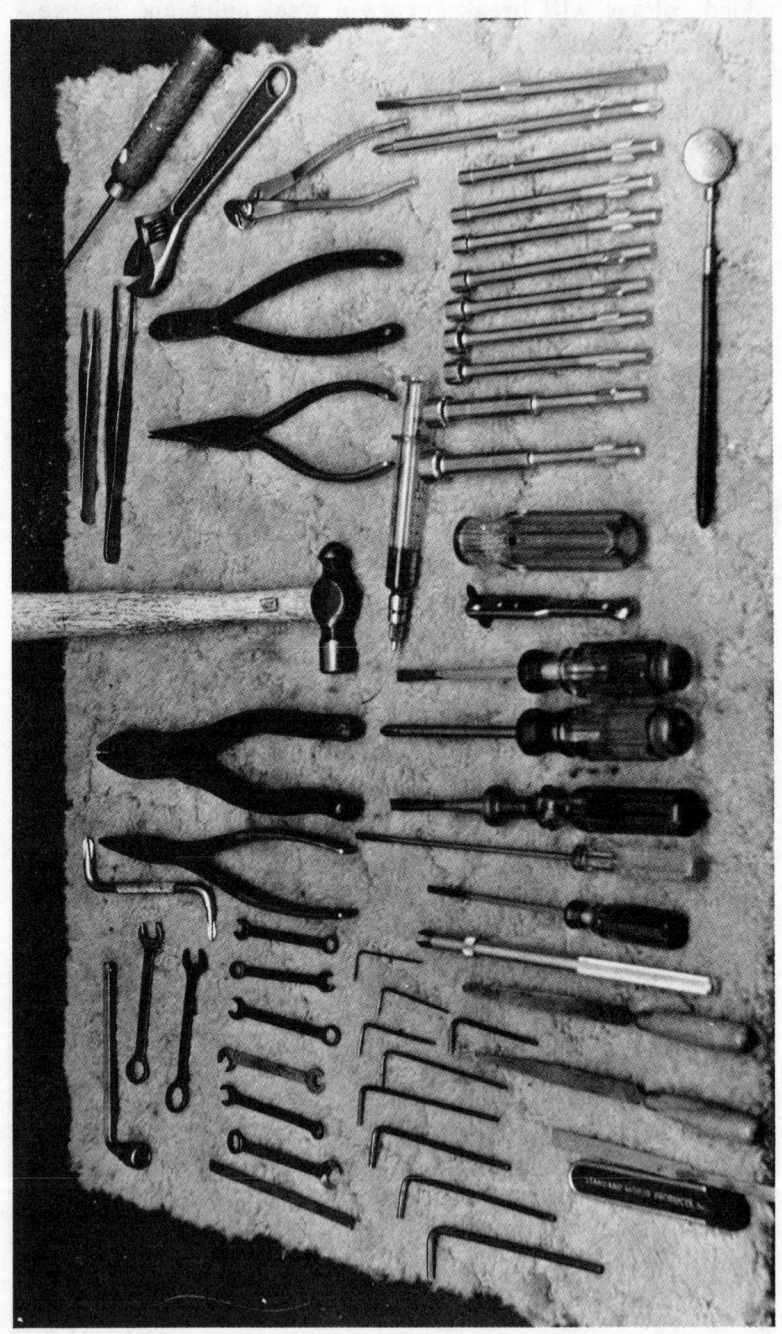

Fig. 1-16. Most of the common tools used in appliance repair.

should have them all. They are available from most any parts supply house. Of course, your tools do not have to be exactly like these, but you should have the equivalent. For example, the "nut drivers" shown in Fig. 1-16 are the plug-in type. You could have individual nut drivers and screwdrivers, but you'll find that you must have them.

Fig. 1-17 shows some of the special tools that you should have. Notice, on the right side of the picture, the "rim tool." It is used to replace rivets in the ring of one type of Sunbeam coffee maker. You may not use it very often, but when you need it, it's about the only thing you can use and do the job right. That's the way it is with most of the other tools shown. You may find that you can use something else, but the right tool always does a better job.

SOLVENTS AND CLEANING MATERIAL

Fig. 1-18 shows a number of different type cleaners, solvents, and lubricants that you should have available. Here again you may not need the exact type shown, but like the special tools, you'll find that they come in handy and in many cases are necessary to complete the job as it should be.

DISASSEMBLY

It would be impossible in a book of this size to even begin to go into all the "trick" ways that have been devised to hold certain appliances together. A small-appliance repairman working on an appliance with which he is not familiar sometimes needs to be part genius to find the secret clip or latch that holds some appliances together. Some repairmen develop an uncanny knack for guessing where the designer has hidden that screw or latch that holds things together, and the ability improves as they work on various kinds.

Disassembly screws are often hidden under name plates or decorative trim. Fig. 1-19 shows a "saddle" plate being pried off an iron. The disassembly screws are underneath the saddle. In recent years it has become increasingly common to find disassembly screws located underneath a "glued-on" escutcheon or name plate. Before tearing off a name plate of this sort, try to make sure there is really a screw underneath. You can often do this with a sharp instrument such as

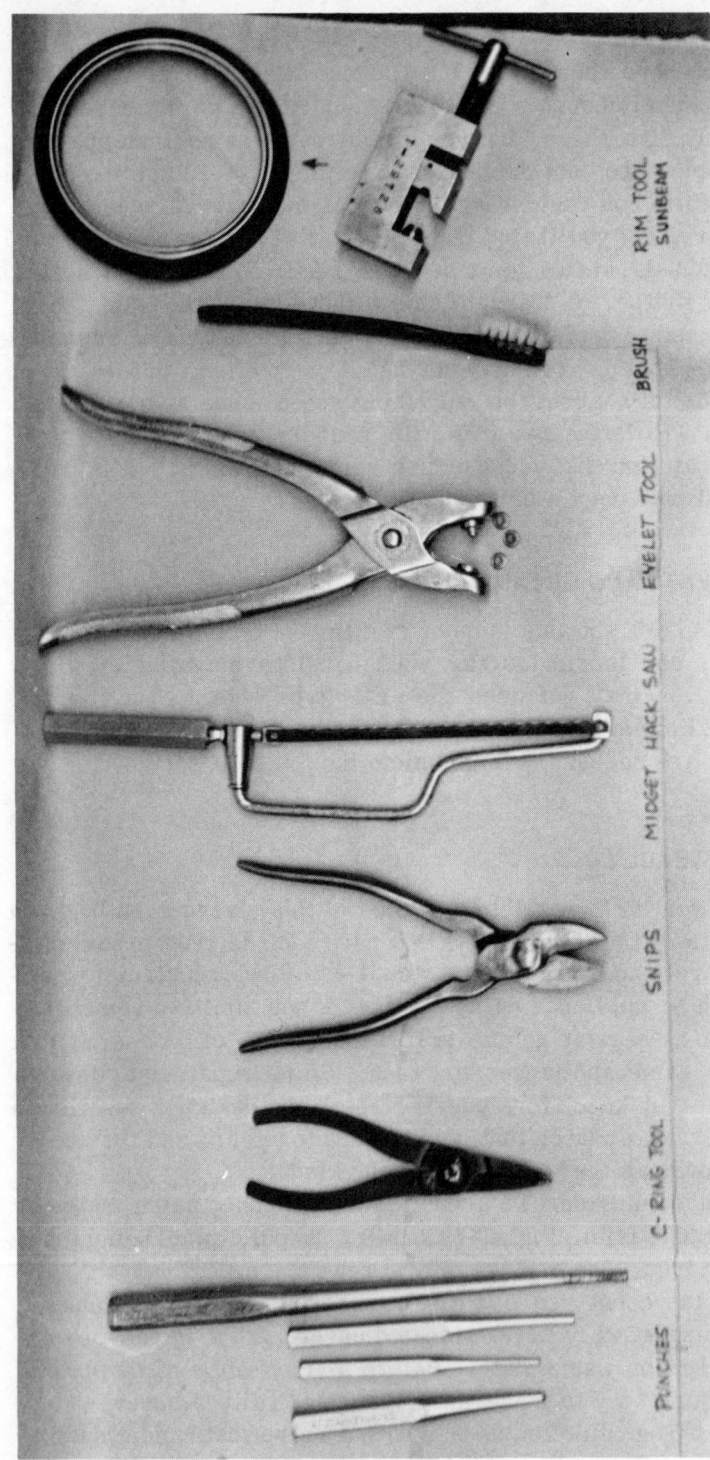

Fig. 1-17. Some special tools you should have available.

Fig. 1-18. Solvents, cleaners, and lubricants used in appliance repairing.

23

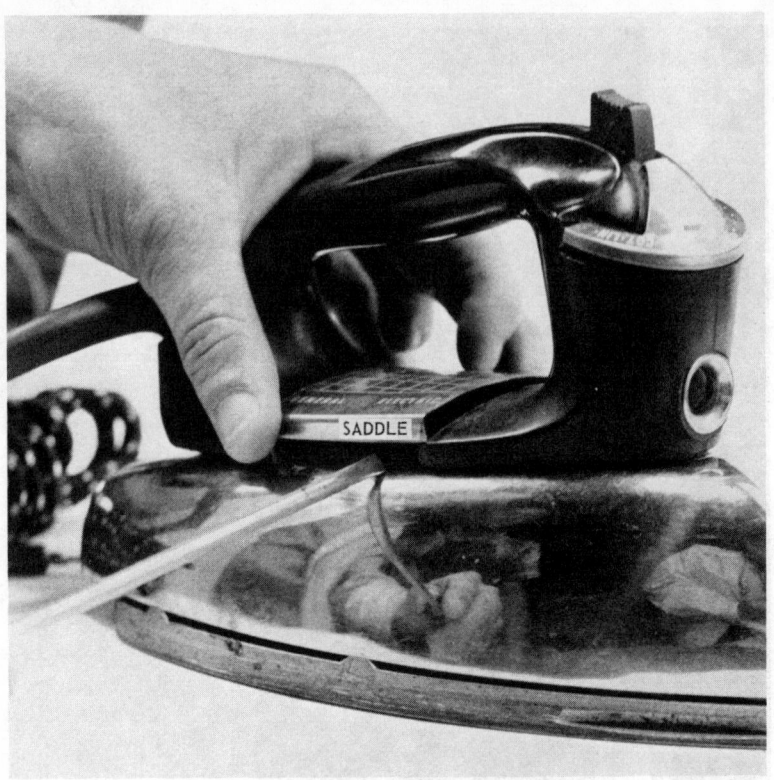

Fig. 1-19. One of the simpler methods of cancealing disassembly
screws is under the saddle on this iron, which can be pried off with
a screwdriver as shown.

an ice pick which will pierce through the escutcheon if there
is a recess underneath that is hiding a screw. If you must
tear off the escutcheon, you should obtain a new one from the
manufacturer or parts house and glue it back on after the repair. You might be willing to use an appliance of your own
without the name plate, but chances are the customer will
feel cheated if you mar the appearance of his appliance, no
matter how well it may work otherwise.

Unusual assembly methods, such as hook and rivet, may test
your ingenuity the first time you disassemble one but after
that there will be no trouble at all. For example, several
years ago a particular make iron used a hook arrangement
to hold the handle to the sole plate. First, a screw had to be

taken out to allow the handle to slide, but to the uninitiated taking out the screw seemed to not release the two parts at all; however, a sharp whack on the handle in the forward direction released the two parts. One part had shoulder rivets on it and the other an eyelet hole as shown in Fig. 1-20.

When you have a part that appears to have no more screws holding it, gentle pressure up, down, or sideways (sometimes you may even have to give it a rather sharp rap with the heel of your hand) may turn up a hidden catch. A few appliances have spring catches that require you to go down through a tiny hole or crevice with a sharp tool to release some parts. These can be among the most difficult to disassemble on a "maiden voyage." Fortunately, there are not too many of this sort.

Take Your Time

Always take your time in a new and strange disassembly situation. Often a rush disassembly will result in a pile of un-

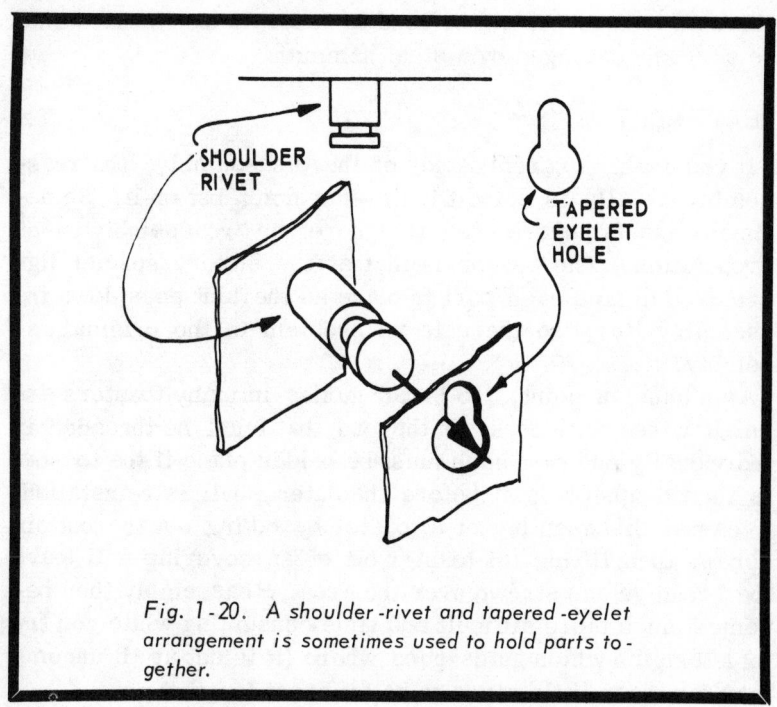

SHOULDER RIVET

TAPERED EYELET HOLE

Fig. 1-20. A shoulder-rivet and tapered-eyelet arrangement is sometimes used to hold parts together.

identified parts and you'll have no idea how they should go back together. It is a good idea to draw a rough sketch when disassembling an unfamiliar unit. Another good practice is to mark internal parts with a light scratch and a mating scratch on another part of the assembly. Many parts can be reassembled in two ways (one right and one wrong) and the light scratch will lead you quickly to the correct positions. Sometimes, parts will go back together in only one way but you don't always know it as you disassemble, so make a mark as a precaution if in doubt.

Use Force Sparingly

Try never to use excessive force in disassembling an unfamiliar item. You may succeed only in bending some part out of shape, thus making reassembly difficult. Or, you may break some part that is difficult to replace.

Though a few manufacturers have built items that require considerable force to disassemble, it is not the usual rule. Even if force is required it usually must be applied in just the right manner and at the right place to prevent damage to other parts. A padded or plastic hammer is a good item for any repairman to have. It can be used to decouple items that would be severely damaged by a steel hammer.

REASSEMBLY

If you make a careful study of the disassembly, the reassembly usually is not difficult—but don't bet on it. Sometimes manufacturers seem to ignore the "reassembly ease" proposition. The reason is that at the factory special jigs are used to hold each part in place as the unit goes down the assembly line, so there is no problem in the original assembly.

As a case in point, the bread guides in many toasters are small wires with hooks on the end that must be threaded in individually and then each must be held in place if the toaster is turned upside down before the outer shell is reinstalled. A casual disassembly of a toaster by taking out the bottom screws then lifting the toaster out of its covering will leave the bread guides strewn over the area. Reassembly then becomes much more difficult and time consuming while you try to determine which guide goes where (it is not at all uncommon for these little wires to be different lengths).

In any reassembly, make sure that no electrical cords or wires are pinched. Sometimes the wiring has a definite channel in which it must be placed or you won't be able to get the case back on. As in disassembly, force is seldom—if ever —needed to get an appliance back together; as a matter of fact, if you use force you will likely have an inoperative appliance when you do get it reassembled.

Make sure that all electrical connections are tight. Experienced repairmen loosen screw or bolt connections at electrical terminals on the appliance and then retighten them. This makes sure that oxidation is broken up and the "scratching" caused by the loosening and retightening means a lower resistance connection. It is the resistance at electrical connections—no matter if it is small—that causes most troubles. The resistance causes the connection to heat up, especially in high-current appliances such as irons and toasters, and the heat produces additional oxidation and more resistance. This vicious cycle eventually results in cord or terminal failure.

Electrical cords that fasten inside an appliance employ some sort of strain relief to prevent a tug on the outside from pulling the internal terminals together, perhaps. The strain relief may be no more elaborate than a knot tied in the cord so that it cannot pass back through the hole it enters, or it may be any number of special devices that clamp the cord in place so as to allow the necessary slack inside. Always make sure that the strain relief is doing its job when the appliance is reassembled.

ABOUT AMPERES AND WATTS

If you do not know, it can sometimes be confusing as to the difference between amperes and watts. The ampere is a measurement of current flow without any regard to the voltage present. For example, you could have 10 amperes (usually shortened to amps) of current at 12 volts or 10 amperes of current at 120 volts. Current flow in amperes is the same in both instances, but the power in an electrical circuit must take into consideration both the voltage (or pressure) and the current flow. In the above example, the first circuit would have a power consumption of 120 watts (12 volts times 10 amperes) and the second circuit would have a power consumption of 1200 watts (120 volts times 10 amperes). Wattage, then, is the current times the voltage.

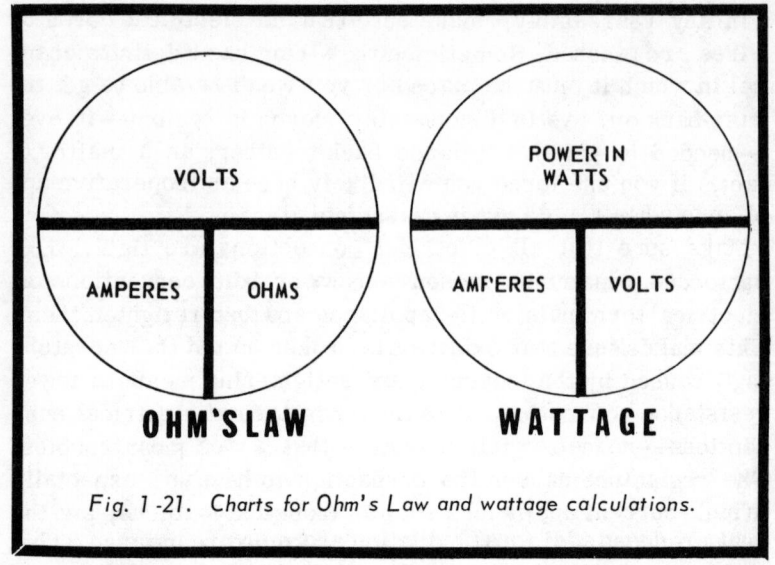

Fig. 1-21. Charts for Ohm's Law and wattage calculations.

When using an ammeter on a 120-volt circuit you can calculate the wattage rating by simply multiplying the ammeter reading by 120. Obviously, this will vary if the line voltage happens to be either more or less than 120, but the calculation will be close enough for most purposes.

ABOUT OHMS

The term "ohms" is a measure of resistance in the circuit. It is pronounced to rhyme with "homes" (without the h). The more resistance in ohms a circuit has, the LESS the current flow through it if the voltage of the circuit is unchanged. For example, if the resistance of one circuit is 10 ohms and another circuit is 20 ohms, the 10-ohm circuit will have twice as much current flow through it if both are connected to the same voltage source.

There is a mathematical relationship between the amount of voltage, amperage, and resistance of a circuit. This is called "Ohm's Law." It is based on the proposition that one ampere of current will flow in a one-ohm circuit when one volt is applied. If we apply 10 volts to that same one-ohm circuit, 10 amperes of current will flow.

As an example of how Ohm's law can be used, let's say an electric blanket element has a resistance of 240 ohms as measured with an ohmmeter. The blanket is to be used on 120 volts. To find the current flow, you divide the resistance into the voltage. In this case the current flow would be one-half ampere. The following relationships below show how you can calculate any unknown if the other two are known.

Voltage = Amperes times resistance in ohms

Amperes = Voltage divided by resistance in ohms

Resistance in ohms = Voltage divided by current in amperes

The charts in Fig. 1-21 may also be helpful. To find an un-known, cover the unknown and the formula for finding the unknown remains on the chart. For example, if you cover "volts" it leaves "amperes" times "ohms." If you cover "amperes" it leaves "volts" divided by "ohms," etc.

CHAPTER 2

Thermostats

Nearly all small electrical appliances which use heating elements also need a thermostat of one form or another. Such thermostats are fixed or in other cases they are adjustable. Fixed thermostats either hold the temperature at one particular value or function as protective devices should the appliance get too hot for some reason. Adjustable thermostats provide customer control of the amount of heat. For example, the customer can adjust an electric iron for the right temperature to iron rayon, wool, silk, cotton, etc., or a fry pan from 200 to 400°, or whatever.

The customer adjustment does not determine the amount of current that flows in an appliance but rather regulates the thermostat which, in turn, controls the on-off cycles of the appliance. For example, an iron may have a 1000-watt heating element but on low-heat settings that element may be turned on by the thermostat only 15% of the time after initial warm up. On high heat settings the element may stay on 75% of the time, etc.

HOW A THERMOSTAT WORKS

In its basic form a thermostat is simply an off-and-on switch that is controlled by heat. The controlling arm is a strip of two metals bonded together, called a bi-metal strip. The two metals are different kinds so each has a different expansion rate. Because of this, when the strip is heated, instead of just expanding lengthwise, it warps or bends. See Fig. 2-1.

In fixed-heat thermostats the bi-metal strip usually has one of the off-on switch contact points fused to it. In adjustable thermostats the bi-metal strip is usually just the actuating arm, see Fig. 2-2. Making the bi-metal strip separate from the electrical circuit eliminates heating caused by the passage of current through it; however, in some instances this is a safety factor since excessive current could cause the thermostat to cut off.

The thermostat turns the heating element off and on to maintain a certain temperature. In an adjustable thermostat, such as in Fig. 2-2, an insulated button at the end of the adjusting shaft is moved up or down by the screw action. The button pushes the bottom contact arm up or down (through a hole in the upper contact arm) and results in the upper contact arm

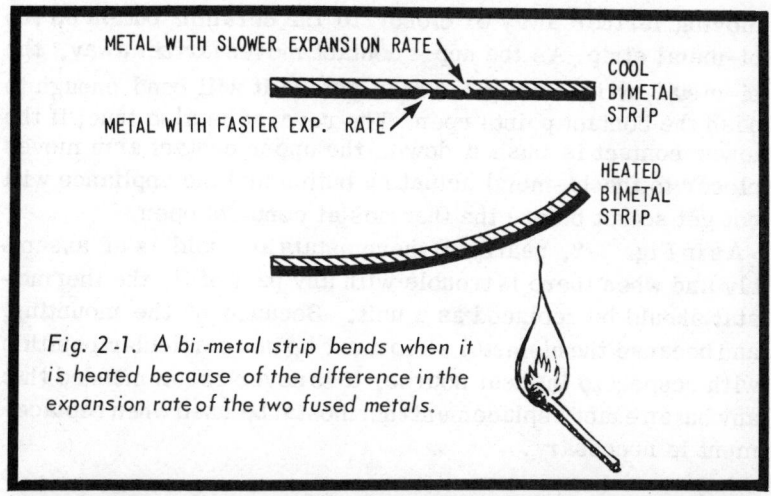

Fig. 2-1. A bi-metal strip bends when it is heated because of the difference in the expansion rate of the two fused metals.

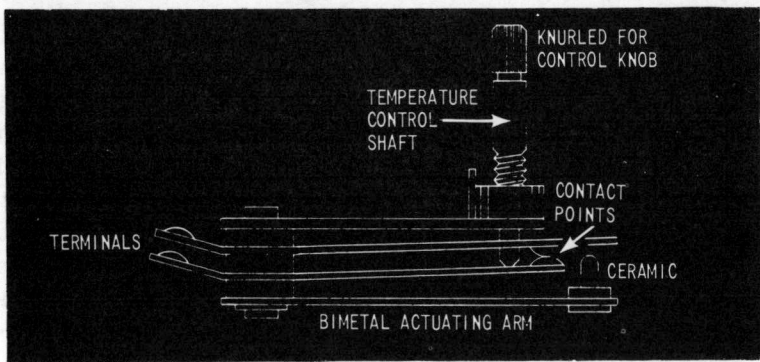

Fig. 2-2. One basic type thermostat. Notice that the temperature control shaft places more or less tension on the lower contact strip (through a hole in the upper contact strip). The bi-metal arm must move farther to open the contacts as pressure is removed from the lower contact strip which moves the upper contact farther away from the ceramic button on the bi-metal arm.

Fig. 2-3. A point file is sometimes used to clean thermostat contacts but not always (see text).

moving farther away or closer to the ceramic button on the bi-metal strip. As the upper contact moves farther away, the bi-metal strip must get hotter before it will bend enough to push the contact points open. The reverse is also true; if the lower contact is pushed down, the upper contact arm moves closer to the bi-metal actuating button and the appliance will not get so hot before the thermostat contacts open.

As in Fig. 2-2, nearly all thermostats are sold as an assembly and when there is trouble with any part of it, the thermostat should be replaced as a unit. Because of the mounting, and because the bi-metal strip must be in a particular position with respect to the heat source, it is never recommended that any but an exact replacement thermostat be used when replacement is necessary.

TROUBLES IN THERMOSTATS

The bi-metal strip itself seldom is a source of trouble. More commonly, trouble occurs because the contact points become pitted and oxidized through repeated use. The contact point material is designed to carry quite a lot of current, as well as withstand the repeated arcing and heating caused by turning the heating element off and on. But after several hundred hours service the points can develop considerable resistance at the contacts, causing additional heat which, in turn, causes additional oxidation and an even greater increase in resistance.

You can "dress" some thermostat points with a point file, Fig. 2-3, if they are not too far gone. Other points, however, will be further damaged by use of a file, because the latter type points have only a hard, thin coating at the contact area and filing will simply finish removing this surface.

Unless you are sure of the kinds of contacts used, don't file any points to remove minor pits or just "for good measure."

If you have a service manual for a particular appliance it will usually indicate whether or not filing or some other method is suitable for routine maintenance of the thermostat contacts. The best idea, unless you have specific instructions to the contrary, is to leave the points alone unless they are definitely proved to be the source of trouble. If they have oxidized or pitted to a point where sustained arcing occurs, or if they no longer pass current, the safest practice is to replace the entire thermostat if possible.

THERMOSTAT ADJUSTMENTS

As indicated before, most thermostats can be adjusted to provide more or less heat. In many cases there are two adjustments—one through a linkage from the customer control knob. The customer knob is provided with stops so that the heat of the appliance can be adjusted only within specified limits. A second adjustment is often (though certainly not always) provided for the service man. This second adjustment is nearly always hidden from view so that the appliance will have to be partially disassembled to find it.

For example, on an iron the control knob may have to be removed, or the saddle plate, or perhaps the handle, before uncovering the second adjustment. On coffee pots you normally have to remove the bottom, but sometimes you may be able to reach the second adjustment through a hole provided or through the center of the control shaft after the control knob is removed. In a few cases the "second" adjustment may be determined by the position of the knob; in other words, the customer control knob may have splines so that the knob can be moved clockwise or counterclockwise on the control shaft. In these cases the stop is controlled by a notch or "pip" on the knob and there will be no stop on the thermostat itself. If the maximum temperature needs to be higher, turn the adjustment screw so that the thermostat contacts are pushed closer together (or farther away from the bi-metal actuating arm). If the minimum temperature needs to be lower, adjust the contacts so there is less tension on the contact points or so they are moved closer to the bi-metal actuating arm.

When the customer control knob reads "off" the contacts should be apart, but they should close by the time the knob

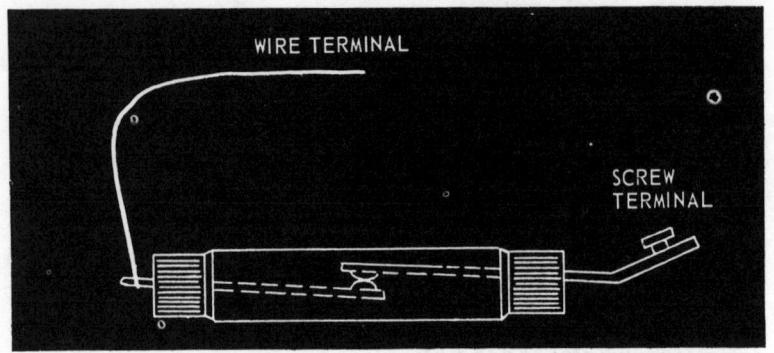

Fig. 2-4. A fixed-temperature thermostat. This one is used in one model coffee pot.

reaches the first mark clockwise on the dial from "off" if the appliance is cool. In other words, unless the appliance is hot, the thermostat points must be together (a closed circuit) at all positions of the control except at "off."

Some thermostats, especially fixed-temperature types, are completely enclosed so that adjustment is difficult, if not impossible. However, the experienced repairman can sometimes make adjustments by using his knowledge of what is inside. For example, the drawing in Fig. 2-4 depicts a fixed thermostat used in a coffee pot. Sometimes this 'stat will turn the element off and on normally, except it will cut off before the temperature rises enough to "perk" the coffee.

Fig. 2-5 shows how the judicial use of pliers can distort the case of the 'stat enough to push the points closer together and so allow the coffee pot element to reach a higher temperature before cutting off. This repair is not necessarily a recommended procedure since a new thermostat is not expensive, but it can be a stop-gap if a new unit is not immediately available.

You can make adjustments on almost any open-type thermostat by carefully bending one of the contact arms in the direction to produce the desired change in operation (more tension on the contacts for higher temperature and vice versa).

Make all such adjustments in small "bites," and allow the thermostat to cycle two or three times in its normal environment. Check your test thermometer for the amount of change. Too radical an adjustment can completely ruin the thermostat and make replacement mandatory.

Be sure that thermostats are tested in the exact location where they are supposed to be. Some 'stats are mounted under friction metal clips. These clips should hold the 'stat firm, but make sure that the clip is not pressed so tightly against the thermostat that the contacts are distorted out of place inside the 'stat body.

CONTACT POINT ARCING

There is a normal amount of arcing anytime a circuit is opened, and the more current that is flowing in the circuit the more severe the arc. However, excessive arcing is a source of trouble and is most often caused by oxidation or pitted contact points. If sustained arcing occurs each time the points open or close, a vicious cycle begins. The arcing causes the points to heat; the heat causes more oxidation; more oxidation causes more arcing, and it isn't long until the contacts are destroyed.

As indicated before, you may be able to clean the contacts with a point file, while in others filing will destroy whatever

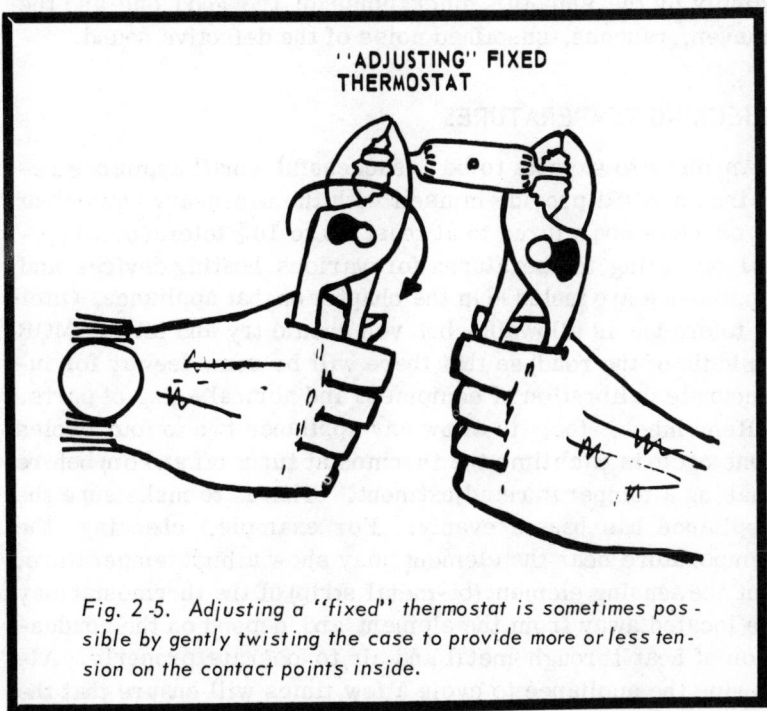

"ADJUSTING" FIXED THERMOSTAT

Fig. 2-5. Adjusting a "fixed" thermostat is sometimes possible by gently twisting the case to provide more or less tension on the contact points inside.

hard metal exists. Any set of points which shows signs of heavy arcing and pitting should be replaced. More often than not the added heat due to the arcing, or the high resistance caused by oxidation, will cause the metal around the contacts to turn a bluish color. The bluish color is a tip-off and if it occurs the chances of cleaning the points is practically nil. Replace the thermostat. (Occasionally, contact point sets have a normal bluish color but it is not usual.)

RADIO METHOD OF FINDING ARCING

A small AM radio will pick up an electrical arc over quite a range even though tuned to a station (if the signal isn't tremendously strong). If you hear a sustained noise in the radio each time a thermostat closes, you can be pretty sure that the thermostat should be replaced or, perhaps if practical, the points cleaned. There will be a short arc and noise in the radio even with a good thermostat, but you'll soon learn to distinguish between the "good" sound and the "defective" one simply by the smooth, quick noise of the good one and the uneven, raucous, sustained noise of the defective sound.

CHECKING TEMPERATURES

Anyone who expects to be a successful small appliance repairman MUST provide himself with the necessary equipment to check temperatures to at least a 5 to 10% tolerance. Typical operating temperatures for various heating devices and appliances are included in the chapter on that appliance. Often a tolerance is allowable but you should try and hit the MOR (middle of the road) so that there will be some leeway for inaccurate calibration of equipment and normal aging of parts.

Remember, too, to allow any appliance two to four cycles (one cycle is each time the thermostat turns off and on) before making a temperature adjustment. This is to make sure the appliance has heated evenly. For example, checking the temperature near the element may show a high temperature, but the sensing element (bi-metal strip) of the thermostat may be located away from the element and depend on the conduction of heat through metal and air to operate properly. Allowing the appliance to cycle a few times will ensure that the

Fig. 2-6. A liquid thermometer of the type often used for checking the temperature of liquid in a coffee pot.

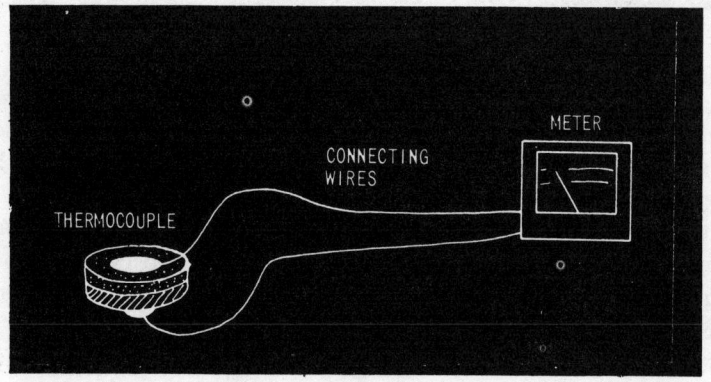

Fig. 2-7. Wiring diagram of thermocouple temperature tester.

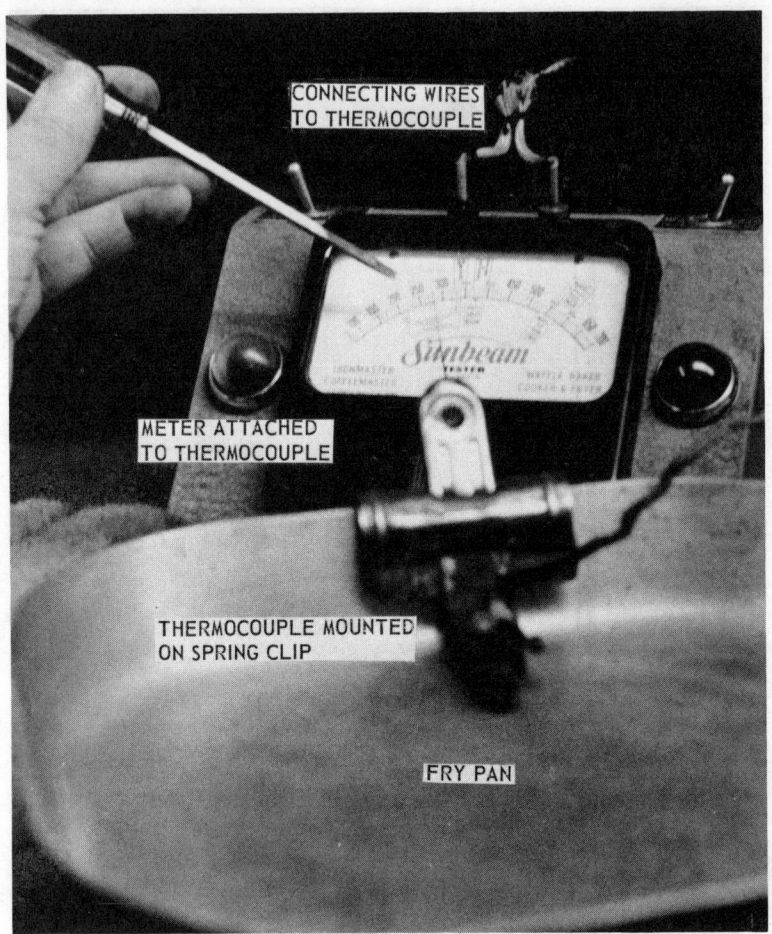

Fig. 2-8. Here, a fry pan is being checked for correct thermostat setting using a clip-on thermocouple and meter indicator.

thermostat is working normally and the temperature tester represents an overall picture of the actual ambient heat in the appliance.

It is because of the thermostat placement that almost all appliances must have thermostat adjustments and checks made when in their normal environment. For example, it is impossible to adjust a toaster correctly if the outside cover is not in place to reflect the heat. The same is true of coffee makers, irons, skillets, broilers, etc. CAUTION: Thermostat contact points as used in AC appliances may fuse together if the appliance is used on DC.

HEAT INDICATORS

For appliances that normally have a liquid inside, such as a coffee pot, sauce pan, etc., use a liquid thermometer such as the one shown in Fig. 2-6 or one of the type shown in Chapter 6.

For irons and often for fry pans, a thermocoupled-type tester is popular. A thermocouple is a device made of two dissimilar metals. When heated, a tiny electric current is generated between the metals. By connecting the thermocouple to a meter the amount of heat can be determined quite accurately. Fig. 2-7 is a wiring diagram of a thermocouple and meter. The one in Fig. 2-8 shows a clip-on type being used to check the temperature of a fry pan.

Fig. 2-9 shows a special thermometer-type test that is used for checking electric irons. The iron rests on the metal tab clamped onto the asbestos base at the top.

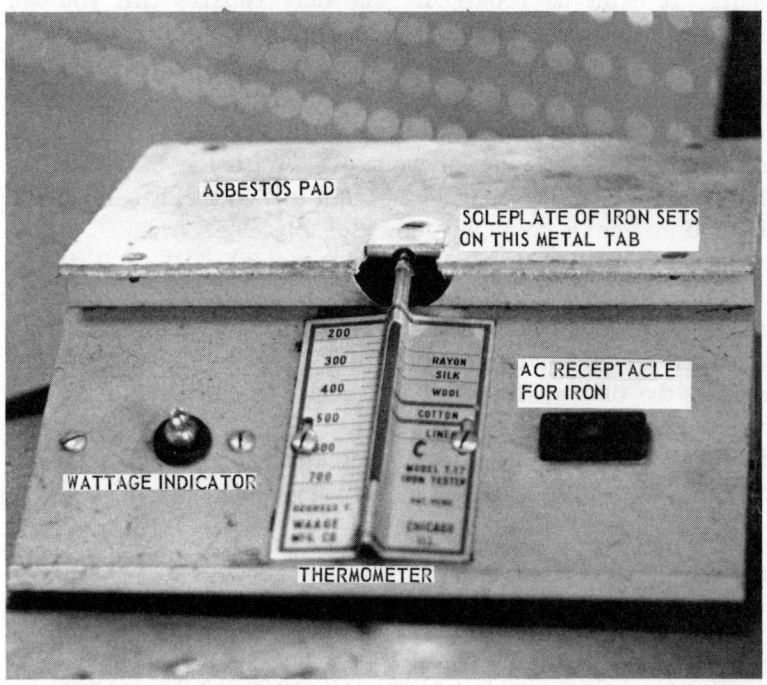

Fig. 2-9. This is a "thermometer"-type iron temperature tester built by the Waage Mfg. Co. The iron rest on the asbestos pad with the edge of the soleplate over the metal tab. The tester also checks thermostat action - with the iron plugged into the receptacle the light goes off and on each time the thermostat opens and closes.

CHAPTER 3

Skillets — Sauce Pans

Electric skillets, sauce pans, fry pans, and similar appliances have a heating element built into the body of the unit (Fig. 3-1). The temperature of the unit is controlled by a thermostat. Should the heating element open in any of these units, it can't be repaired. The only repairs that you can make are to the thermostat, control unit, or cord/plug.

Two types of controls are commonly used. In one case the thermostat and control are built together and the unit plugs into the utensil as shown in Fig. 3-2. Fig. 3-3 shows three different types of plug-in controls. With the other, older type the thermostat and control unit are in the handle of the utensil and can't be unplugged. See Fig. 3-4.

Fig. 3-5 is a wiring diagram of a typical skillet. With the unit plugged into the AC outlet and the control turned on, the thermostat contacts close and the skillet starts to heat. When the skillet reaches the temperature indicated on the control setting the thermostat contacts open. Up until this time the neon lamp has been on. When the thermostat contacts open the neon lamp also goes out, indicating the utensil is ready for use.

COMPLAINTS

Complaints about the pan itself are confined to defective or damaged parts, or perhaps faulty assembly, and there isn't much you can do about it either. Warping of the pan may be caused by repeated insertion in cold water while the pan is still hot. Complaints about the temperature involves the probe, thermostat, temperature control, or plug/cord assembly.

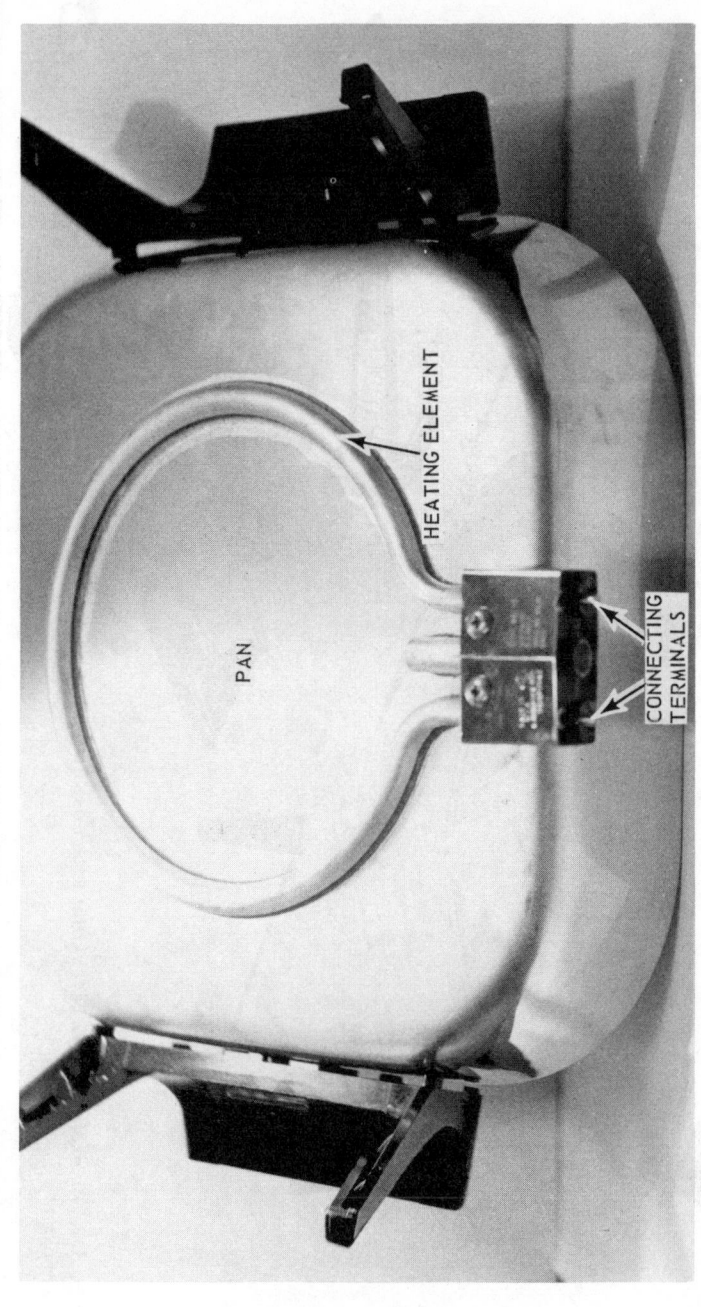

PAN

HEATING ELEMENT

CONNECTING TERMINALS

Fig. 3-1. Fry pans, sauce pans, pop corn poppers, and grills all have much in common. Most have an interchangeable cord with probe thermostat.

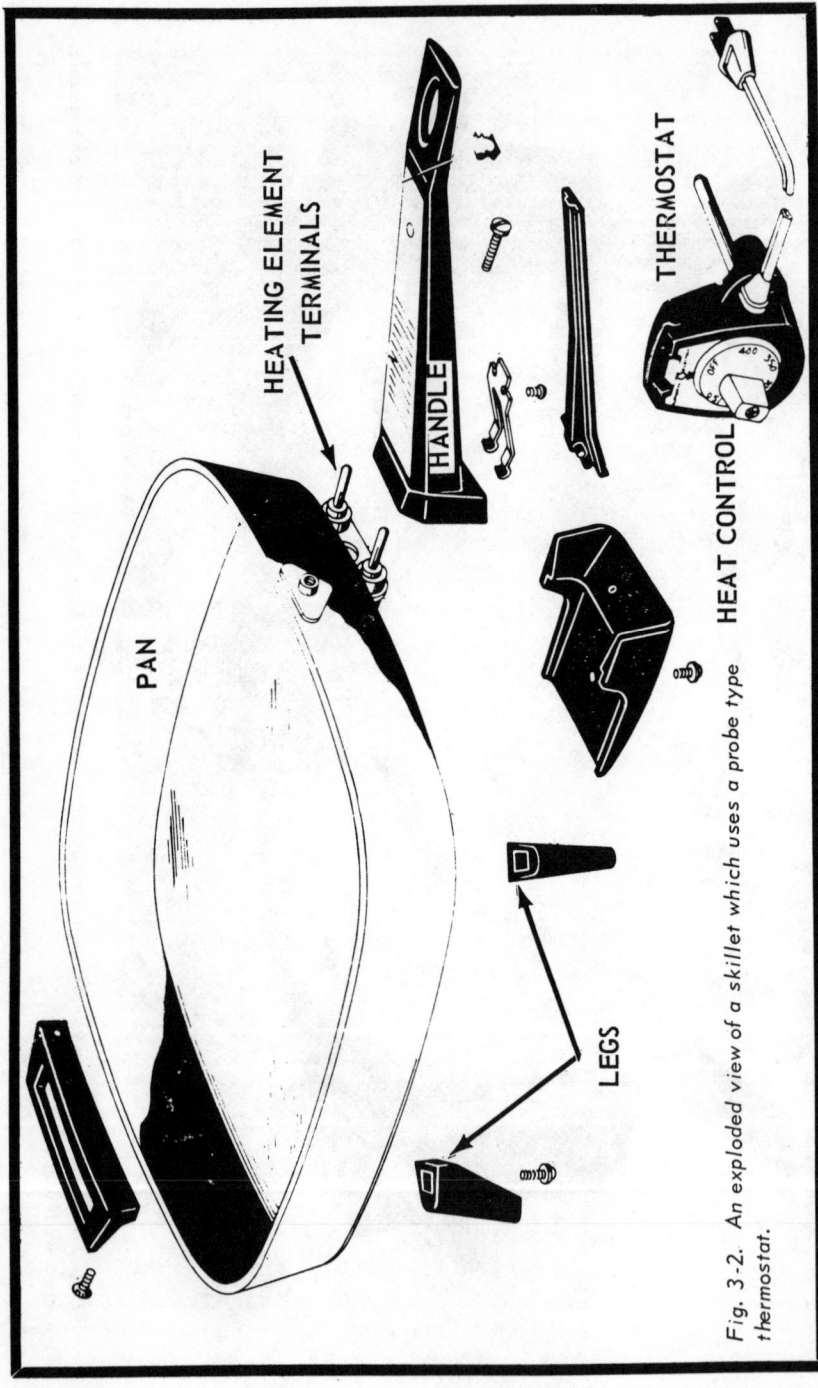

HEATING ELEMENT TERMINALS

HANDLE

THERMOSTAT

PAN

HEAT CONTROL

LEGS

Fig. 3-2. An exploded view of a skillet which uses a probe type thermostat.

No Heat

Use your appliance tester and check the line cord, plug, and thermostat connections for continuity, Fig. 3-6. A very simple way to check these parts is shown in Fig. 3-7. Connect a jumper wire between the two connecting terminals of the probe and plug the probe into the series section of the appliance tester. Turn on the switch connected in series with the 40-watt bulb. The temperature control on the probe can be at any position. If you have continuity the 40-watt bulb will light. This is a good time to check to see if there is a loose connection in the probe, or perhaps a partly broken line cord, or a broken plug. Move the cord and plug around. If there is a loose connection and continuity is lost, the lamp will go out or flicker off and on.

A word of caution. DO NOT connect a jumper wire between the probe connecting terminals and plug the probe into an AC outlet. You would have a definite shock hazard—and in addition, with no load (the heating element in this case) the thermostat will burn out or the points weld together. Replace any defective parts found. Don't try to repair the cord unless there is no replacement available.

If the cord, plug, and thermostat assembly are good then the heating element is probably open. Don't throw the pan away just yet. To be sure of yourself, take the test leads and your appliance tester and check the continuity of the heating element, Fig. 3-8.

As stated before, if the heating element is open you can't repair the utensil. If the probe and cord are good but the skillet still won't heat, then more than likely the heating element is open. But should you get continuity through the heating element, it's just possible that the connecting terminals between the heating element and the probe are bad, and these can be changed on some pans (Fig. 3-9) by screwing off the old ones and replacing with new ones.

Temperature Incorrect

Complaints about temperature involve the probe, thermostat, temperature control, or the plug and cord assembly. Plug the skillet into an AC outlet and connect a temperature test jig to the skillet (Fig. 3-10). Set the temperature control on the skillet to 200°. Let the skillet cycle a few times.

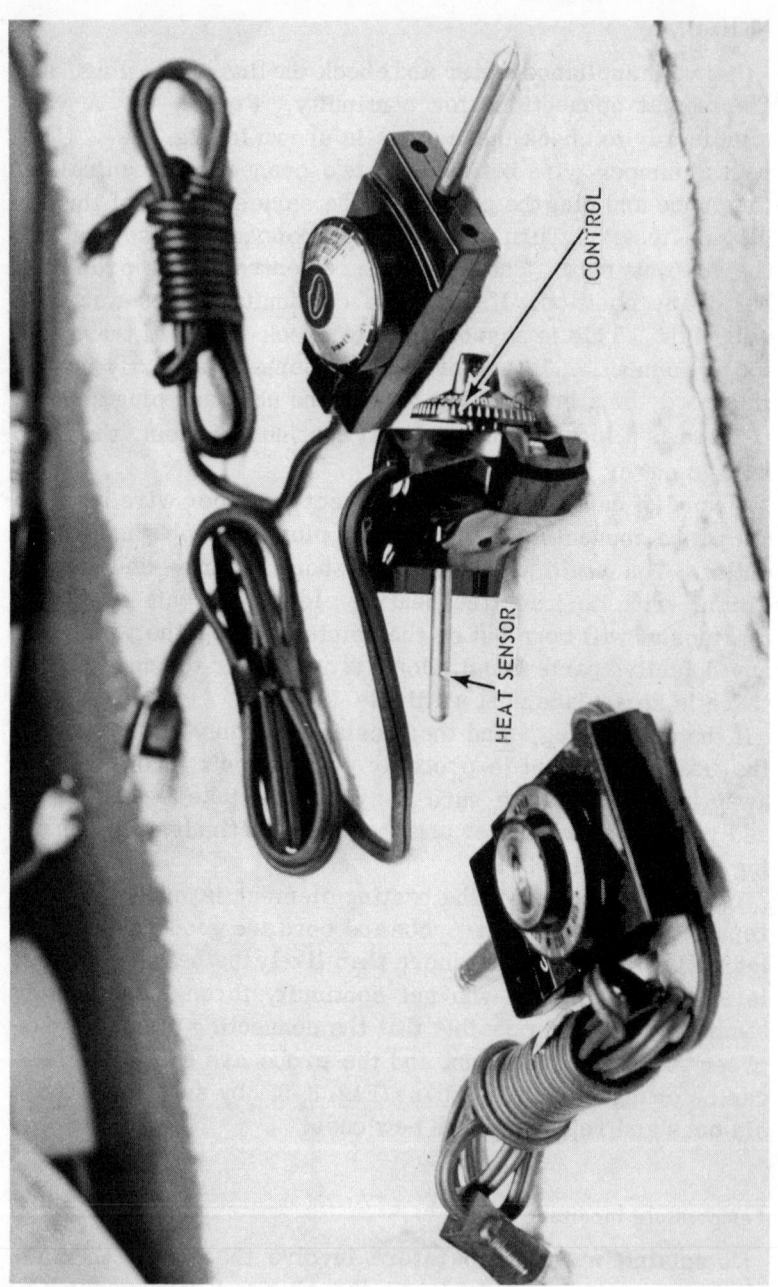

CONTROL

HEAT SENSOR

Fig. 3-3. Here are some different type probe thermostat units. All work in essentially the same manner.

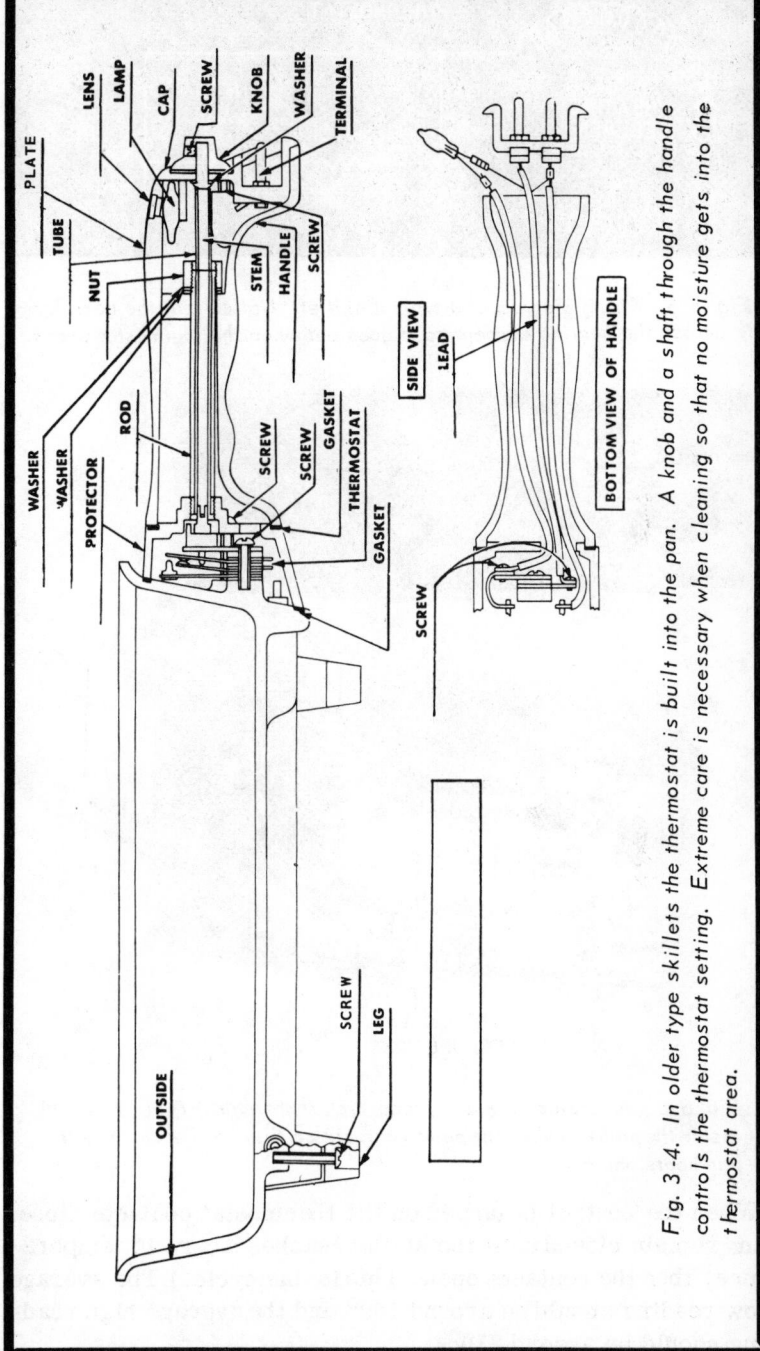

Fig. 3-4. In older type skillets the thermostat is built into the pan. A knob and a shaft through the handle controls the thermostat setting. Extreme care is necessary when cleaning so that no moisture gets into the thermostat area.

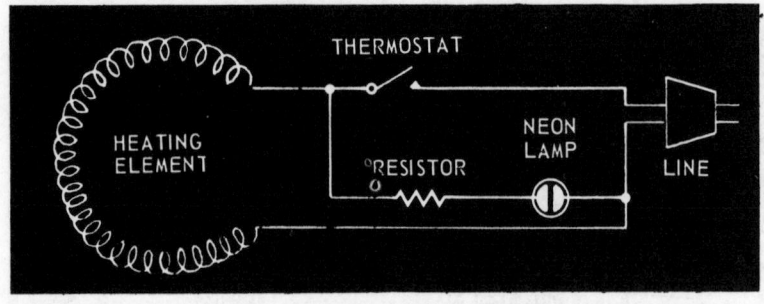

Fig. 3-5. Wiring diagram of a typical skillet. Notice that the neon lamp is across the heating element so it goes out when the thermostat opens.

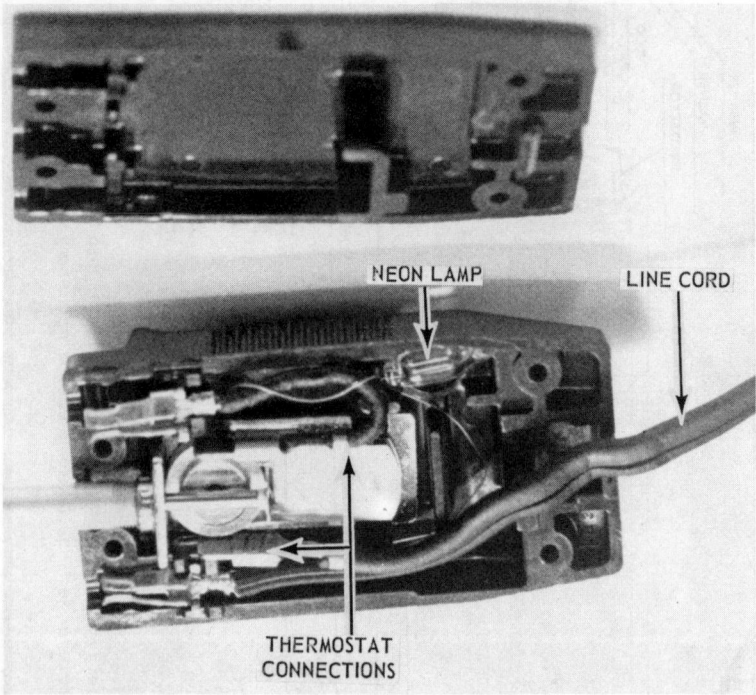

Fig. 3-6. An inside look at a probe-type thermostat. A bi-metal rod inside the probe pushes the point contacts so they open or close as the pan heats and cools.

(When the control is turned on the thermostat contacts close, and remain closed until the skillet reaches a certain temperature, then the contacts open. This is one cycle.) The average low reading should be around 180° and the average high reading should be around 210°.

46

Keep in mind that the test jig is over the heating element and the thermostat is located at the back of the skillet, so for uniform heat over the entire pan you must wait a few cycles. Skillets with "pull-out" controls usually are not quite as accurate as the type with the controls built into the handle. If the temperature is not correct the thermostat, temperature controls, connections, etc., can be cleaned as stated in other Chapters. If you find considerable damage in a plug-in type probe, it's best to replace the complete unit.

Neon Bulb Doesn't Light, But Skillet Heats

The bulb on the unit goes out when the correct temperature is reached, so it's important to the customer that the bulb works. Check the resistor in series with the neon bulb. If it is open you can tell just by looking as a rule. But if you want an accurate check use an ohmmeter; it should read between about 22,000 and 82,000 ohms.

If the resistor checks good, look for a cracked or broken bulb. Also, the leads of the neon might be touching, which would short circuit the lamp and keep it from working. Re-

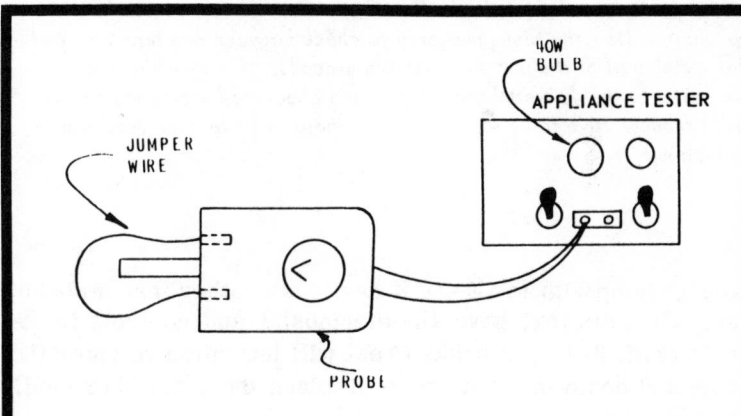

Fig. 3-7. Shown here is a quick way to check the cord, plug, and control unit for continuity. Connect a jumper wire between the connecting terminals on the probe. Plug into the series test (40-watt lamp switch only on) and turn the probe control to some temperature setting. If all parts are good the 40-watt lamp on the tester will light. Wiggle the cord to make sure it is not intermittently opening.

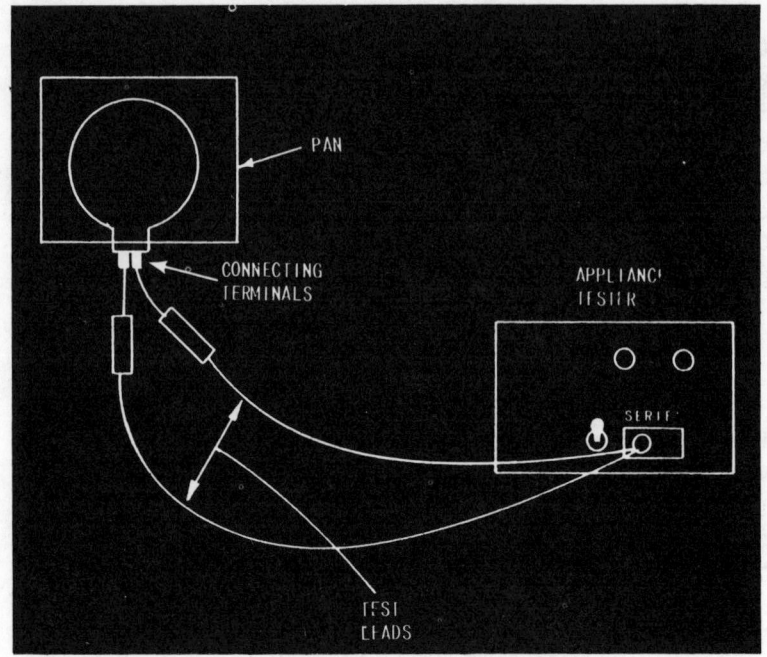

Fig. 3-8. The heating element can be checked for continuity with the appliance tester. Switch in the heating element to make sure there are no shorts. Use the test lamp only to check between one terminal and the metal part of the pan for possible grounds. If either the neon on the tester or the 40-watt lamp lights when checking for grounds the pan will probably have to be replaced since there is little that can be done to repair it.

place the lamp with an NE-2 if it has leads rather than a socket base. On units that have the thermostat and controls in the handle (Fig. 3-11), a broken seal will let moisture enter the handle and could cause a short. Replace the seal if damaged.

Overheating

If the contact points on the thermostat are fused together, the skillet or pan will overheat. Recall that the contact points open when the skillet reaches the proper temperature. Check the thermostat. The temperature adjustment could be incorrect. Refer to the previous section on Temperature.

Low Heat

Check for loose terminal connections. Replace if worn, dirty, or pitted. The contact points on the thermostat could also cause this trouble. If they are not making a good connection they act as a high resistance which reduces the current to the heating element. It's best to replace the thermostat.

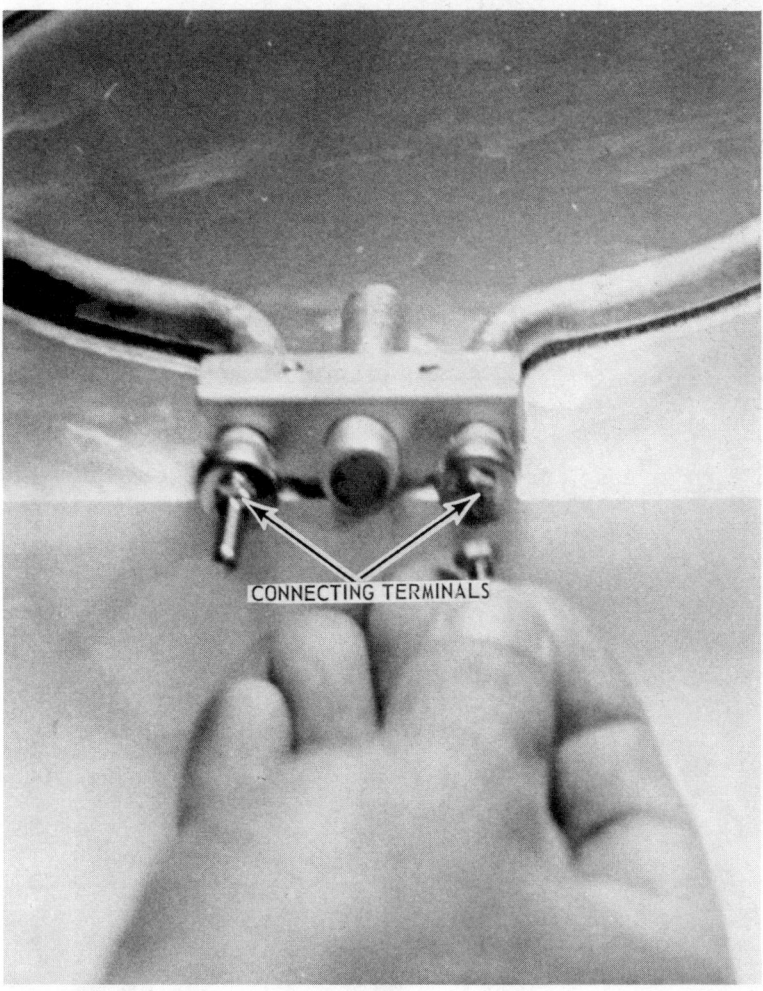

Fig. 3-9. Some pans have replaceable terminals as shown here. If the terminals develop bad pitting, lose their shiny appearance, or do not fit the plug, they must be replaced.

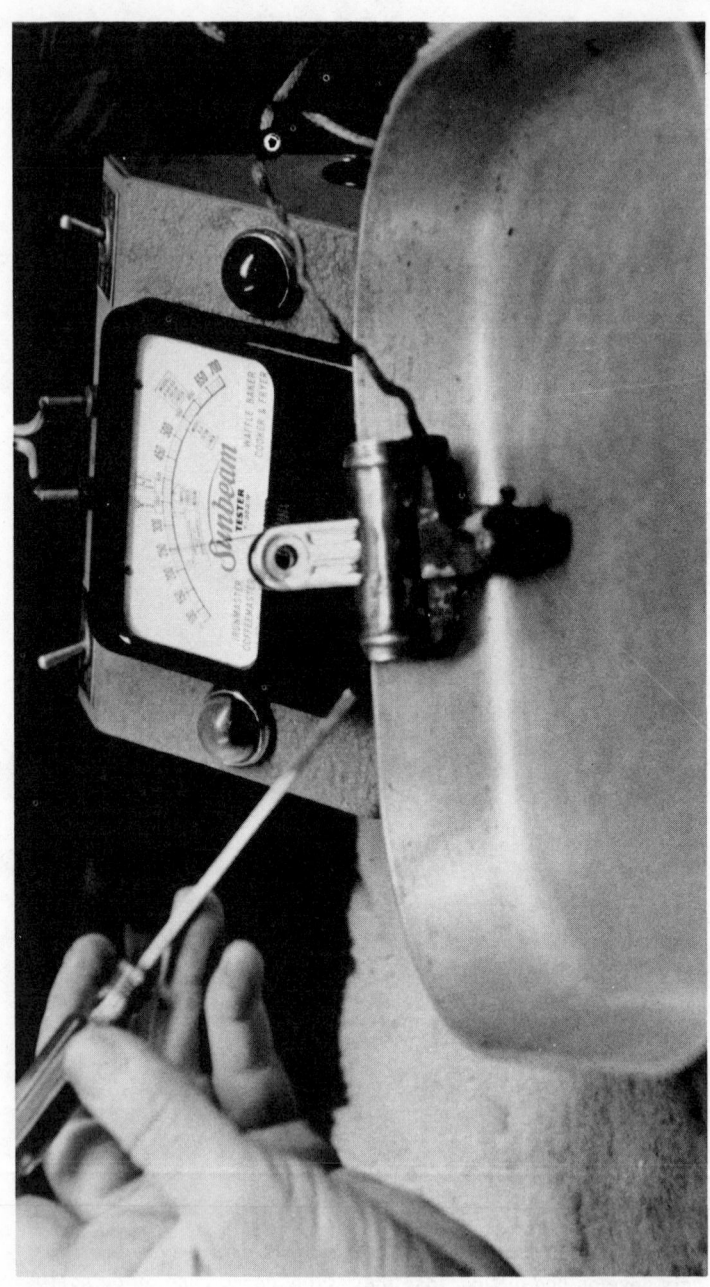

Fig. 3-10. Here, a clip-on thermocouple and a meter is used to check the thermostat setting of a skillet.

Fig. 3-11. A broken seal on this skillet allowed moisture to enter, causing a short as well as damage to the thermostat control gears.

Dented Utensil Body

Those small dents in the aluminum body can be hammered out with a leather or rubber mallet, with a little care. Aluminum bends easily so don't hit too hard.

Terminal Post Burnt or Pitted

This can be caused by a loose cord or probe connection. Replace both terminal posts if they are burned so bad you can't smooth them up, or if they're badly discolored. When replacing the terminals be sure you get a good solid connection.

DISASSEMBLY INSTRUCTIONS

Usually, no specific instructions are needed to disassemble the control probe, but on some models you have to remove the decal to get to the screws that hold the control together. If the decal is glued on, you will have to tear the decal off and glue a new one on when you have completed the repairs.

CARE AND CLEANING INSTRUCTIONS

Always allow an appliance to cool before washing. Washing a hot appliance in cold water could cause warping of the pan. Place the appliance in the sink and wash with warm water and a mild detergent. Only in extreme cases will it be necessary to scrub lightly with a fine steel wool cleaning pad. Rinse with clean water.

To remove stubborn food particles, pour in enough water to cover the food particles, add a small amount of mild detergent. Cover and set temperature control for 200° and let the skillet heat. Food particles will be loosened in a few minutes. Do not mar or scratch the cooking surface with a spoon, knife, or abrasive. Also, do not immerse the plug-in type controls in water. Just wipe clean with a damp cloth.

CHAPTER 4

Irons

There are three types of modern electric irons: dry (Fig. 4-1), steam (Fig. 4-2), and steam and spray (Fig. 4-3). They all use a sealed, tubular-type heating element which is cast into the aluminum soleplate (Fig. 4-4). The element heats the soleplate, and the amount of heat is controlled by a thermostat. A heat regulator control, conveniently mounted on the iron (Fig. 4-5), can be adjusted for different temperatures, by one of many types of thermostats currently being used. (Thermostats are covered in Chapter 2.)

Steam irons have a built-in water container or reservoir (Fig. 4-6) which holds a few ounces of water; a separate control turns the steam on and off. The heating element in the iron heats both the soleplate and the water in the reservoir. A small tube (Fig. 4-6), called a valve assembly, connects the spray nozzle with the water tank. When the spray button is pressed, water and steam are forced from the water tank through the connecting tube to the opening of the nozzle.

Setting the temperature dial or knob controls the thermostat, which in turn controls the heat of the iron. When the thermostat is closed (Fig. 4-7) the iron draws current and heats up. When the correct temperature is reached the thermostat opens and shuts off the current. This opening and closing of the thermostat is called a cycle. (If the iron is working properly it should reach a fairly steady temperature after about three cycles.) Regardless of the control setting, when the iron draws current it consumes its full wattage, around 1000 to 1100 watts, until the thermostat automatically shuts off the current. Fig. 4-8 shows a cut-away view of an assembled steam and spray iron.

GENERAL REPAIR PRACTICES

Repairing an iron takes good, common - sense procedures, and it's a sure thing that the right approach will pay off. Here

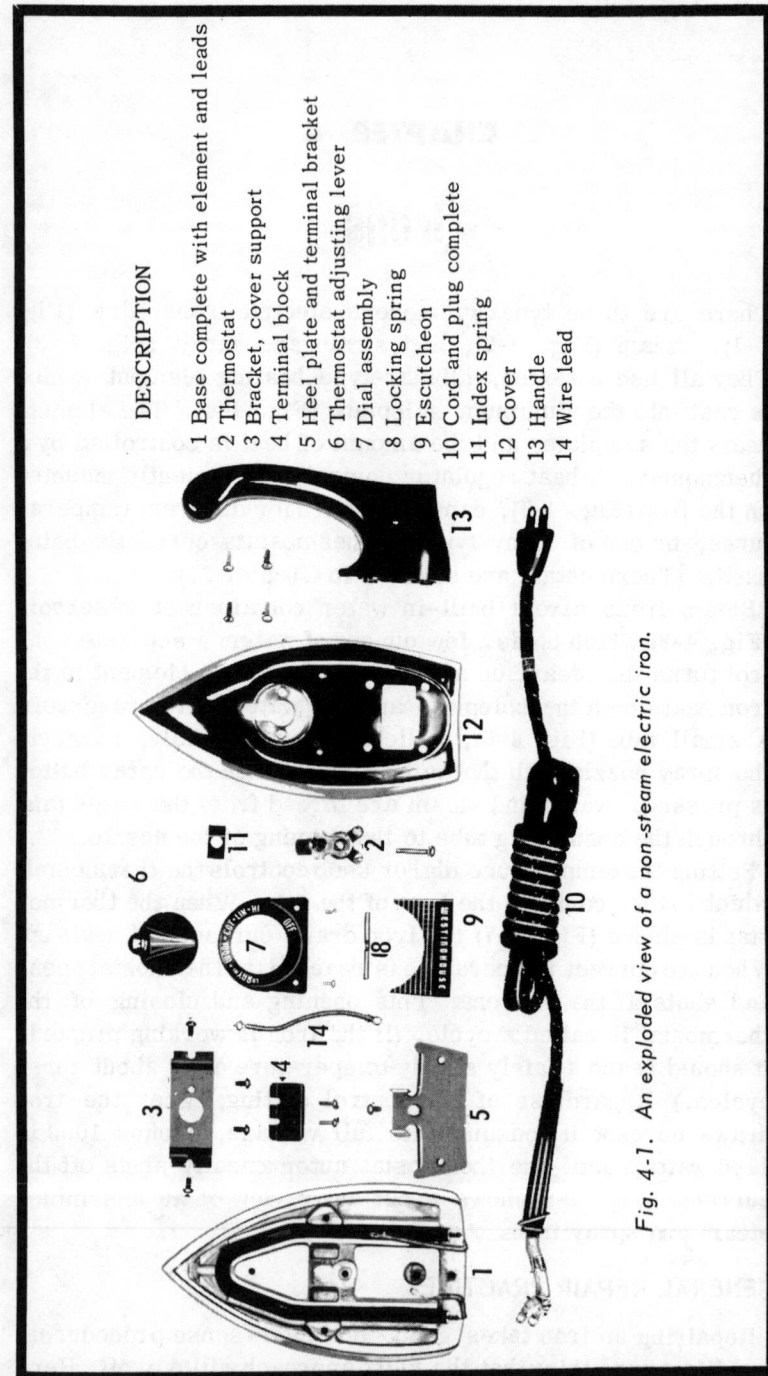

DESCRIPTION

1 Base complete with element and leads
2 Thermostat
3 Bracket, cover support
4 Terminal block
5 Heel plate and terminal bracket
6 Thermostat adjusting lever
7 Dial assembly
8 Locking spring
9 Escutcheon
10 Cord and plug complete
11 Index spring
12 Cover
13 Handle
14 Wire lead

Fig. 4-1. An exploded view of a non-steam electric iron.

are many good ideas—learn them...use them; if you do, repairs will be much faster and easier.

(1) During disassembly and assembly don't "force" anything —all the parts in the iron were made to fit. If you get them together the way they should be, or take them apart right, you generally won't have to use force. When you disassemble the iron keep all the parts in one place, or perhaps in a small box. You won't have to hunt them up when you get ready to put the iron back together.

(2) Good troubleshooting techniques will save you lots of time. For example, if the iron heats but there is no control over the temperature, there is no need to check the cord or plug. With this trouble the cord, plug, or connecting terminals could not be at fault, but you should always check their condition anyway. If they are damaged, replace if possible. Repair the cord only when a replacement is not available. The connecting terminals should be tight and free from corrosion, Fig. 4-9. Tighten and clean when necessary.

(3) Most all companies publish service bulletins or manuals. If there is one available on the iron you are working on, use it. Read it carefully. Who knows better what the iron is upposed to do than the company that made it? The more you use the bulletins the more familiar you'll become with the iron.

(4) Know what you are trying to fix—know what the iron does or doesn't do before you start. It probably doesn't need a complete overhaul. If you know the symptoms of trouble, you can save yourself a lot of unnecessary work. When possible, ask the customer about the behavior of the iron. Don't guess. Know what you are looking for.

(5) Everything in an iron was put there for a reason. It has a job to do. Don't overlook a part just because it's small. It could be your trouble. In addition to being small, many of the parts in the iron are very fragile and easy broken. Handle with care!

(6) Small fragile parts are broken many times by not using the right tool for the right job. I know you have probably heard

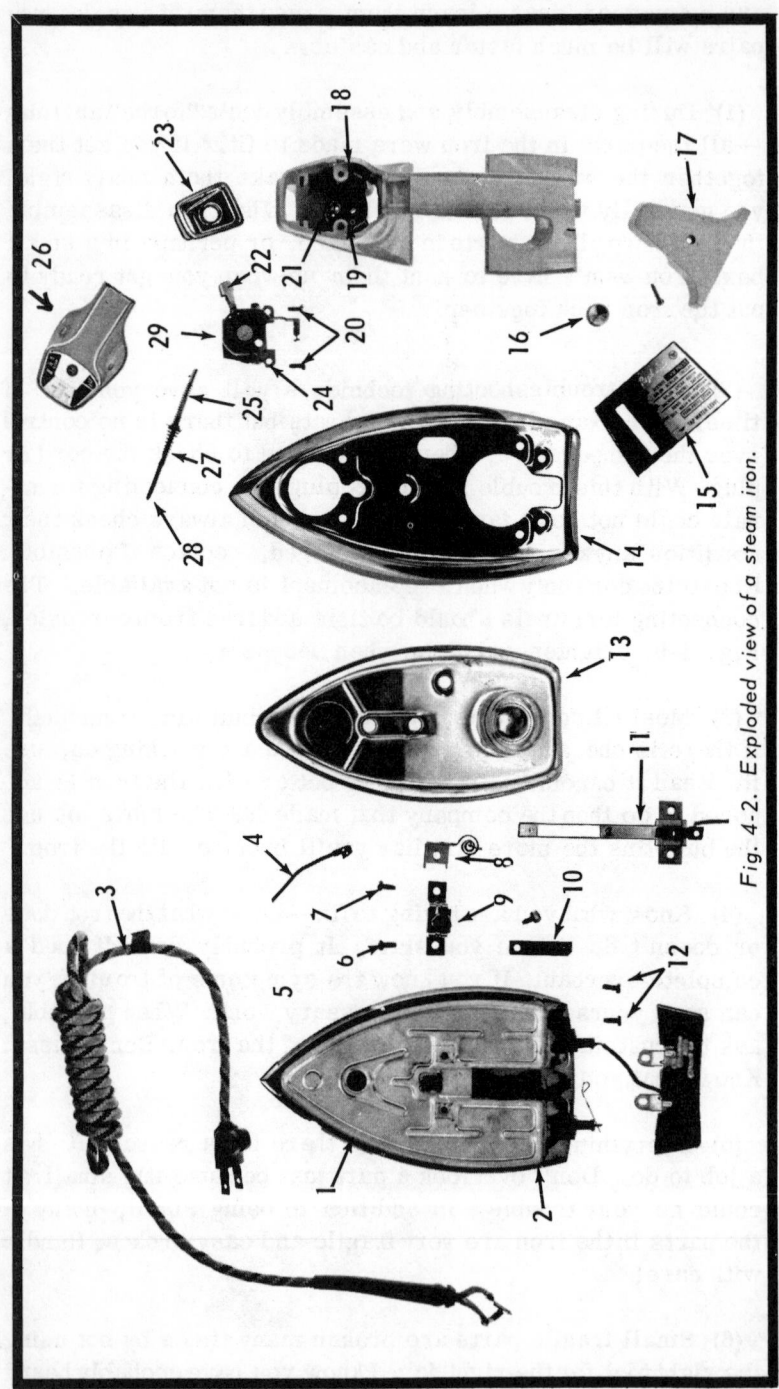

Fig. 4-2. Exploded view of a steam iron.

NO	DESCRIPTION
1.	Cover plate for base with valve seat
2.	Base complete with cover plate
3.	Cord and plug
4.	Indicator hand
5.	Screw
6.	Screw
7.	Screw
8.	Indicator bi—metal complete
9.	U Bracket with stud
10.	Bi—metal assembly & mounting screw
11.	Thermostat assembly with bi—metal
12.	Screws
13.	Tank complete
14.	Cover
15.	Escutcheon
16.	Plug button
17.	Cover plate, cord
18.	Spring clip
19.	Spring Clip
20.	Screws
21.	Guide cup, valve assembly
22.	Knob, control lever
23.	Trim, front of handle
24.	Can assembly complete
25.	Spring valve assembly
26.	Adjusting Screw, can assembly
27.	Spring valve assembly
28.	Valve assembly
29.	Top cap, dial plate assembly

this often, but it's still true. Use the right tool. (Check Chapter 1.)

(7) Do a good job. Repair the iron the way it should be repaired. Have the iron working properly before you return it to the customer. Repair it like it was your own, and you were the customer.

COMMON COMPLAINTS

The complaints listed here are general and apply to all irons.

Won't Heat

First make a visual check of the cord, plug, and terminals connecting the cord to the iron, for any sign of defects. Re-

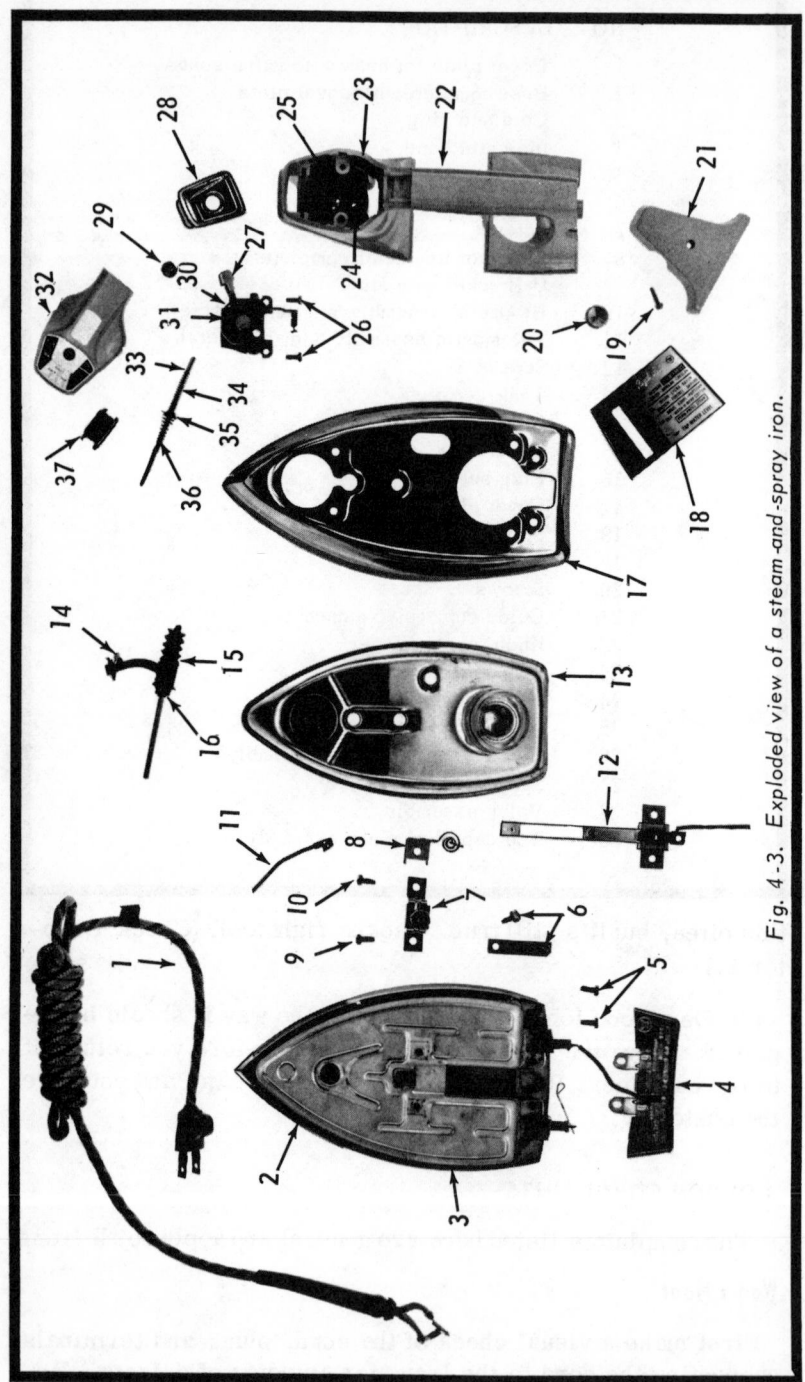

Fig. 4-3. Exploded view of a steam-and-spray iron.

NO.	DESCRIPTION
1	Cord and plug
2	Cover plate for base
3	Base assembly
4	Heel plate
5	Screws
6	Bi—metal assembly & mounting screw
7	U Bracket with stud
8	Indicator bi—metal complete
9–10	Screws
11	Hand indicator
12	Thermostat assembly with bi—metal
13	Water tank
14	Gasket nozzel
15	Pump, complete
16	Gasket, pump to handle
17	Cover
18	Escutcheon
19	Screw
20	Plug button
21	Cover plate, cord
22	Handle
23	Spring clip
24	Spring clip
25	Guide cup valve assembly
26	Screws
27	Knob, control lever
28	Trim
29	Spray nozzle
30	Cam assembly complete
31	Adjusting screw, cam assembly
32	Top cap, dial plate assembly
33	Hex cap nut cam follower
34	Spring valve assembly
35	Valve assembly
36	Spring, valve assembly
37	Spring clip

place the cord if necessary. If no visual defects are noted, make a continuity check of the cord with your appliance tester, Fig. 4-9. If you find an open or short, replace the cord.

If no defect is found in the cord or plug, check for an open heating element, using the tester, Fig. 4-10. If you don't have an appliance tester, you can check the heating element for continuity with an ohmmeter.

If the heating element is open, you must replace the soleplate. If the element has continuity, check the contact points on the thermostat; they may be dirty or pitted and not making a good connection, Fig. 4-10A. In some cases you can clean the

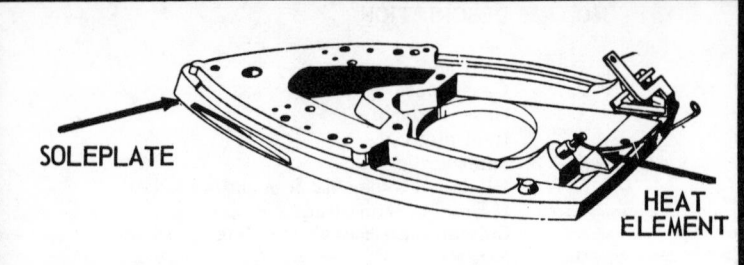

SOLEPLATE
HEAT
ELEMENT
Fig. 4-4. A typical soleplate and heating element. The heating element in modern irons is cast into the soleplate and cannot be repaired.

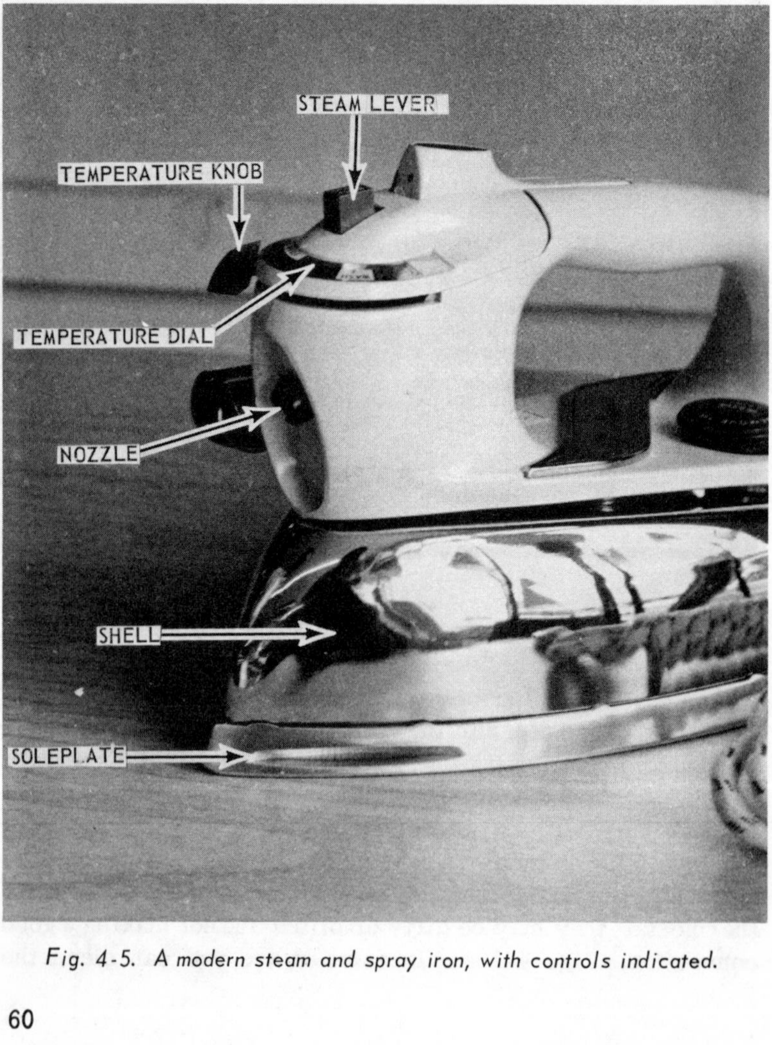

STEAM LEVER
TEMPERATURE KNOB
TEMPERATURE DIAL
NOZZLE
SHELL
SOLEPLATE
Fig. 4-5. A modern steam and spray iron, with controls indicated.

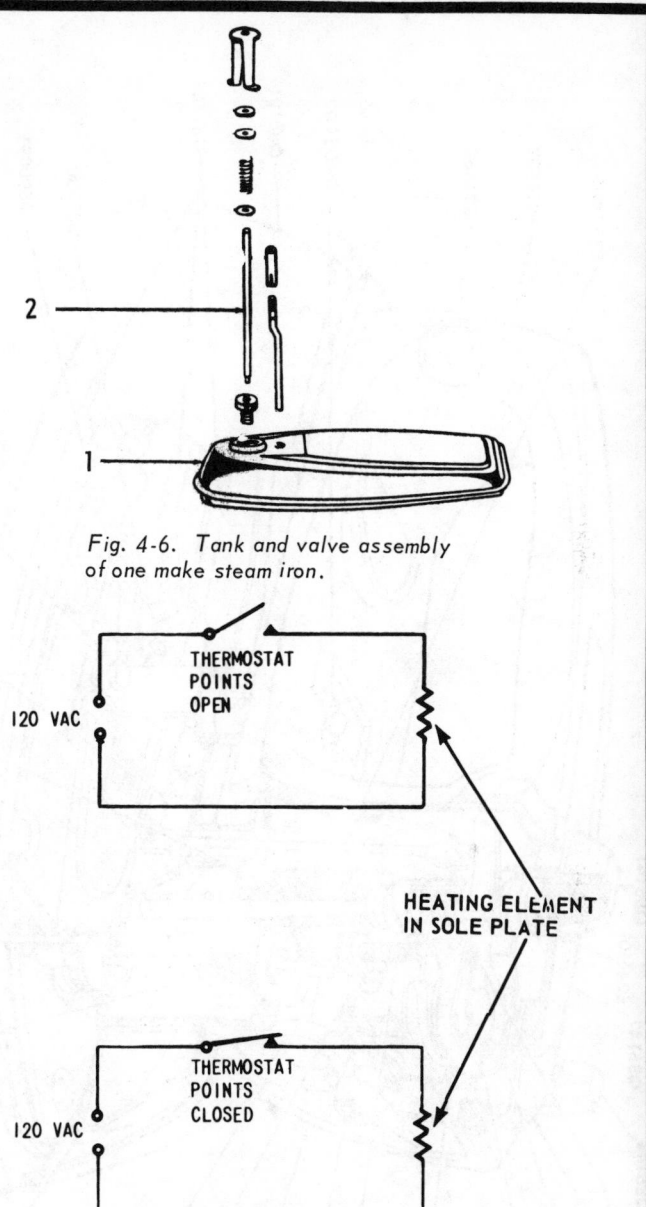

Fig. 4-6. Tank and valve assembly of one make steam iron.

THERMOSTAT POINTS OPEN

120 VAC

HEATING ELEMENT IN SOLE PLATE

THERMOSTAT POINTS CLOSED

120 VAC

Fig. 4-7. Wiring diagram of an electric iron. When the thermostat is closed the iron draws current and heats. When the thermostat opens the iron begins to cool. This opening and closing is called a cycle. If working properly the iron should reach a steady temperature after about three cycles.

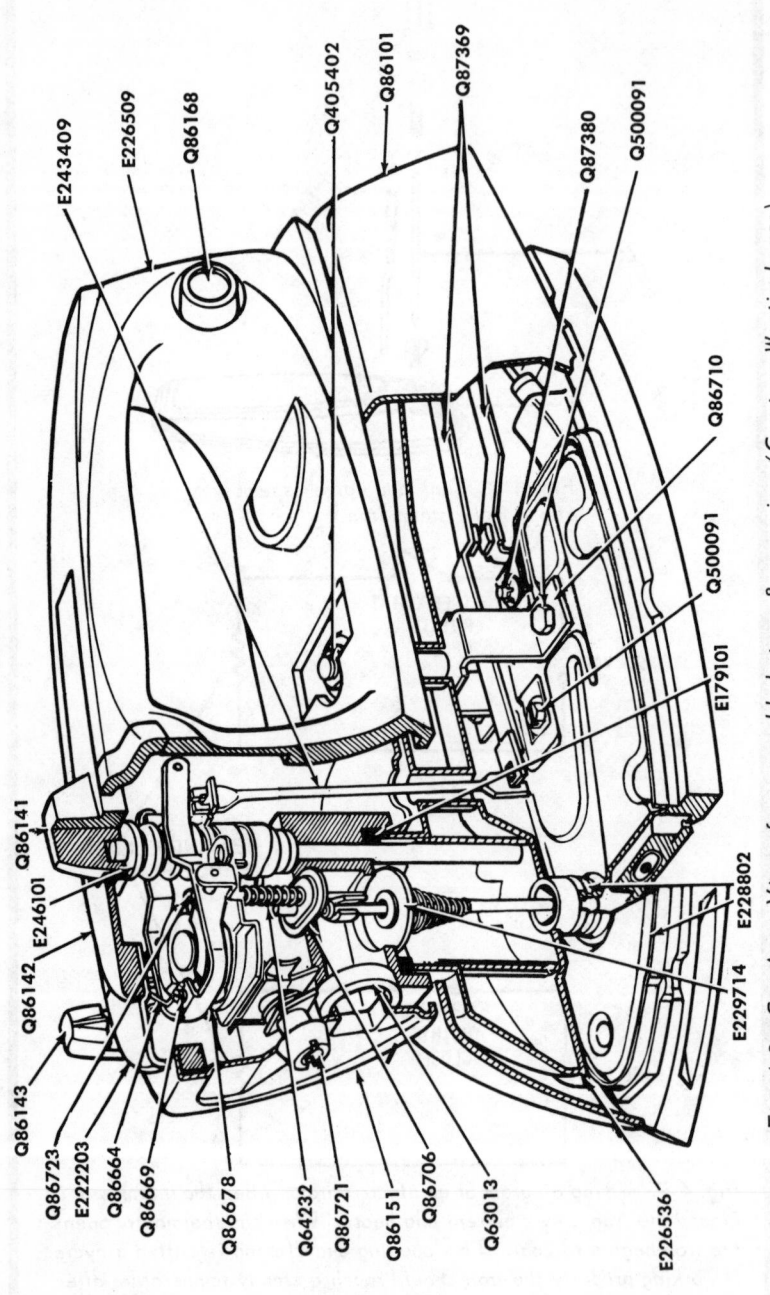

E243409
E226509
Q86168
Q405402
Q86101
Q87369
Q87380
Q500091
Q86710
Q500091
E17910I
Q86141
E24610I
Q86142
Q86143
Q86723
E222203
Q86664
Q86669
Q86678
Q64232
Q86721
Q86151
Q86706
Q63013
E226536
E229714
E228802

Fig. 4-8. Cut-Away View of an assembled steam & spray iron.(Courtesy Westinghouse)

NO	DESCRIPTION
Q86141	Spray lever
E246101	Pump kit complete
Q86142	Top cover dial plate to handle
Q86143	Knob, control lever
Q86723	Hex cap nut, cam follower, valve assembly
E222203	Dial plate
Q86664	Spring, cam assembly
Q86669	Adjusting screw, cam assembly
Q86678	Cam assembly complete
Q64232	Spring, top, valve assembly
Q86721	Spray nozzle
Q86151	Trim, Front of handle
Q86706	Guide cup, valve assembly
Q63013	Gasket, front trim
E226536	Tank complete with level indicator
E229714	Valve assembly
E228802	Cover plate for base with valve seat
E179101	Gasket, between tank throat & handle
Q500091	Screw, thermostat and bi—metal
Q86710	U—bracket with stud
Q500091	Screw, thermostat and bi—metal
Q87380	Bi—metal assembly
Q87369	Thermostat assembly with bi—metal
Q86101	Cover
Q405402	Nut, U—bracket to cover
Q86168	Plug button
E226509	Handle
E243409	Control link, thermostat arm to cam

contact points with a small file, but it's not always a good idea. The coating on the contact points is so thin that slight filing removes most of the coating. By cleaning dirty or pitted points you may get the iron working again, but you are probably just delaying replacement of the thermostat, and your reputation certainly won't be enhanced by such tactics! Replacement is best.

Heat Too High or Too Low

Using an iron temperature test stand, check the iron for operation within the limits shown in Fig. 4-12. Plug in the iron; set on the "steam" position (if it's not a steam iron set it to the middle of the dial), and place it on the test stand (Fig. 4-11). Allow the iron to heat through three cycles, then check the temperature against the chart in Fig. 4-12. Each manufacturer chooses slightly different temperature settings, also different plus-minus values for their irons, but this is a good average of those values.

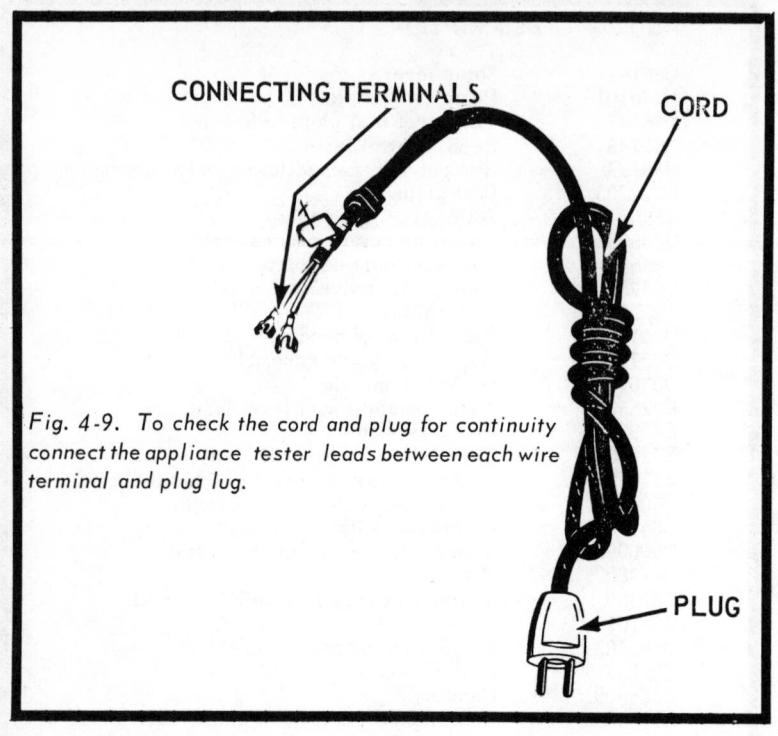

CONNECTING TERMINALS

CORD

Fig. 4-9. To check the cord and plug for continuity connect the appliance tester leads between each wire terminal and plug lug.

PLUG

Check to see that the iron is "off" when the temperature control is in the "off" position. The iron should come on (when it's cold) about the first mark after the "Off" position, usually a 1/4" or so. Try more than one temperature setting to make sure the iron is changing temperature when the control is moved. Here are two conditions that could occur. First, the iron could be changing temperature at the various settings but be either too high or too low. The other condition is that the iron does not turn off.

If the iron changes temperature as you move the temperature dial but is not the correct temperature, you may be able to adjust the thermostat to correct it. There are many different types of adjustment screws (Fig. 4-13) and most can be reached by a hole in the cover assembly after the iron has been partially disassembled. Turning the adjustment screw clockwise decreases the temperature and turning the adjustment screw counterclockwise increases the temperature on most irons. You can't always count on this; it may be the reverse.

If you have the iron disassembled to where you can see the

bi-metal strip and contact points, you can tell which direction a turn of the screw will increase the temperature. If the contact point moves away from the bi-metal strip or if the contact points move away from each other, the temperature will increase. The greater the distance between the two, the longer it takes for the bi-metal strip to bend enough to open the contacts.

If the iron heats but the thermostat does not turn it off, the iron will become very hot, so hot it could even melt the sole-plate. The contact points are probably stuck or fused together, or the bi-metal strip is not functioning correctly. In either case the thermostat assembly should be replaced.

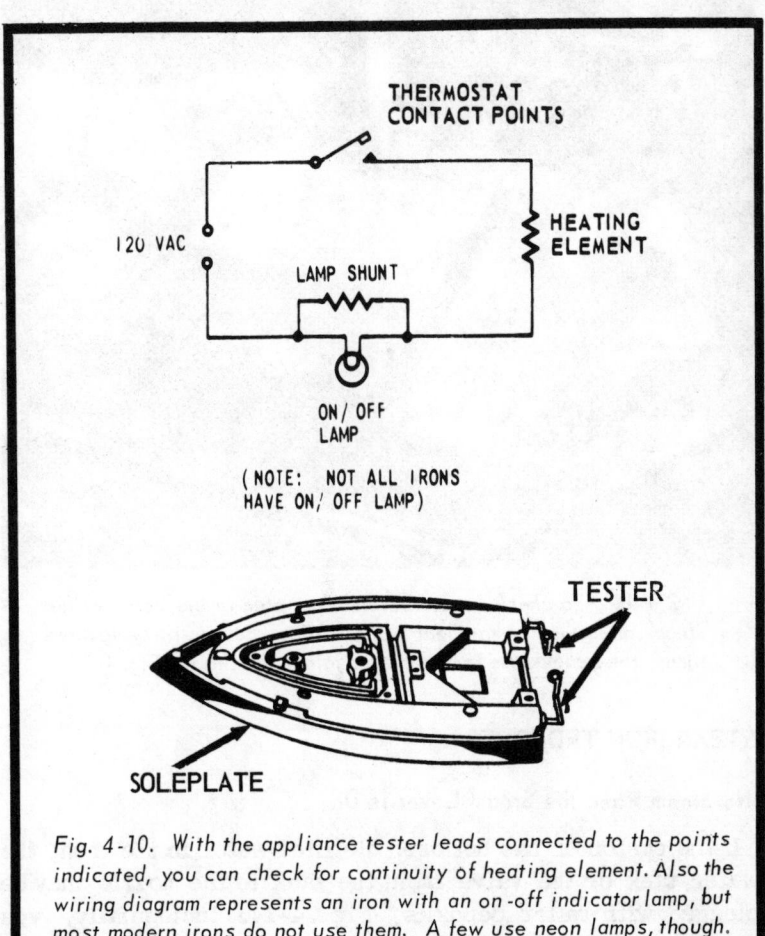

Fig. 4-10. With the appliance tester leads connected to the points indicated, you can check for continuity of heating element. Also the wiring diagram represents an iron with an on-off indicator lamp, but most modern irons do not use them. A few use neon lamps, though.

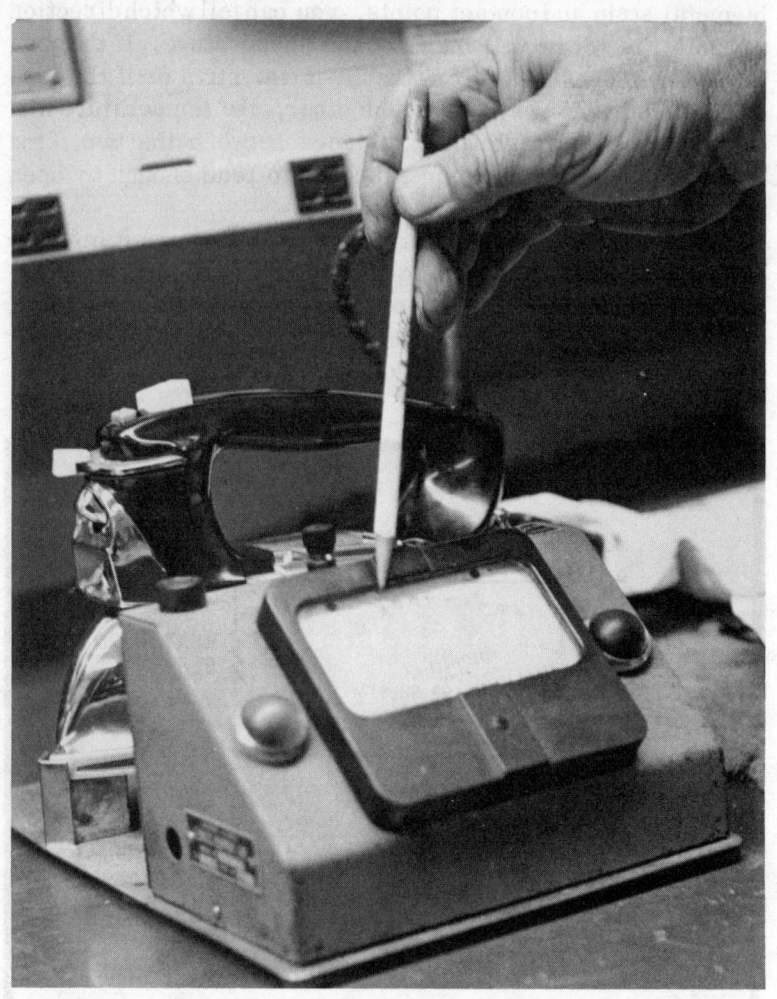

Fig. 4-11. To check for correct heating, plug in the iron, set for steam, and place on the heat stand. Allow the iron to cycle three times, then check the temperature against the chart in Fig. 4-12.

STEAM IRON TROUBLES

No Steam When the Steam Lever is On

If the customer has not used distilled water in the iron, the water tank or the valve from the tank to the nozzle may be clogged with water deposits, Fig. 4-14. Incidentally, you should advise the customer to use distilled water in steam

AVERAGE TEMPERATURE CHART

Synthetic	220°
Rayon	275°
Steam	300°
Wool	340°
Cotton	400°
Linen	455°
Maximum	500°

(All temperatures ± 50° ; control set in the middle of each range)

Fig. 4-12. Average temperature chart

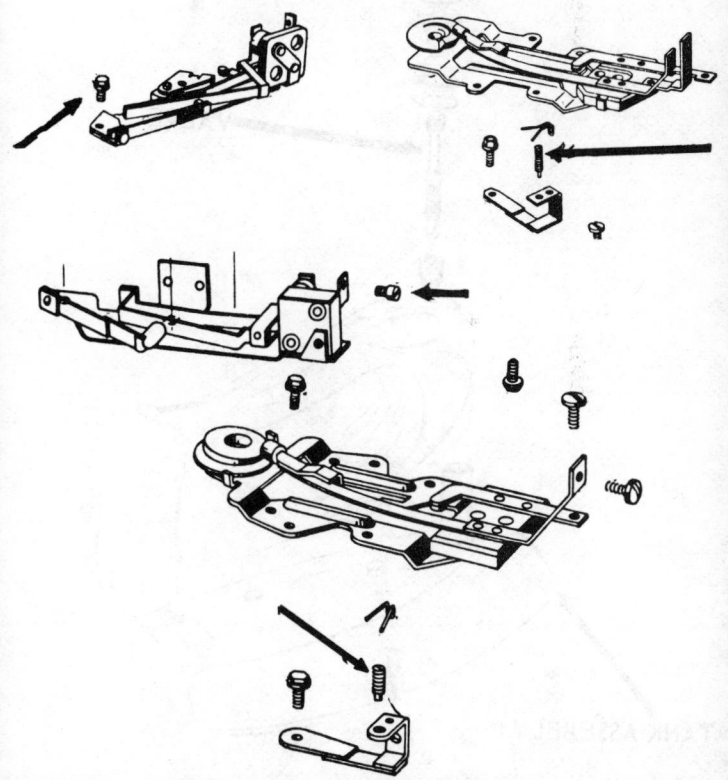

Fig. 4-13. Examples of internal temperature control adjustments used in electric irons.

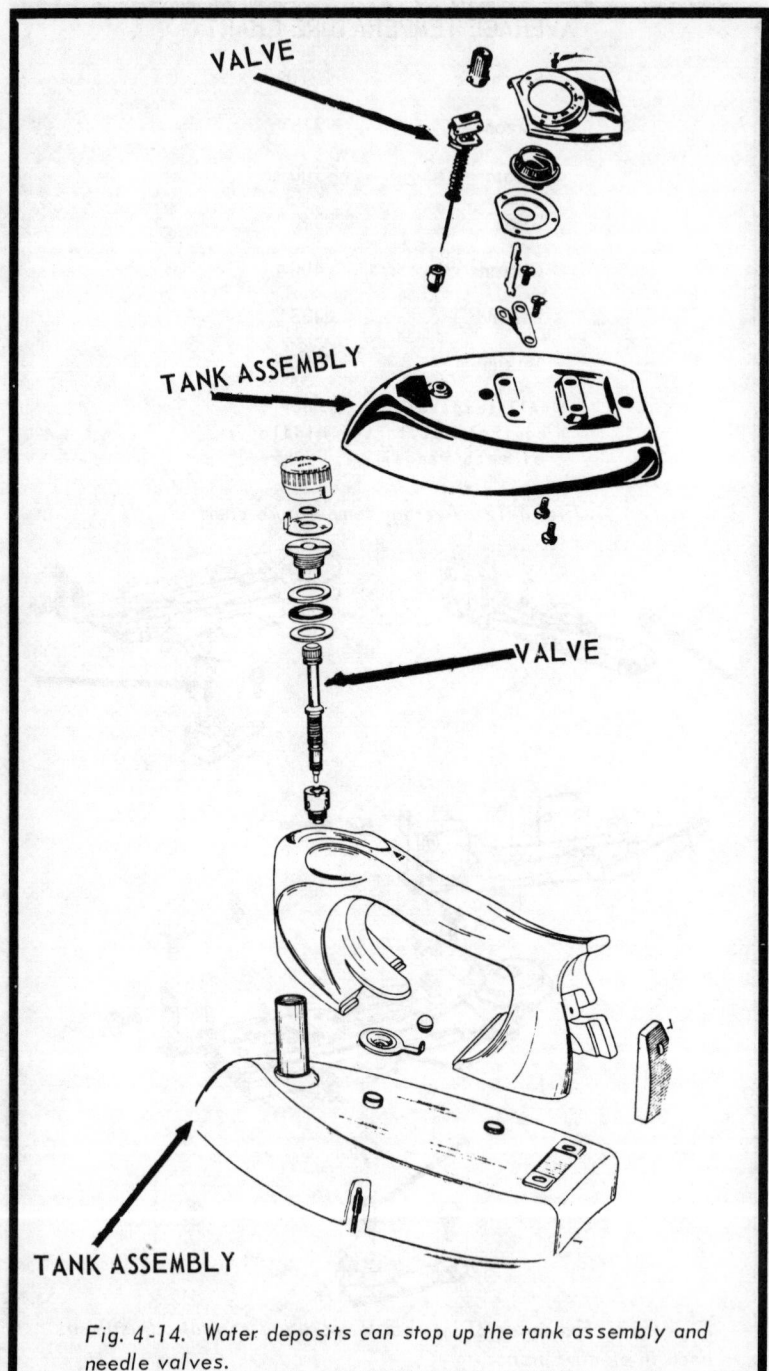

VALVE

TANK ASSEMBLY

VALVE

TANK ASSEMBLY

Fig. 4-14. Water deposits can stop up the tank assembly and needle valves.

and spray irons to prevent deposit build-up. If the customer is unable to purchase distilled water, rainwater caught in a plastic container strained through nylon hose is satisfactory.

In most cases water deposits can be removed without too much trouble. There are a number of suitable products on the market. One type of iron cleaner is called SSS-T, manufactured by Fast Chemical Products Corp., Yonkers, N.Y. Take a small amount of the cleaner, mixed with water, and pour into the iron. Place the iron in the sink or other heat-proof surface which will allow the mixture to drip through the holes. Set the iron for "steam" and use the lowest temperature you can and still have steam. On spray-type irons turn the temperature to steam and press the spray button a few times. About one minute should be sufficient to clean the iron. After the spray parts have been cleaned, allow the rest of the solution to drip through the iron. After cleaning, rinse the iron according to the directions on the cleaner container.

Another good cleaner is distilled white vinegar. Fill the tank with vinegar, set the temperature for low heat and plug in the iron. Put the steam button on and let the vinegar pass through the valve and nozzle. One tank full usually removes the deposits. If the valve or the cavity of the valve seat is coated with stubborn deposits, a cotton swab soaked in muratic acid will usually remove them. Of course, in a case of this type you would have to disassemble the iron.

Oil and grease film can also clog the valve. To correct this, operate the iron at least an hour at maximum heat to bake out the oil fim. Sometimes it may be necessary to heat the valve itself with a small gas flame to drive the oil off. Keep the flame about an inch away from the valve. Be careful not to overheat and melt the valve! Let the valve cool naturally, as compressed air could deposit another film.

Iron Steams When the Steam Lever Is Off

Check the pin on the bottom of the valve body and the valve spring. If the pin is bent or damaged, or if the spring is weak, the valve body will not seat properly. This allows water to pass, even though the steam lever is set to off, Fig. 4-15.

Iron Leaks Water

Look for a bad gasket. If any of the gaskets shown in Fig. 4-16 were cracked, worn out, or not seating properly, the

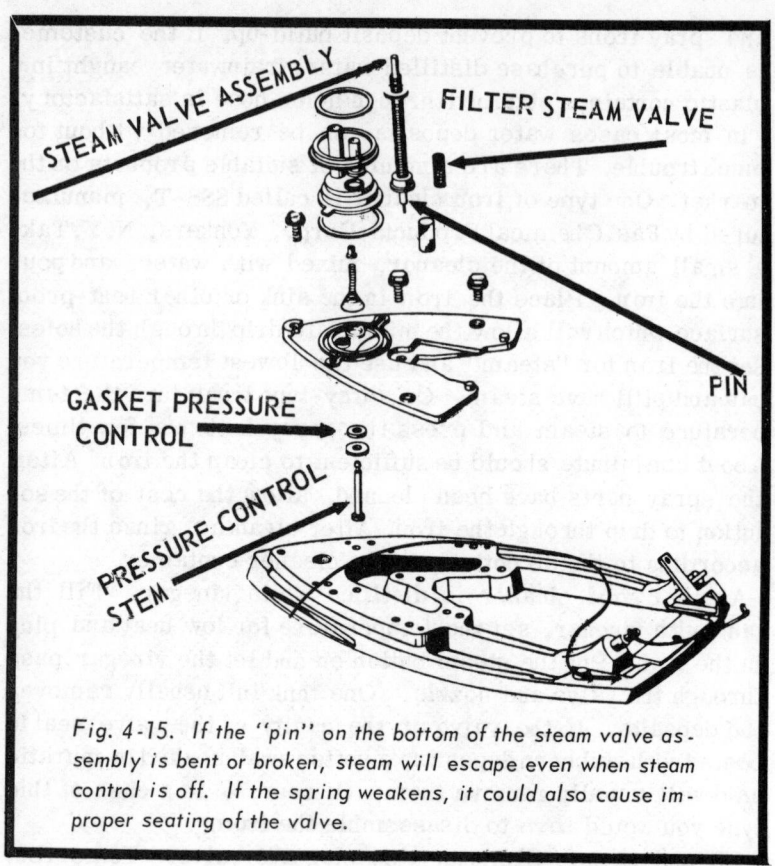

STEAM VALVE ASSEMBLY

FILTER STEAM VALVE

GASKET PRESSURE CONTROL

PIN

PRESSURE CONTROL STEM

Fig. 4-15. If the "pin" on the bottom of the steam valve assembly is bent or broken, steam will escape even when steam control is off. If the spring weakens, it could also cause improper seating of the valve.

iron could leak water. Should the iron leak between the soleplate and the cover, check for leaks in the steam chamber assembly. The most common trouble here is a leak in the seam of the steam chamber. If the leak is large enough you can find it visually, but should the leak be a small one it may be necessary to apply soapy water around the seams and blow compressed air through the opening in the tank. "Soap bubbles" will indicate the position of the leak. See Fig. 4-17.

Small leaks can be patched with a sealing compound called "Silastic." It's a silicone rubber sealing compound that is heat and pressure resistant, stays pliable, and is safe and easy to use.

Check the valve assembly; is it binding in the handle? If it is, the steam valve will not seat properly.

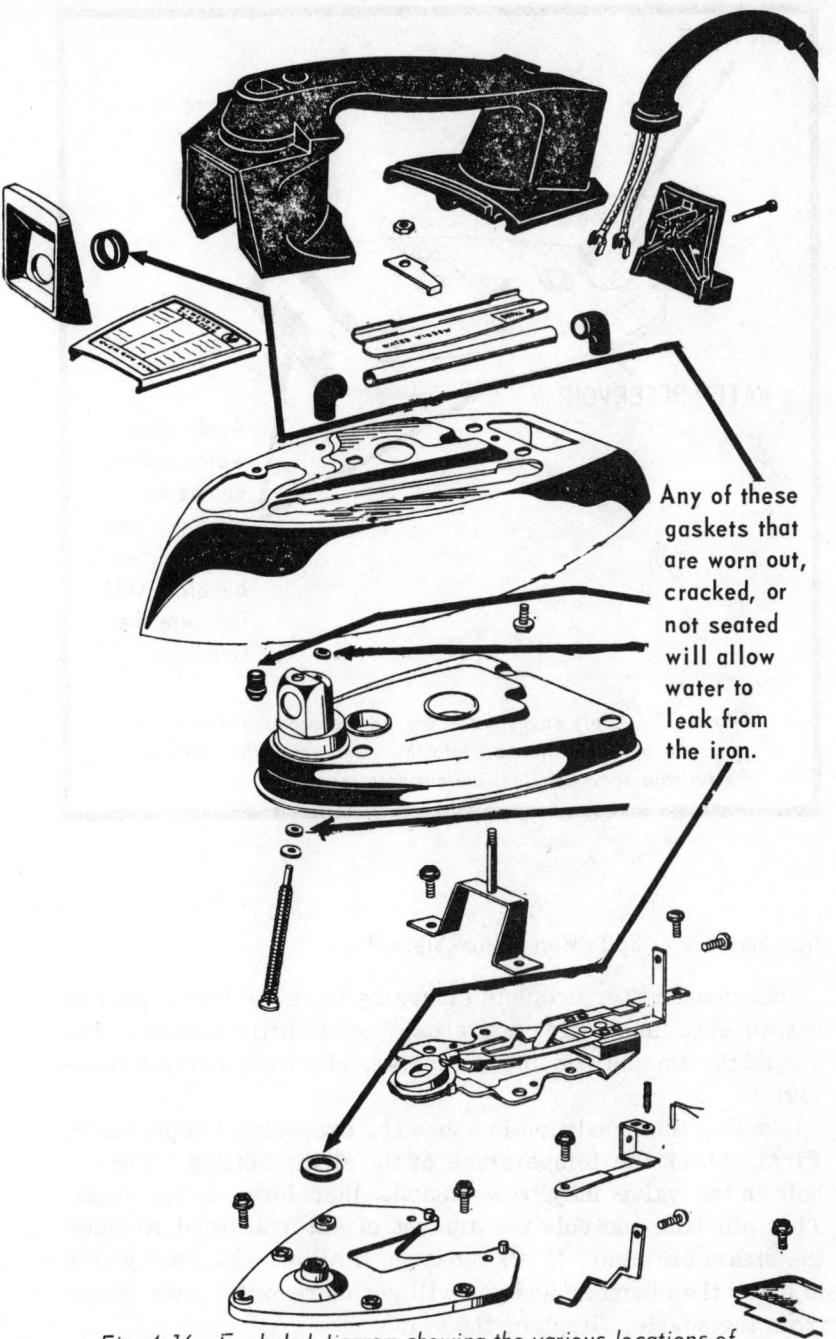

Any of these gaskets that are worn out, cracked, or not seated will allow water to leak from the iron.

Fig. 4-16. Exploded diagram showing the various locations of gaskets in one model steam and spray iron.

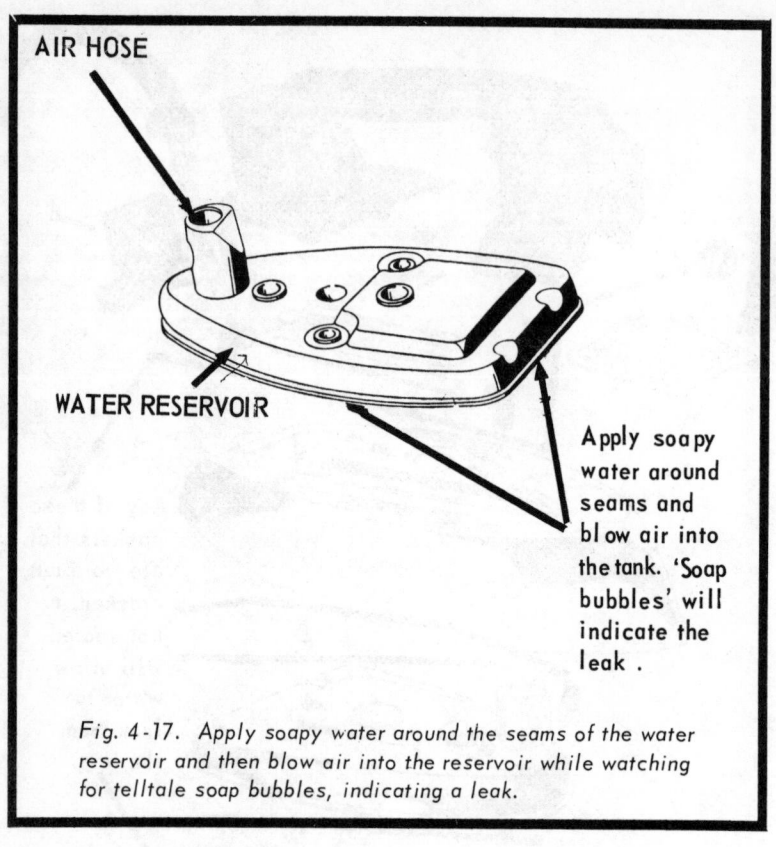

AIR HOSE

WATER RESERVOIR

Apply soapy water around seams and blow air into the tank. 'Soap bubbles' will indicate the leak.

Fig. 4-17. Apply soapy water around the seams of the water reservoir and then blow air into the reservoir while watching for telltale soap bubbles, indicating a leak.

Iron Sputters or Spits Water From Steam Port

Occasional water droplets emerging from the steam port is not an uncommon thing and should cause little concern, but should the amount become excessive, check one of the following:

Usually, this condition is caused by excessive temperature. First, check the temperature at the steam setting. The pin hole in the valve may be worn and, therefore, is too large. This pin hole controls the amount of water allowed to enter the steam chamber. If it's too large it allows too much water to enter the chamber and you will get more water than steam from the nozzle. Replace the valve.

Some irons have a special coating inside the steam chamber. If this coating is damaged in any way, you'll have to

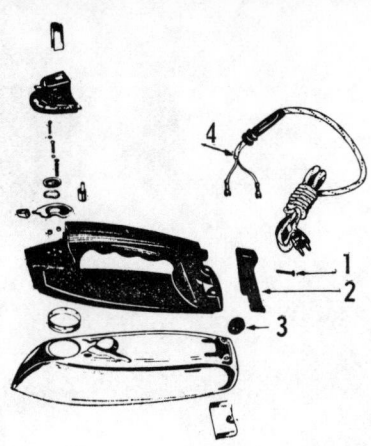

Fig. 4-18. Exploded view of cord, handle, and shell assembly to show how an iron is disassembled.

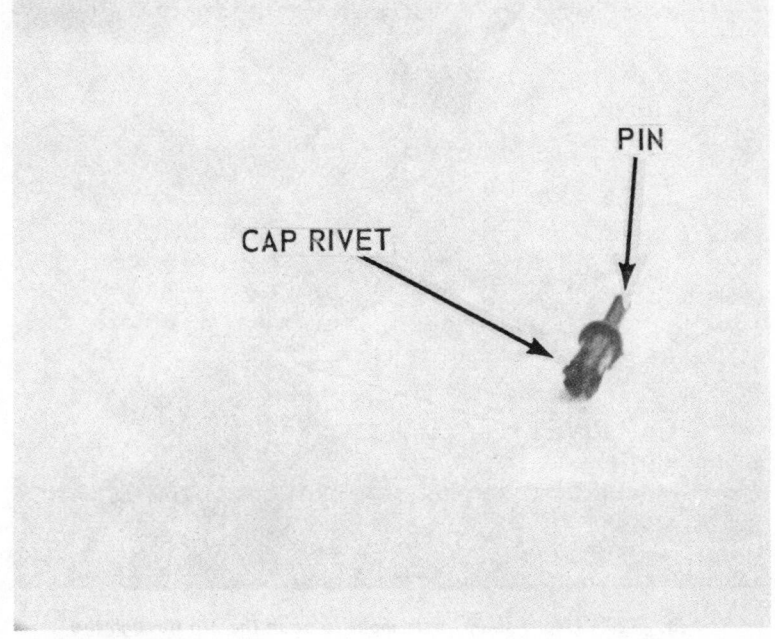

PIN

CAP RIVET

Fig. 4-19. A pin and cap rivet is used on many Sunbeam irons. It is a puzzle to remove if you don't know how. See Fig. 4-20.

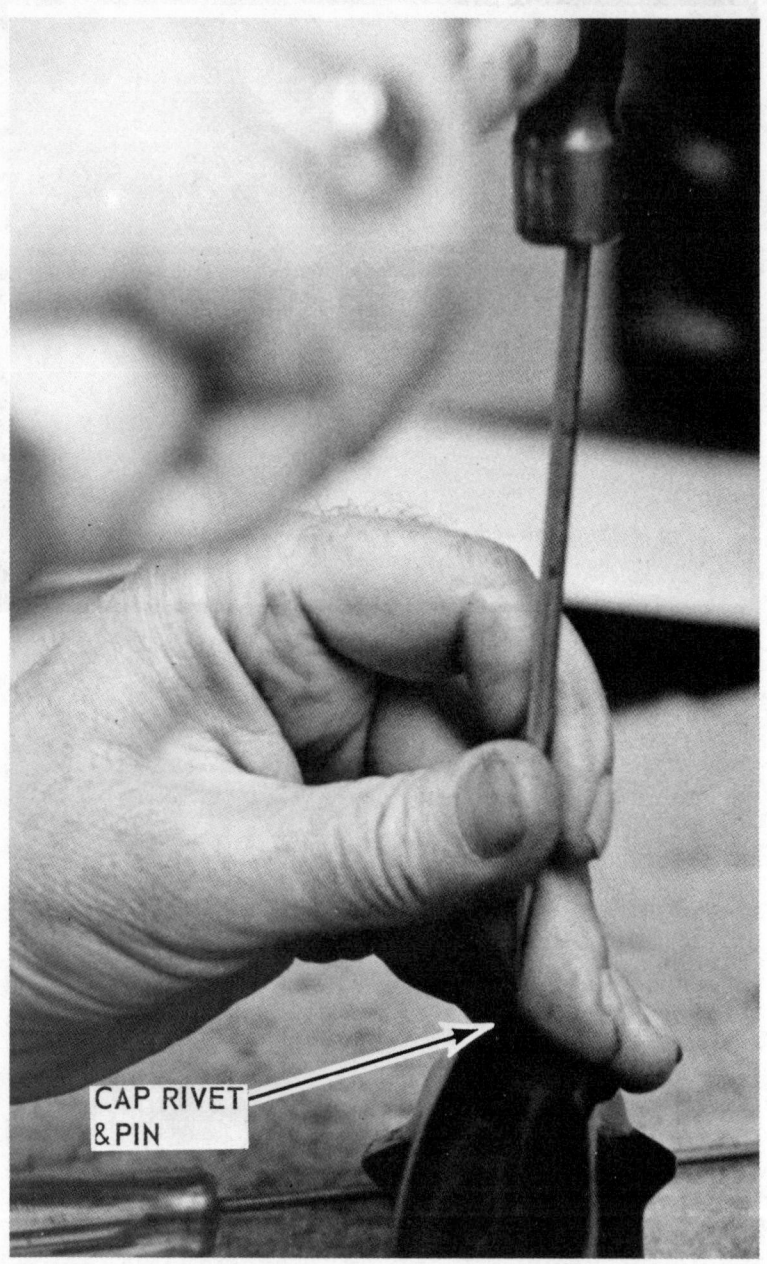

CAP RIVET & PIN

Fig. 4-20. Use a sharp instrument to push the pin through the cap rivet and down into the iron where it can be retrieved after the iron is disassembled. Then use a knife blade to pry the rivet up and out of the iron handle.

TROUBLESHOOTING CHART

Trouble	Cause	Correction
Won't heat	Cord and:/ or plug	Replace the cord or plug as necessary
	Cord connecting terminals	Be sure they are clean, tight, and making good connection
	Heating element	Check for open heating element. If open, replace soleplate
	Contact points dirty or pitted	Replace thermostat
Heat too high or too low	Temperature setting off	Adjust thermostat
	Contact points fused togeather	Replace thermostat
	Bi-metal strip damaged	Replace bi-metal strip
No steam	Water tank or valve clogged	Clean iron with iron cleaner or vinegar
	Valve clogged by film from oil or grease	Remove the film by heating iron to maximum temperature for an hour, or use small flame
Steam when lever is off	Valve not seated properly	Check pin of valve and the valve spring; replace if damaged
Iron leaks water	Bad gasket	Replace any worn or cracked gaskets
	Seam of steam chamber cracked	Repair with sealing compound if crack is not too large; replace the steam chamber if necessary

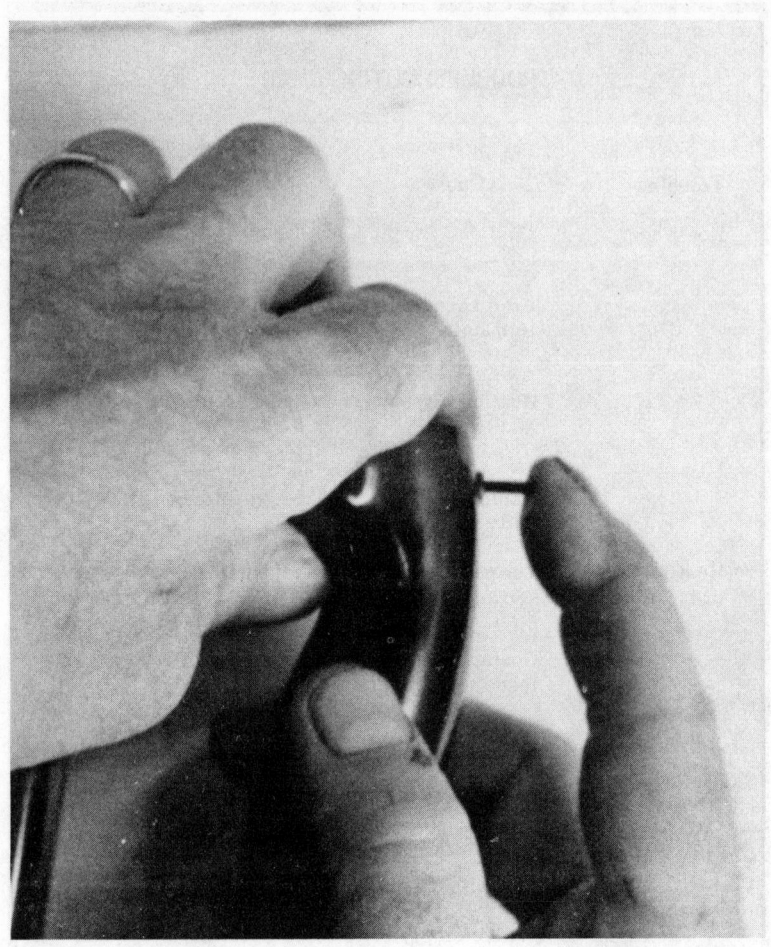

Fig. 4-21. To replace the cap rivet, push or hammer the pin down until flush with the rivet head.

change the soleplate to stop the spitting. Water deposits in the steam chamber will cause spitting, too. Clean the steam chamber with iron cleaner or vinegar as suggested earlier. Trying to steam iron with the temperature control at some position other than the steam position will cause spitting in some irons.

Iron Spots Material

If lint has worked its way into the steam chamber or valve, it will burn and turn brown when the iron is used for dry ironing. This will cause brown spots to appear on the material. Fill the iron with water and place the temperature control on the steam position. The boiling water and steam should flush out the lint. You may have to do this a couple times to insure that all the contamination has been removed.

General Hints

Water left in the iron could cause pitting and rusting of the soleplate. When finished with the iron pour the water out. What little water is left in the tank will dry from the heat of the iron.

If the point of the soleplate is bent or rough, smooth with small file.

Starch buildup on the soleplate can be removed with a soap pad used lightly.

Scratches on the soleplate can be removed with fine grade sandpaper.

For many years bread wrappers were used to give the soleplate a slick finish. The waxed paper did give the iron a slight wax coating on the soleplate, but don't try it with the bread wrappers of today! Most are plastic and will practically vulcanize to the soleplate.

GENERAL DISASSEMBLY INSTRUCTIONS

To disassemble the type iron shown in Fig. 4-18, remove the rear plate screw (1), rear plate (2), and circular cap (3). The cord (4) can now be removed by pulling the solderless connectors off the switch terminals.

To remove the handle and shell, there is a small pin in the cap rivet, Fig. 4-19, that must be pushed through the cap rivet down into the iron, Fig. 4-20. (After you get the handle removed look for the pin; it's down inside the iron.)

After pushing the pin through, take a thin-bladed knife and pry the cap rivet upward and remove. Now the temperature knob, steam lever assembly, and handle can be removed. After you have repaired and assembled the iron push the pin into the cap rivet as shown in Fig. 4-21.

CHAPTER 5

Toasters

Most modern toasters are automatic and their operation is controlled, basically, by a bi-metal strip. A toaster (Fig. 5-1) consists of a number of heating elements, racks to hold the slices, controls to lower and raise the slices, and a bimetal strip for heat control. The bread slices are placed on racks and the racks are lowered into the toaster, either mechanically or electrically. When the racks are lowered a switch is closed to turn the toaster on and a mechanical latch or catch holds the racks down during the toasting cycle. The heat from the elements toasts the bread to the desired color. When the desired degree of toasting is reached the bi-metal strip turns the toaster off and the racks return to their starting position.

Fig. 5-2 is a wiring diagram of an automatic toaster. Not all wiring diagrams are like this one, but it is one common circuit. A little later in this Chapter we will discuss another circuit arrangement where the elements are in series-parallel and a relay controls the hold-down latch. For the discussion on general operations, however, the diagram in Fig. 5-2 will do quite well.

When bread slices are placed in the racks and the handle is pressed down, switch #1 closes and current flows through the bi-metal strip and the main heating elements (5). After the racks are lowered into the toaster, a lever or catch (Fig. 5-3) holds the racks down until the toaster has completed its cycle. The bi-metal strip causes the lever to be released and the return spring raises the racks back to the starting position. As the bi-metal strip heats, it starts to bend; when it bends a predetermined amount switch #2, Fig. 5-2, closes. How long it takes this switch to close depends on the setting of the "light-dark" control.

Notice on the wiring diagram that when switch #2 is closed, the bi-metal strip is shorted out of the circuit—that is, no

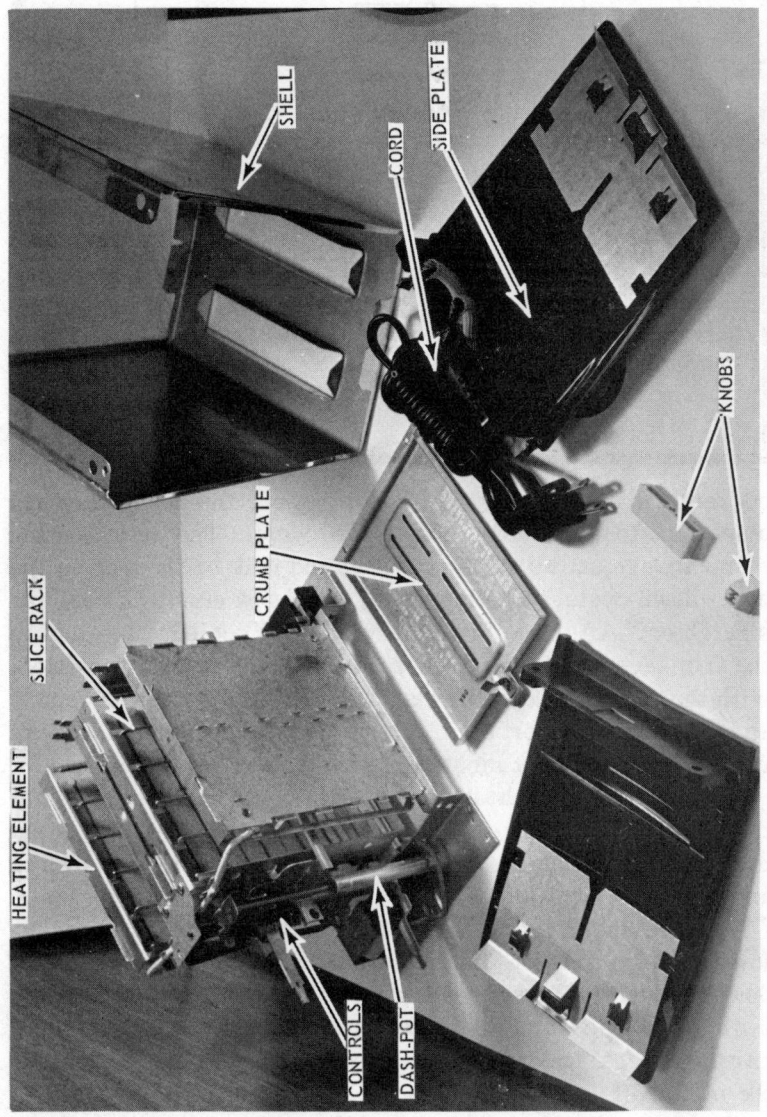

Fig. 5-1. Main parts of a typical modern toaster.

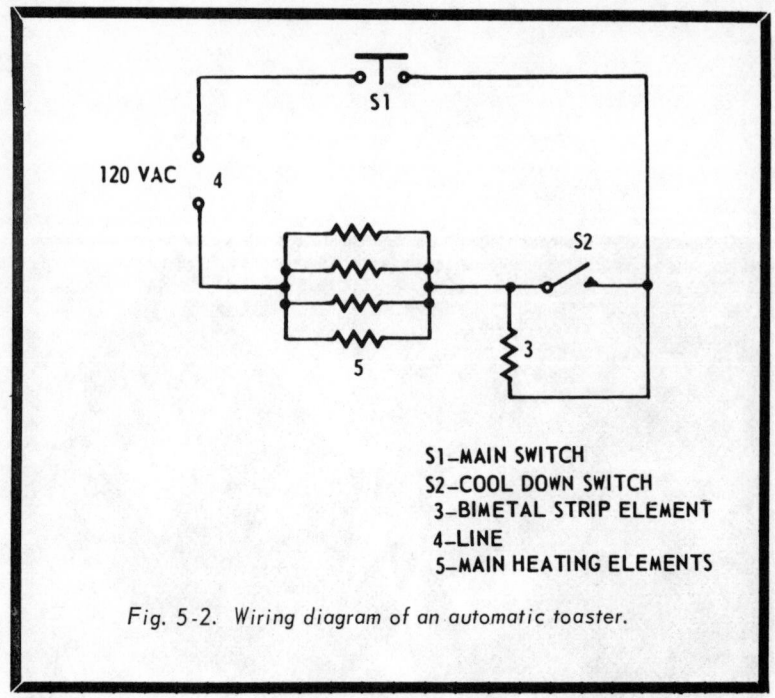

S1—MAIN SWITCH
S2—COOL DOWN SWITCH
3—BIMETAL STRIP ELEMENT
4—LINE
5—MAIN HEATING ELEMENTS

Fig. 5-2. Wiring diagram of an automatic toaster.

current can flow through it. Shorting out the bi-metal strip places the toaster in the cool-down cycle. The main heating elements are still drawing current and will be throughout the cool-down cycle. The bi-metal strip now starts to cool and straighten. After the bi-metal strip has cooled, it releases the trip lever and the racks raise to their starting position. With the racks back to the starting position, switch #1 opens and turns the toaster off. There are different methods of raising the racks but most modern toasters use a spring.

The adjustment on the bi-metal strip controls the duration of the toasting cycle by changing the degree the bi-metal strip must bend to control the operation of the cool-down switch and trip lever.

Fig. 5-4 shows a drawing of a toaster that uses a motor to lower the bread racks, instead of a handle that has to be pushed down manually. When bread is placed in the toaster the motor switch is closed and the motor lowers the racks. When the carriage rack is lowered the motor switch opens and turns the motor off. A lever holds the rack down until the toasting cycle is completed. At the end of the toasting cycle the motor raises the rack.

SERVICE

A toaster is another of those appliances where you run into either electrical and/or mechanical troubles. The electrical

Fig. 5-3. The bi-metal strips trip the hold-down latch when the cycle is over. The return spring raises the racks to the starting position.

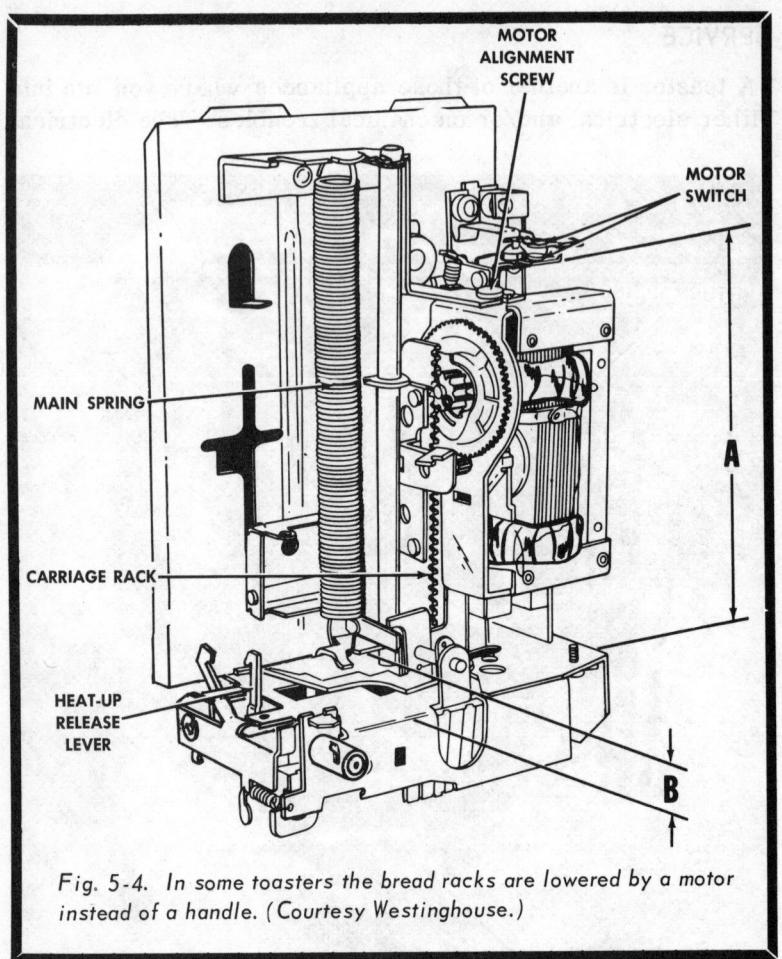

MOTOR
ALIGNMENT
SCREW

MOTOR
SWITCH

MAIN SPRING

CARRIAGE RACK

HEAT-UP
RELEASE
LEVER

A

B

Fig. 5-4. In some toasters the bread racks are lowered by a motor instead of a handle. (Courtesy Westinghouse.)

troubles are not very difficult, but sometimes mechanical problems can become very trying.

A frequent problem with toasters is caused by food particles, which can affect both electrical or mechanical operations. Small crumbs, or burnt raisins and the like, can contaminate the contacts of the switches or "gum up" the mechanical works. An air hose does a good job of removing most of the particles. Raisins or jelly, something of this type, after it has been burnt usually has to be scraped off contacts or other parts. When cleaning be careful not to damage a heating element! The contacts of the switches can be cleaned without too much difficulty. A small file or knife will do if you don't scrape too hard.

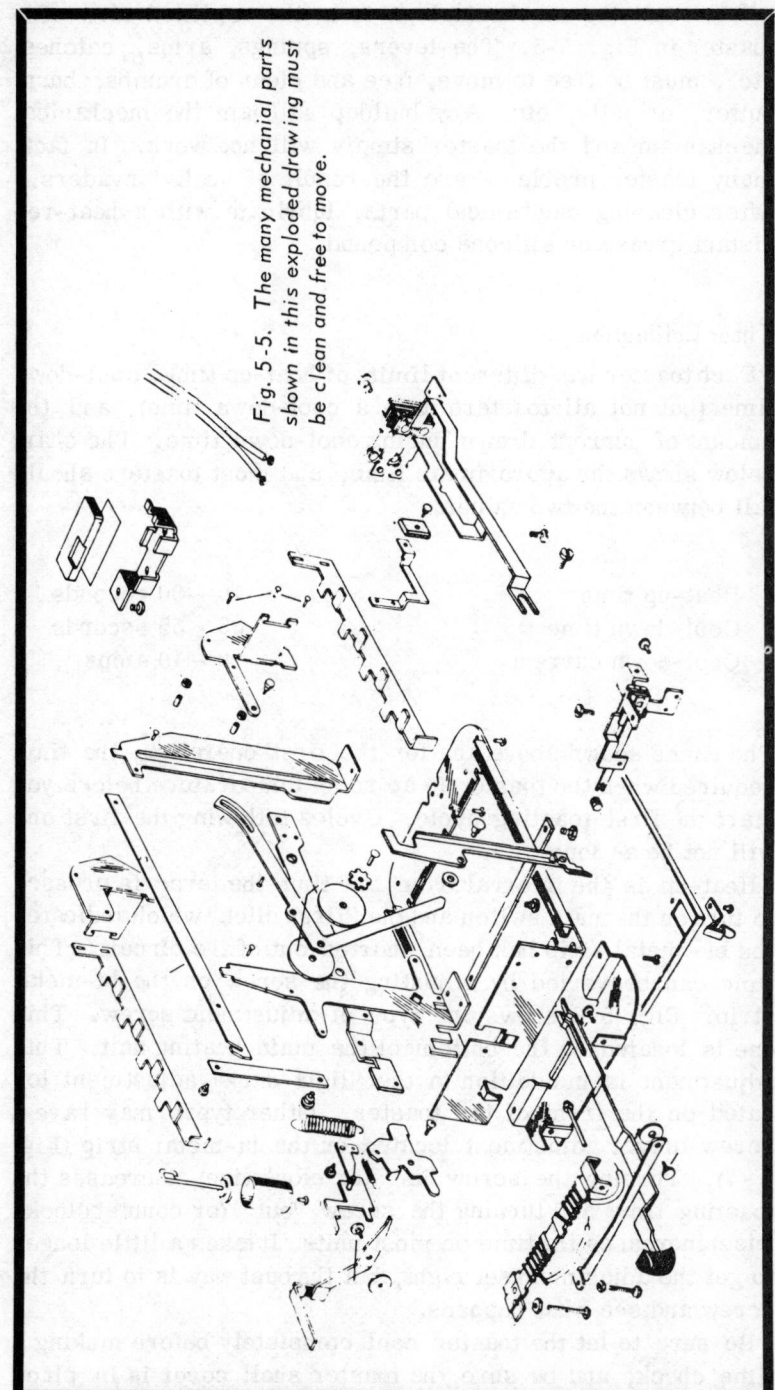

Fig. 5-5. The many mechanical parts shown in this exploded drawing must be clean and free to move.

Notice all the mechanical parts in the exploded view of a toaster in Fig. 5-5. The levers, springs, arms, catches, etc., must be free to move, free and clean of crumbs, burnt butter, or jelly, etc. Any buildup will jam the mechanical mechanism and the toaster simply will not work. In fact, many toaster problems are the result of such "invaders." After cleaning mechanical parts, lubricate with a heat-resistant grease or silicone compound.

Timer Calibration

Each toaster has different limits of heat-up time, cool-down time (but not all toasters have a cool-down time), and the amount of current drawn during cool-down time. The chart below shows the approximate time, and most toasters should fall between the two values.

Heat-up time	70 - 90 seconds
Cool-down time	35 - 55 seconds
Cool-down current	9 - 10 amps

The times shown above are for the first operation, the time required when the toaster is at room temperature before you start the first toasting cycle. Cycles following the first one will not be as long.

Heat-up is the interval from the time the lever is pressed to turn on the main switch and the "first click" which indicates the bi-metal strip has been shorted out of the circuit. This time can be varied by adjusting the screw on the bi-metal strip. Fig. 5-6 shows one type of adjustment screw. This one is located on the bottom of the main heating unit. This adjustment is in addition to the "light-dark" adjustment located on the front of the toaster. Other types may have a screw-driver adjustment located on the bi-metal strip (Fig. 5-7). Turning the screw "in" (or clockwise) decreases the toasting time and turning the screw "out" (or counterclockwise) increases the time on most units. It takes a little longer to get the adjustment set right, but the best way is to turn the screw and see what happens.

Be sure to let the toaster cool completely before making a time check, and be sure the toaster shell cover is in place when timing the cycle. Without the shell cover the heat is not distributed normally inside the toaster and so timing cycles

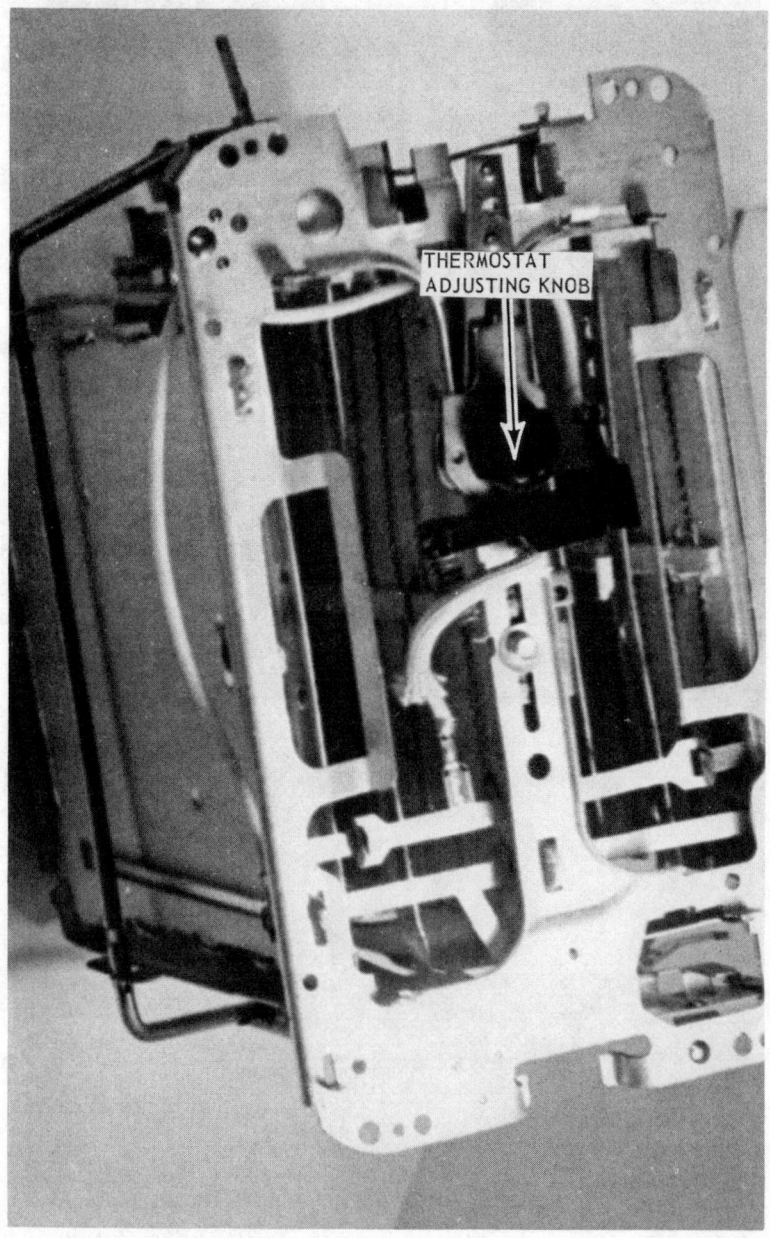

Fig. 5-6. The thermostat adjusting knob is located as shown here in some toasters.

Fig. 5-7. Some toasters have a screw-driver adjustment on the bi-metal strip.

and thermostats can't be correctly adjusted. In toasters with a cool-down cycle, check the timing from the first click (indicating the bi-metal strip has been shorted out) and the time the racks pop up.

Not all toasters have a cool-down cycle, but a wiring diagram for one with the cool-down cycle is shown in Fig. 5-2. On this type, when the bi-metal strip shorts out, the heating elements are still drawing current and continue to do so until the bi-metal strip returns to its straight position and pops up the toast. There is an adjustment, generally, on both the heat-up and cool-down times. A change in heat-up time also changes the cool-down time. Don't adjust the cool-down time until the heat-up adjustment is completed.

The final test of any toaster is how it toasts a slice of bread. With the "light-dark" lever about midway, you should be able to get several consecutive slices of toast with a uniform brown color, neither too dark or light. Some breads have more or less moisture content and so will toast to varying degrees of brown at the same setting. Use the same kind of bread when testing toasters so that you can establish a standard for yourself.

Fig. 5-8 is a wiring diagram of a toaster not using a cool-down cycle. In this toaster when the racks are down, switch S1 closes, supplying current to the heating elements (2). In addition to their usual function, the elements heat the bi-metal strip (3) which starts to bend and after a period of time closes switch (5) which energizes relay (4). When the relay pulls in the catch (6) is released and the spring pulls the rack and bread up.

The difference between this type and the one previously discussed is that the thermostat need only switch enough current to close the relay. The relay then does all the work necessary to release the racks. Fig. 5-9 shows a toaster with the relay rack release in the "off" or raised position and Fig. 5-10 shows the toaster "on."

There are other kinds of timing devices which have been used on toasters, such as clock mechanisms, but these are no longer used in home-type toasters. The problems with these, as with other toasters, are often cured by a good cleanup and judicious lubrication. Commercial toasters often use a clock mechanism with a bi-metal strip to set the timing according to the pre-heated condition of the toaster.

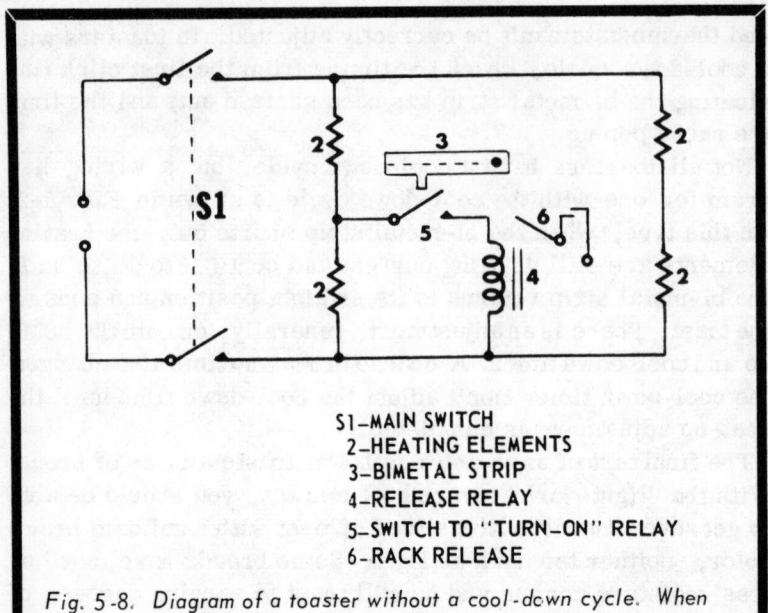

S1 — MAIN SWITCH
2 — HEATING ELEMENTS
3 — BIMETAL STRIP
4 — RELEASE RELAY
5 — SWITCH TO "TURN-ON" RELAY
6 — RACK RELEASE

Fig. 5-8. Diagram of a toaster without a cool-down cycle. When the relay (4) is energized it releases the racks. The racks return to the starting position and open switch S-1.

A FOUR-SLICE TOASTER

Several companies make four-slice toasters, which are essentially the same as their two-slice "brothers." An exploded view of a four-slice toaster is shown in Fig. 5-11. The essential parts of the toaster with the names given them by the manufacturer are included. A list of this sort is handy when ordering parts for any toaster, since you can describe a particular part by its name. Of course, if possible, you should always order by part number, although sometimes this is not practical and a correct or near correct name for a part can make it much easier for a parts distributor to determine which part you need.

TOASTER PROBLEMS

Won't Heat

Plug the toaster into the appliance tester and check for continuity. Remember, continuity is possible only when the rack

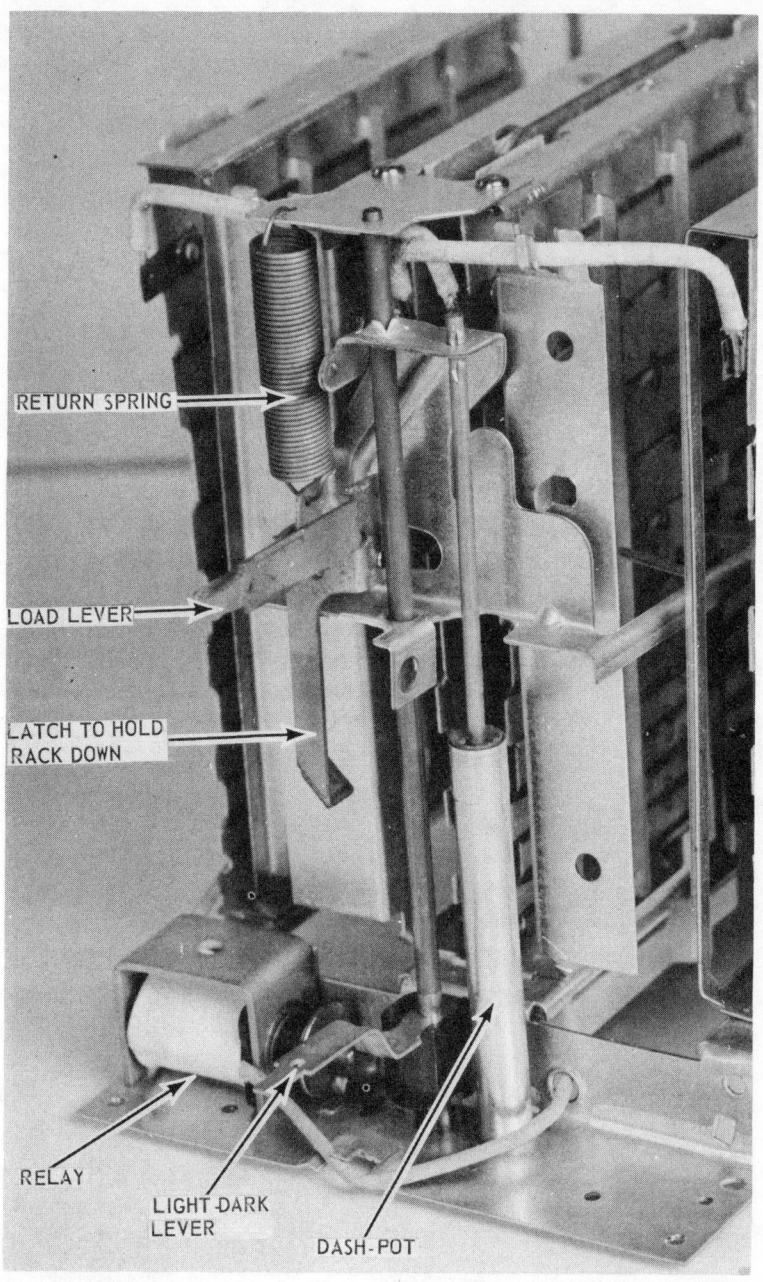

RETURN SPRING

LOAD LEVER

LATCH TO HOLD
RACK DOWN

RELAY

LIGHT-DARK
LEVER

DASH-POT

Fig. 5-9. Toaster with the racks in the off position.

RETURN SPRING

LOAD LEVER

RELAY

HOLD DOWN
LATCH

Fig. 5-10. Toaster with the racks in the on position.

is pushed down to close the main switch. Be sure to bend and move the cord and plug to check for possible intermittent connections.

If there is no continuity, disassemble the toaster to the point where you can check the main switch contacts (Fig. 5-12). Nearly all toasters use a double-pole switch (a switch that opens both sides of the power line). Check to see that both points make contact and that they are clean. Sometimes a crumb can lodge in the switch contacts or in the activating mechanism so that the switch cannot close. Check carefully for any foreign matter. Use an air hose to blow out the toaster everytime you have it apart for repair.

If the main switch is badly pitted or burned you likely cannot make a satisfactory repair since all the "hard" metal coating of the points will be burned away. Replace the switch if practical. If the toaster is an inexpensive one it may be cheaper for the customer to purchase a new toaster, especially if the switch is a difficult one to replace.

Another problem may be that the mechanical pressure of the rack is not strong enough to close the switches. You can correct this sometimes by bending an arm which controls the switch contacts, sometimes by pushing the switch assembly up and sometimes by readjusting the catch which holds the rack down.

Burns Toast

Check the toaster timing through two or three cycles. If the toaster is turning off and popping up but not doing it quickly enough, you may be able to adjust the thermostat. Some toasters have an extra "customer" knob on the bottom of the toaster and this may get turned without the customer knowing it.

Uneven Toast

If one side of the bread browns and the other doesn't, it is most often due to an open heating element. Make a visual check for an element that doesn't glow red. Some elements are in series-parallel and in this case two elements will not heat.

A difference in the reflection of heat may be the result of aging heating elements. A new element beside an old one can

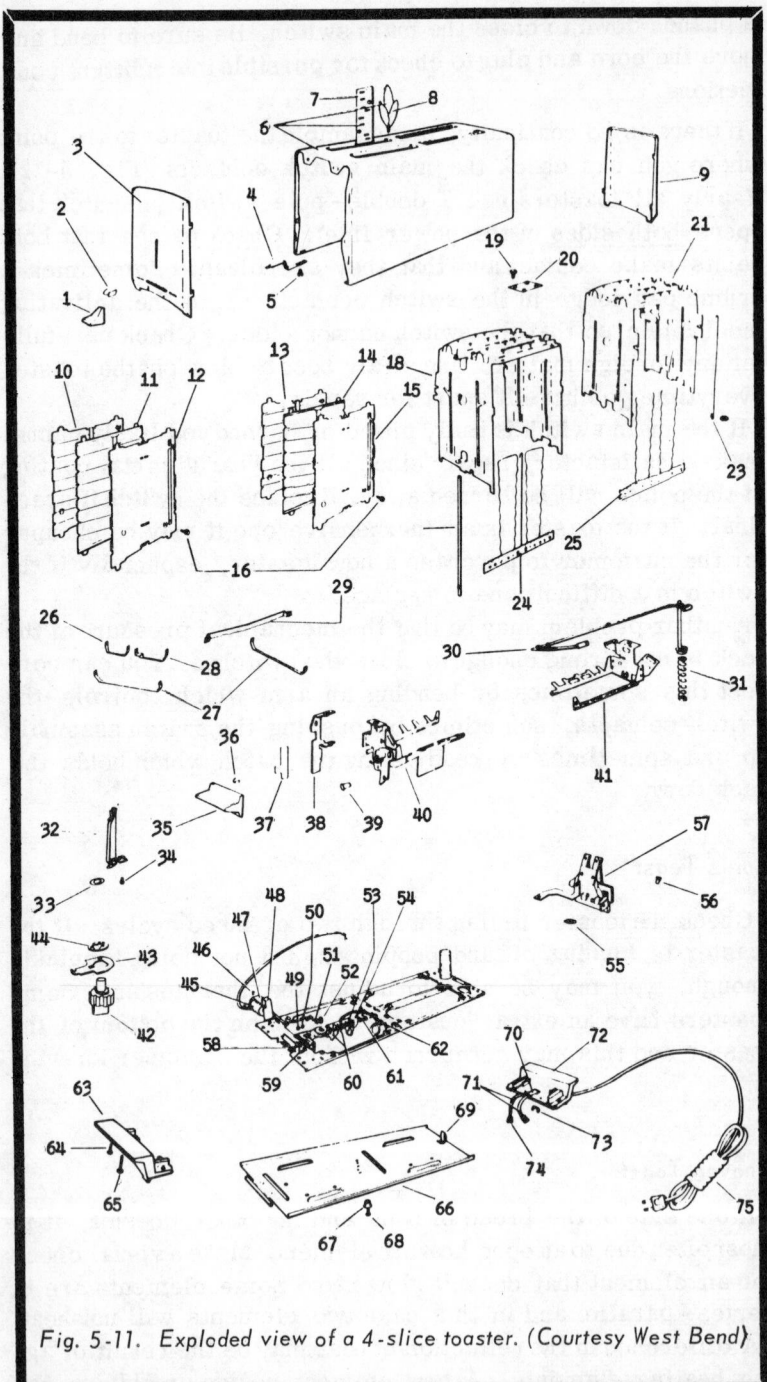

Fig. 5-11. Exploded view of a 4-slice toaster. (Courtesy West Bend)

PARTS	DESCRIPTION
1.	Color control knob
3.	Front body plate
6.	Body assembly
7.	Body emblem fastener
8.	Body emblem
9.	Rear body plate
10, 11, 12, 13, 14, 15.	Element assemblies
18.	Front frame
21.	Rear frame subassembly
24, 25.	Grille wire assembly
30.	Lifter arm and piston assembly
31.	Dashpot spring
32.	Thermostat assembly
35.	Lifter knob
42.	Color setting knob
45.	Latch release assembly
49 to 62.	Base subassembly
66.	Crumb tray assembly
70 to 75.	Cord assembly and rear foot

cause this trouble also. If the reflecting surfaces inside the shell have become discolored, rusty, or covered with burnt food particles, the bread may not toast evenly.

A sometimes common situation may be "customer" trouble. If the bread used does not have equal moisture distribution, it will come out of any toaster uneven. The only thing that can be done in this case is to inform the customer, after checking the toaster for other possible faults.

Won't Pop Up

This may be caused by a worn catch that "hangs up" the rack so it won't release. Sometimes a catch can be put back in service by dressing it with a small file. Other times gum and foreign matter may have built up on the slides so that the rack is not free enough to move. If the toaster has been dropped the rack transport may be binding. Often you can "re-distort" the rack so that it will move up and down freely. Another reason for pop-up trouble may be a defective thermostat or misalignment of the thermostat with the trip mechanism.

In a solenoid (relay) type toaster the solenoid coil may be open. Check it for continuity when the thermostat points are

TROUBLESHOOTING CHART

Problem	Cause	Correction
Won't heat	Burned-out element	Repair broken element, or replace
	Open cord or broken plug	Replace cord and plug
	Main switch defective	Replace switch
	Rack pressure not strong enough to close switch	Bend the lever to make good contact
Burns toast	Timing calibration not set correctly	Adjust timing
	Distorted bi-metal strip	Replace
	Shorted cool-down or heat-up switch	Replace
	Permanent heat-up	Clean switch or replace
Won't pop up	Distorted bi-metal strip	Replace
	Shorted cool-down or heat-up switch	Replace
	Trip lever stuck	Check mechanical action, oil and lube as necessary
	Return or carrier spring broken or not connected	Replace if broken or has no tension
Toast too light or too dark	Timing calibration	Adjust timer
Uneven toasting	Heating element(s) open	Replace or repair
	Aged heating element	Replace
	Reflection surface dirty	Clean
Throws toast out	Dash-pot inoperative	Replace

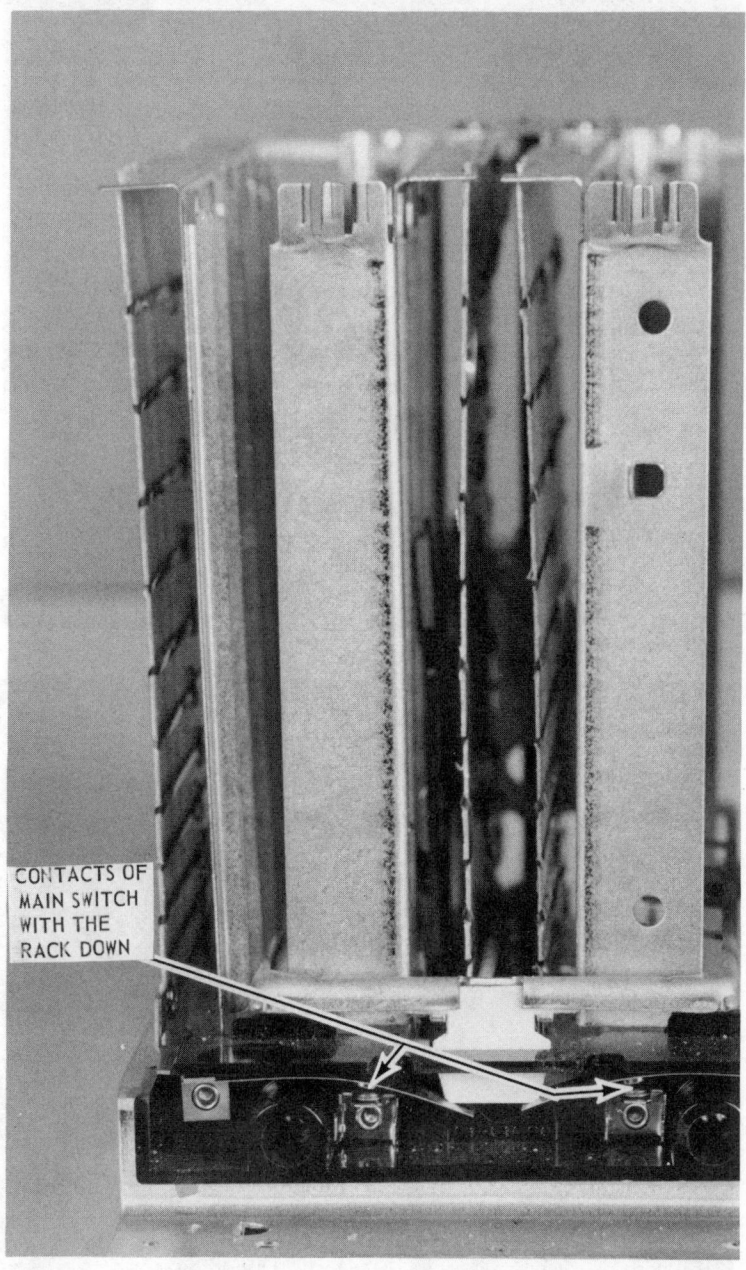

CONTACTS OF
MAIN SWITCH
WITH THE
RACK DOWN

Fig. 5-12. Checking the contacts of the main switch. The contacts of the main switch close with the rack down.

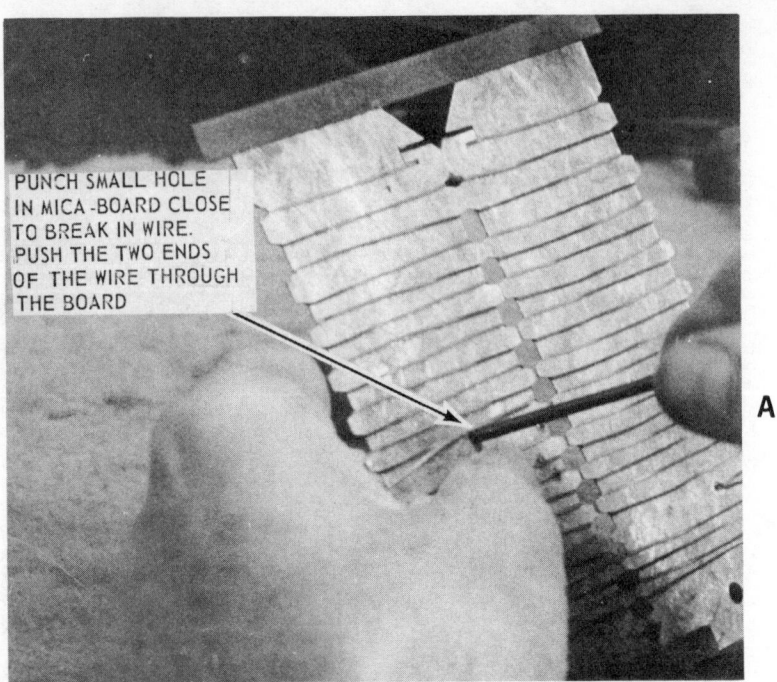

PUNCH SMALL HOLE IN MICA-BOARD CLOSE TO BREAK IN WIRE. PUSH THE TWO ENDS OF THE WIRE THROUGH THE BOARD

A

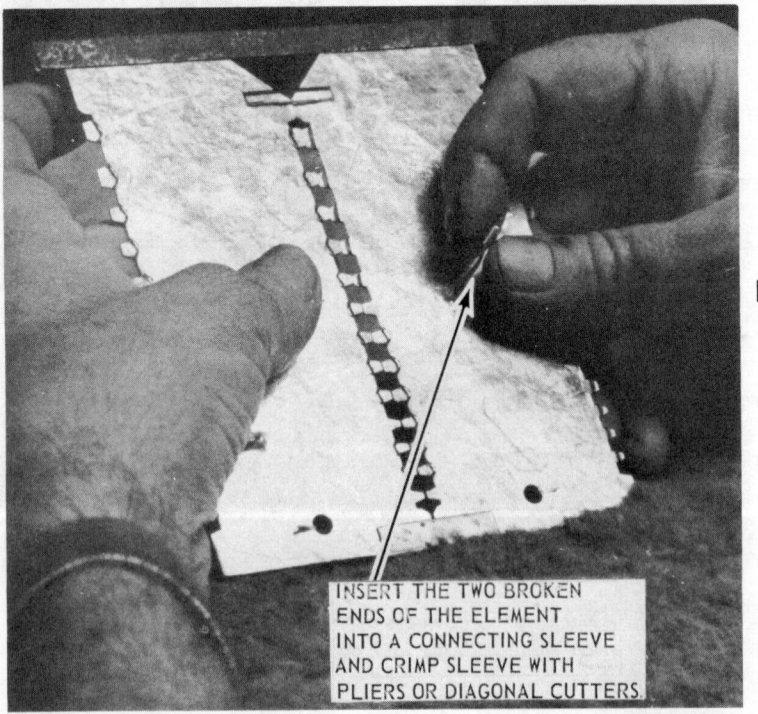

B

INSERT THE TWO BROKEN ENDS OF THE ELEMENT INTO A CONNECTING SLEEVE AND CRIMP SLEEVE WITH PLIERS OR DIAGONAL CUTTERS.

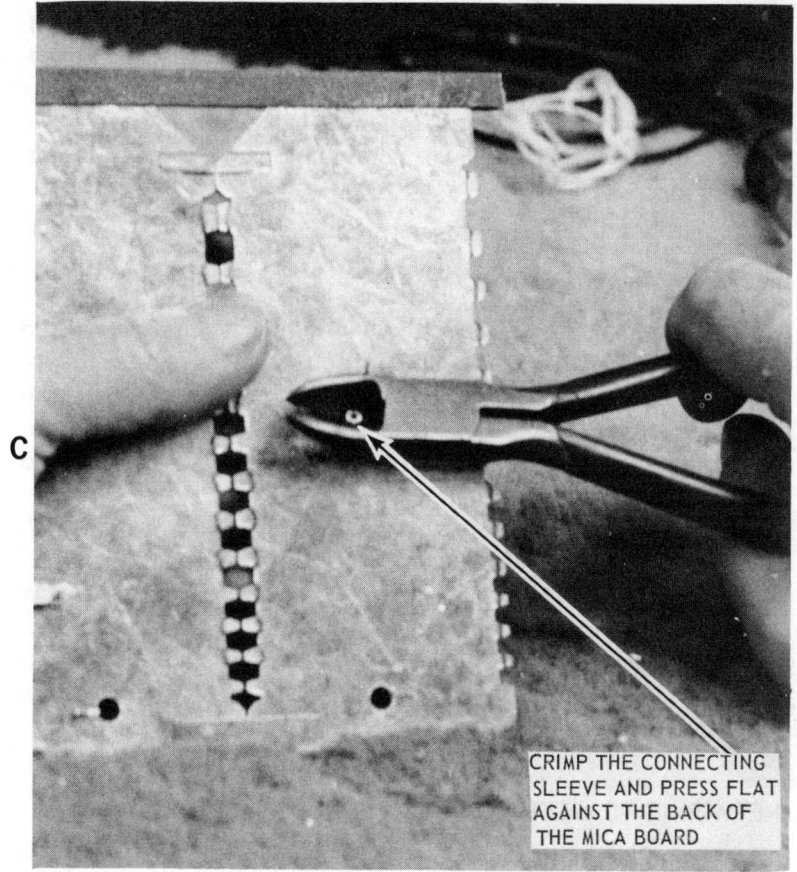

C

CRIMP THE CONNECTING
SLEEVE AND PRESS FLAT
AGAINST THE BACK OF
THE MICA BOARD

*Fig. 5-13. To repair an open element, punch a small hole (A) in mica
board close to break in wire. Push the two ends of the wire through the
board (B) and insert into a connecting sleeve. Crimp the sleeve (C).*

open; if the points are closed the heating element will act as
a continuity path across the coil and make it impossible for
you to tell whether the coil is open or not.

Won't Stay Down

Such trouble is normally caused by a worn catch, and it can
often be corrected by using a small file to reshape the notch
or bracket. In some cases you will be able to use long-nose
pliers and bend the catch so that it will hold the racks.

Sometimes the catch won't hold because of dirt, grease, and

grime, especially in the pivot of the catch lever. Clean and lubricate with heat-resistant grease. Some catches use a tiny coil spring that may break, fall out of the toaster and be lost, and unless you know the spring was supposed to have been there you may be at a loss to determine why the catch is not working properly.

Bread Pops-Out of Toaster

The "dash-pot" (Figs. 5-1 and 5-9) on the toaster keeps the racks from returning to the up position too fast when the toasting cycle is over. When the lever or catch is released, the return or carrier spring moves the racks to the up position. If the "dash-pot" is not working the racks will move up too fast and throw the toast out of the toaster.

There are different types of dash-pots. Some work with liquid, others on air pressure, friction, or suction. The types shown in the Figs. 5-1 and 5-9 work on air pressure and friction. The tube has a plunger inside with a fiber washer that rubs against the side of the tube when the spring pulls the racks up. The resulting friction slows down the racks. On most toasters the dash-pot can be replaced.

REPAIRING TOASTER HEATING ELEMENTS

If it is possible to remove or gain access to a toaster element you probably can repair it. One method is shown in Fig. 5-13. Take an ice pick or other sharp instrument and punch a small hole through the mica (Fig. 5-13A) near the break in the heater wire. Push the two ends of the broken heater wire through the hole so they can be connected on the back side (away from the toast). Insert the two broken wires into a connecting sleeve and crimp with a special tool or with a pair of diagonal cutters, Figs. 5-13B and C. Press the sleeve flat against the back of the mica board so it will not touch some metal part of the toaster. If necessary use a piece of asbestos tape to make sure the sleeve will not become grounded. Tape is always a good idea because as the elements heat and cool, expansion and contraction can cause the splice to move. But if you choose the spot for the splice with care and slide the connecting sleeve close to the mica, tape won't be necessary.

CHAPTER 6

Coffee Makers

A great variety of coffee makers has been placed on the market over the years. The vacuum, drip, and pressure types have come and gone, come back again, and now seem to be virtually pushed into the background by the old standby percolator.

All coffee makers use a heating element (Fig. 6-1) controlled in most cases by a thermostat (Fig. 6-2) of some sort. Many models rely on a fixed-heat thermostat while others provide the user with an adjustable one (weak-strong). Some have rather sensitive thermostats that "bump" off and on within fairly narrow limits and keep the coffee hot after it has perco-

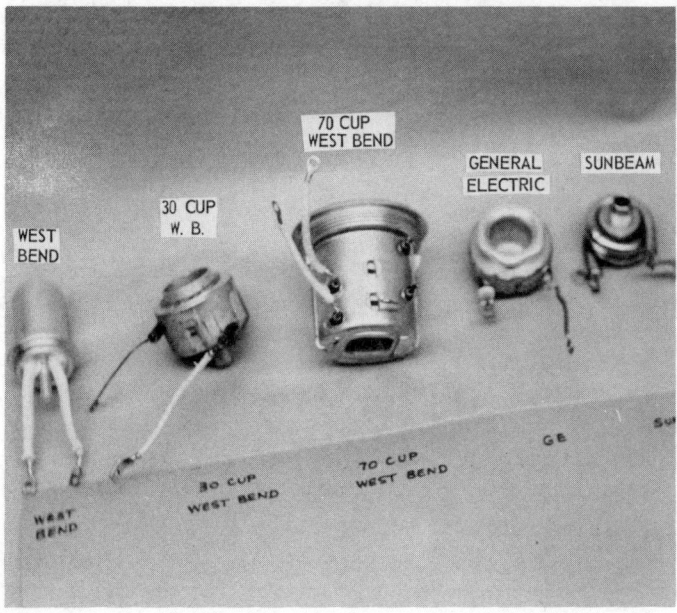

Fig. 6-1. Pictured here are several types of heating elements.

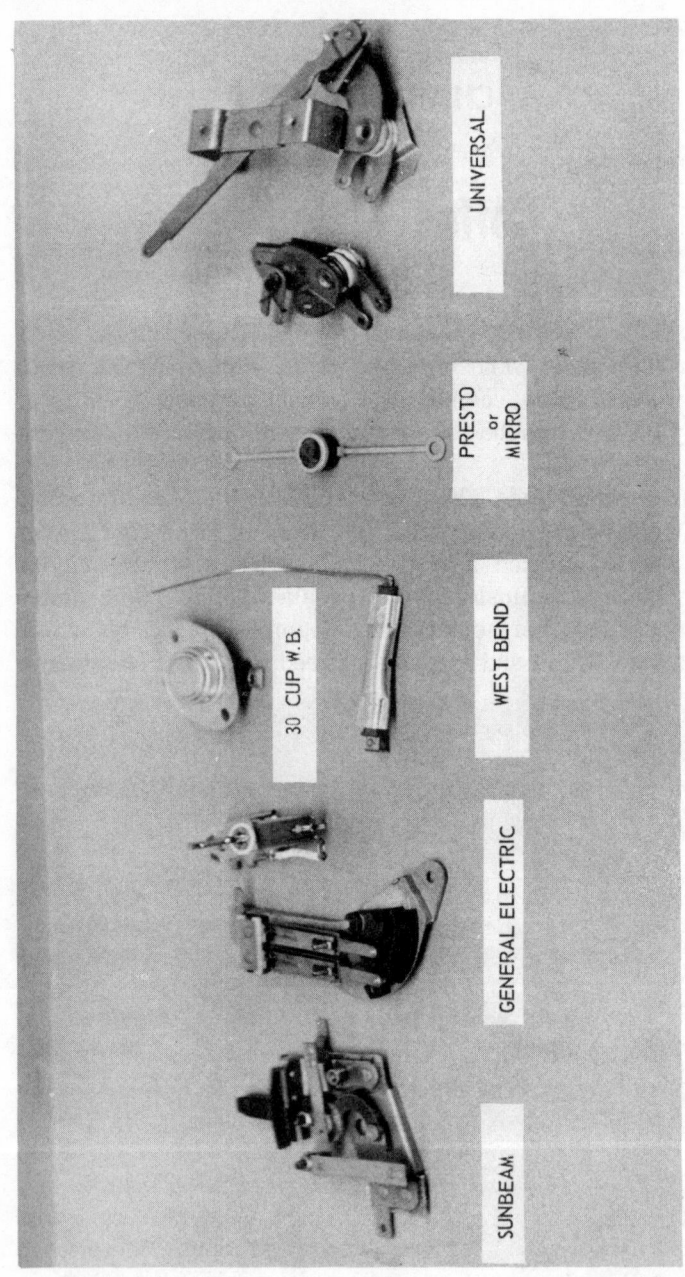

Fig. 6-2. These are some of the thermostats found in typical coffee makers.

lated or otherwise processed. Others, especially adjustable percolators, use a "warming" element which turns on to keep the coffee hot after the "main" element has turned off.

Fig. 6-3 shows the wiring diagram of a coffee pot using a "bump" type thermostat. A small amount of water is heated, perks up through the pump and drips down through the coffee in the basket. The rest of the water at the bottom of the pot remains relatively cool. Since the thermostat is located at the bottom of the pot, the cool water keeps the heating element turned on until the water at the bottom of the pot has become sufficiently hot to turn off the thermostat. When the coffee starts to cool down the thermostat turns on and reheats the coffee, but not enough to start it perking again.

Fig. 6-4 shows the circuit of a coffee pot using a warming element. The warming element is connected across the thermostat so that it heats when the thermostat opens. This warming element not only keeps the coffee hot but also provides enough heat in the bottom of the pot to keep the thermostat from closing again. If everything is working right, once the coffee has perked it will not perk again unless the pot is turned off and allowed to cool. We should point out here, perhaps, that one common trouble with this type of pot (if the complaint is continuous reperking), is an open warming element. Without the warming element there is nothing to keep the thermostat from closing again as soon as the coffee cools.

As can be seen from the wiring diagram, the warming element is in series with the main element, but because the warm-

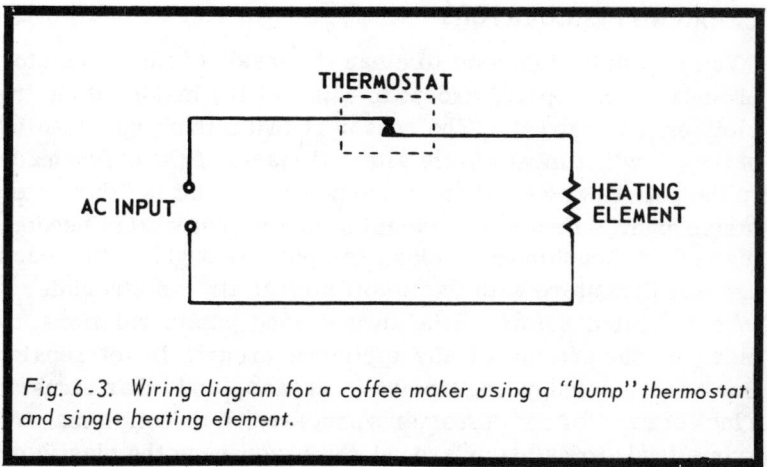

Fig. 6-3. Wiring diagram for a coffee maker using a "bump" thermostat and single heating element.

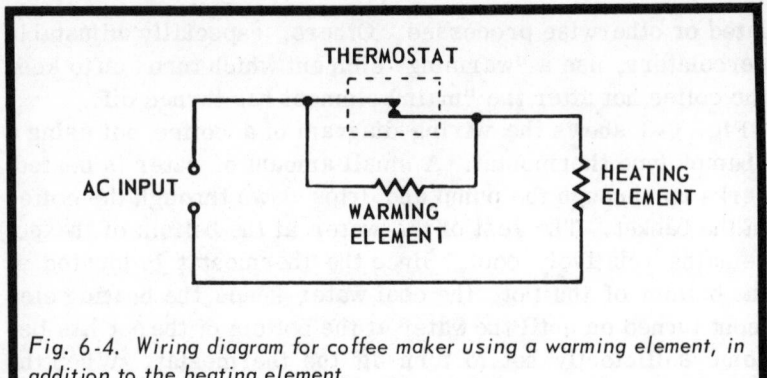

Fig. 6-4. Wiring diagram for coffee maker using a warming element, in addition to the heating element.

ing element is a higher resistance (lower wattage rating) most of the heat is developed across the warming element. When the thermostat points are open, the two elements—heating and warming—are in series with each other and the warming element will develop about six times the heat of the main element. However, the main element, when turned on by itself (thermostat points closed), develops about six times as much heat as the warming element does when it's turned on. In other words, the warming element is rated at about 85 to 100 watts while the main element is about 600 watts, although this varies with the manufacturer; some have warming elements that draw as little as 35 watts and others have heating elements with ratings up to about 1000 watts.

CLEANING PERCOLATORS

You should be reluctant to clean the inside of any percolator brought in for repair, except to wipe out the inside with a dry cloth or paper towel. The reason is that a thorough cleaning of the pot will almost surely affect the taste of the coffee made in the pot. However, if the customer complaint is "the coffee tastes funny," then a good cleaning may be just what is needed. Instruct the customer to clean the pot thoroughly after each use and then store with the lid off so that air can circulate.

As indicated before, it's always good public relations to clean up the outside of any appliance brought in for repair. Don't leave smudgy fingerprints, grease, and other signs of a lack of care for the customer's property. With coffee makers grime tends to build up around the base where the plastic or bakelite parts meet the metal parts. As a repairman you can do a good job of cleaning this "ring" of dirt when you disassemble the pot—don't neglect to do so.

Use a laundry detergent and a damp cloth or one of the specially prepared cleaners. Don't use an abrasive such as steel wool unless absolutely necessary, and then be careful not to mar the finish that is not dirty.

No matter what the instructions say, advise your customers that they are asking for trouble if they submerge any percolator for cleaning. This is especially true if the percolator is still warm, or if the percolator is a year or so old. Old seals which are cracked or hard will often allow moisture to be trapped inside, which then has a very hard time finding its way out. It is not unusual at all for a repairman to dismantle a "submergible" percolator and find the thermostat and other moving parts badly corroded by moisture.

COFFEE MAKER TROUBLE

Fails to Percolate

Fill the pot with cold water and plug it into your appliance tester. See if it draws current. If a wattmeter is available check the power consumption. If the wattmeter reading is zero be sure the cord and plug are OK and also make sure that the switch is on. If the wattmeter reading is less than 100 watts, the most likely trouble is an open thermostat. Recall that with the thermostat points open the warming element still heats, but it's not hot enough to cause the pot to perk. Pots not having a warming element will not draw any current if the thermostat, cord, plug, or the heating element are open.

A defective thermostat may allow the water to heat but not hot enough to perk. Use a thermometer, either the type shown in Figs. 6-5 and 6-6, or one of the clip-on tubular thermometers available for this purpose, as shown in Fig. 6-7. On pots that have an adjustable thermostat you can make slight adjustments that will cure minor trouble, but be sure you allow the pot to cycle at least two or three times before considering the job finished.

With fixed (non-adjustable) thermostats you may be able to make a repair by carefully bending the ends of the case. The

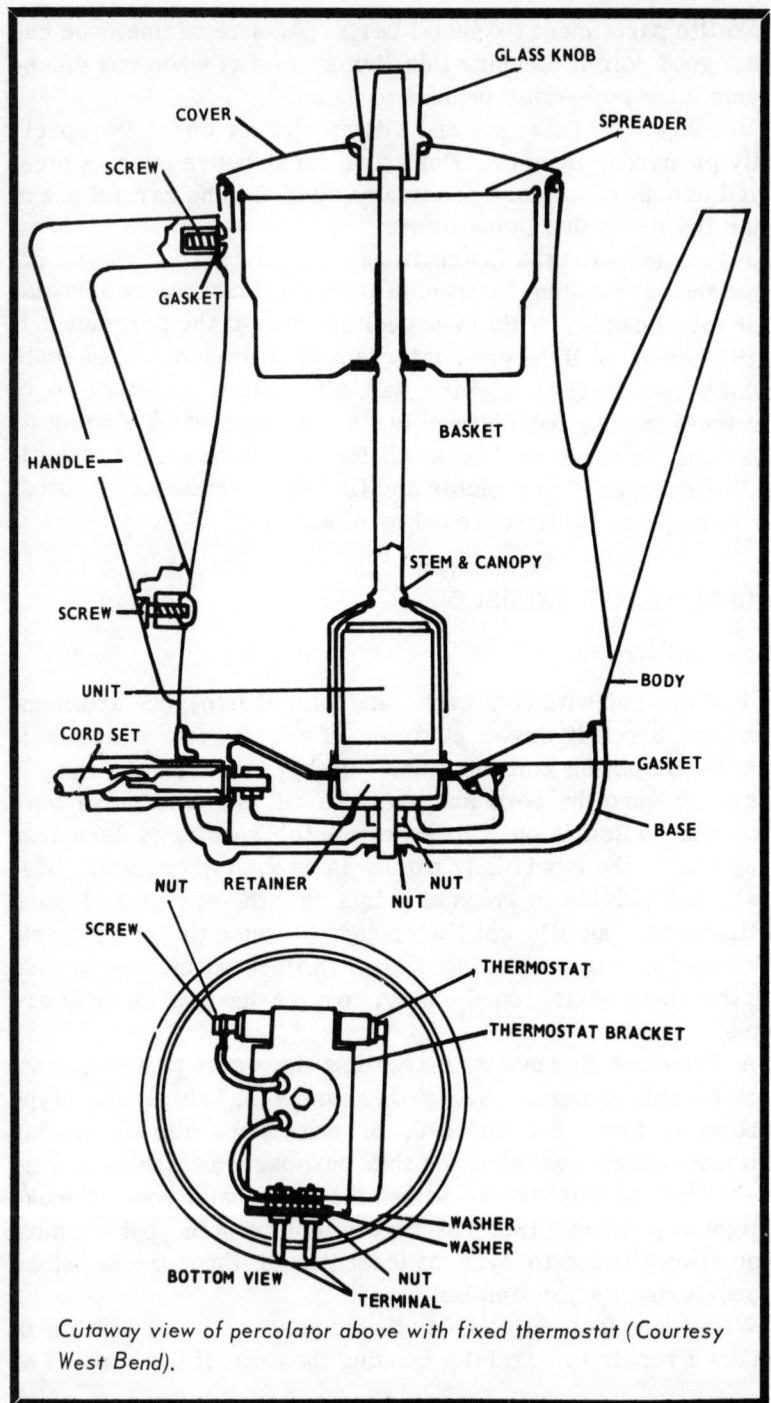

Cutaway view of percolator above with fixed thermostat (Courtesy West Bend).

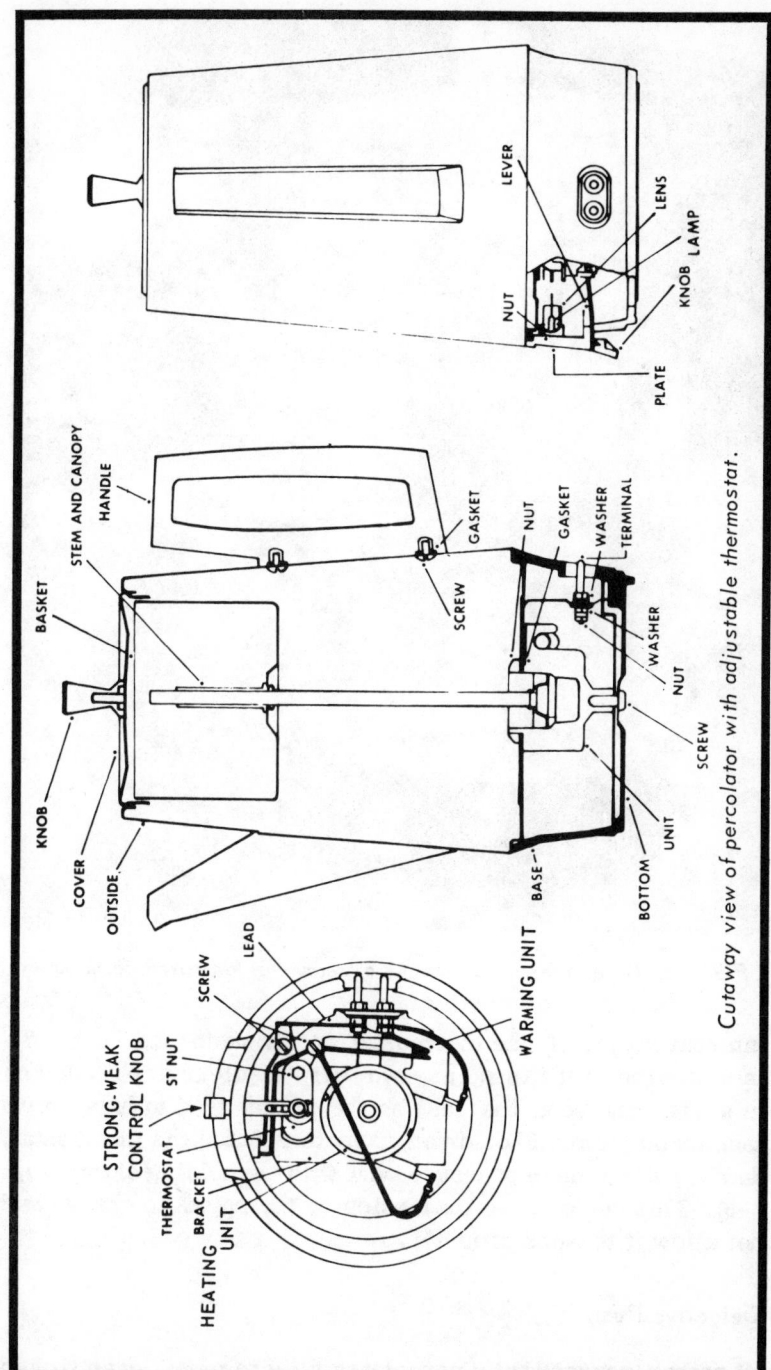

Cutaway view of percolator with adjustable thermostat.

LEVER

LENS

KNOB LAMP

NUT

PLATE

STEM AND CANOPY

HANDLE

BASKET

GASKET

SCREW

NUT

GASKET

WASHER

TERMINAL

WASHER

NUT

SCREW

KNOB

COVER

OUTSIDE

BASE

BOTTOM

UNIT

LEAD

SCREW

WARMING UNIT

STRONG-WEAK
CONTROL KNOB

ST NUT

THERMOSTAT

HEATING
UNIT

BRACKET

Fig. 6-5. Here, a repairman checks a thermostat for correct temperature.

internal layout of one thermostat is shown in Fig. 6-8. To increase the heat range, use two pairs of pliers or put one end in a vise and bend the case so the points tend to have more tension on them. Should you have to replace the thermostat, do not put too much pressure on it with the holding clamp (Fig. 6-9). This could cause the tension on the points to change and not allow it to work properly.

Defective Pump

Another reason that a percolator fails to perk, even though

Fig. 6-6 Here is another way to check thermostat operation.

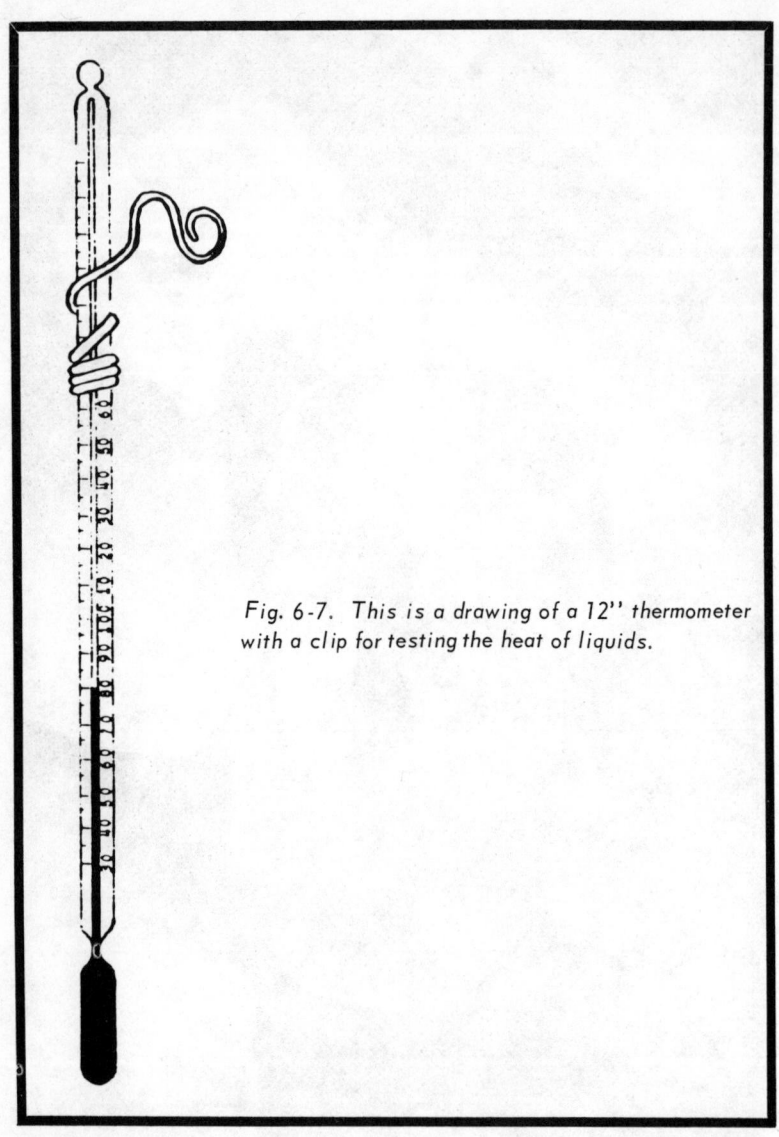

Fig. 6-7. This is a drawing of a 12" thermometer with a clip for testing the heat of liquids.

the temperature is normal, is a defective pump. The pump's purpose is to hold a small amount of water close to the heating element so that the water is heated quickly and forced up through the pump and out the opening into the percolator top where it is spread over the coffee. If the pump is clogged, or if the valve will not work, or if there is a leak in it, the water can not be forced up through the pump stem, Fig. 6-10. Often, a simple cleaning is all that's necessary to put the pump back into service. A pipe cleaner or a thin wire will unclog the pump.

Some types of pumps have the stem fastened to the cup by "swedging." If the stem is loose enough to allow pressure to escape, you may be able to set the cup and stem in a vise and, using the proper size bolt head or punch, re-swedge the joint, Fig. 6-11.

We must say again that repair of a part such as suggested above is not normally as satisfactory as replacement but in many cases, where a part is not readily available, a little ingenuity will solve the problem and prevent a long wait for the customer until the part arrives.

Pot Shuts Off Too Soon or Repercolates

Check the thermostat and the continuity of the warming element if one is used.

Pot Fails to Shut Off

Check according to the following approximate rate: The median percolating time for eight cups of coffee is from 14 to 18 minutes and seven to ten minutes for four cups. If the pot doesn't work within these general limits you should replace the thermostat.

Pot Leaks Around Element

Replace the asbestos washer between the element and the pot. If the leaks appear to have damaged the thermostat, replace

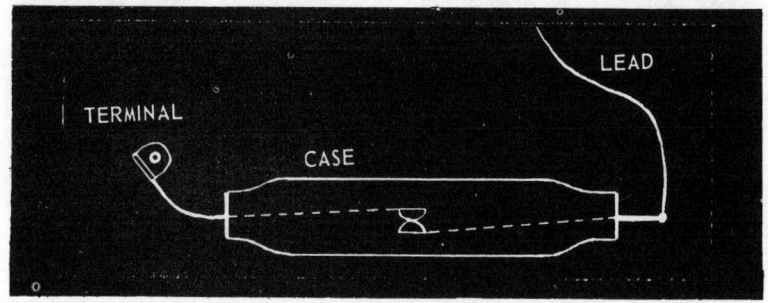

Fig. 6-8. Drawing of one type fixed-heat thermostat used in a coffee percolator.

Fig. 6-9. *When replacing a thermostat, don't put too much pressure on it with the holding clamp.*

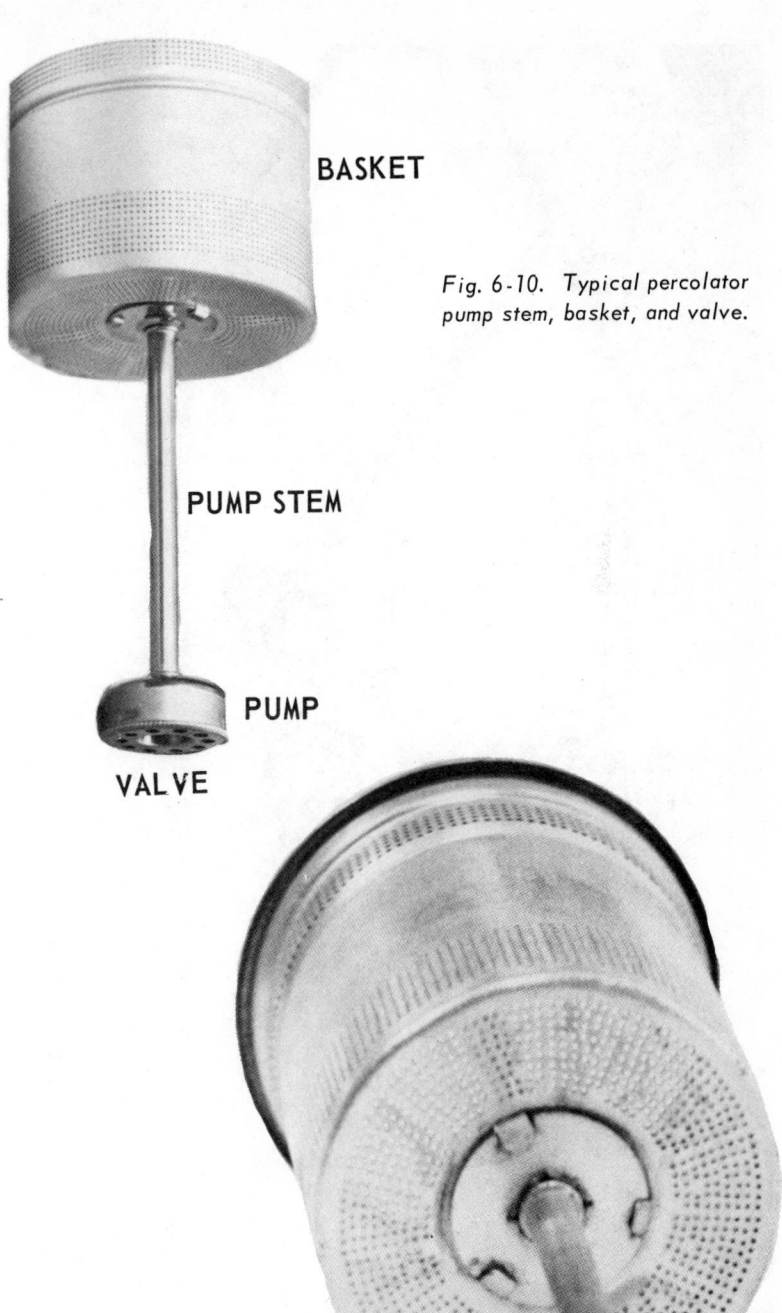

BASKET

Fig. 6-10. Typical percolator pump stem, basket, and valve.

PUMP STEM

PUMP

VALVE

Fig. 6-11. If the stem is loose enough to allow pressure to escape, you may be able to "reswedge" the joint with a punch or proper size bolt head.

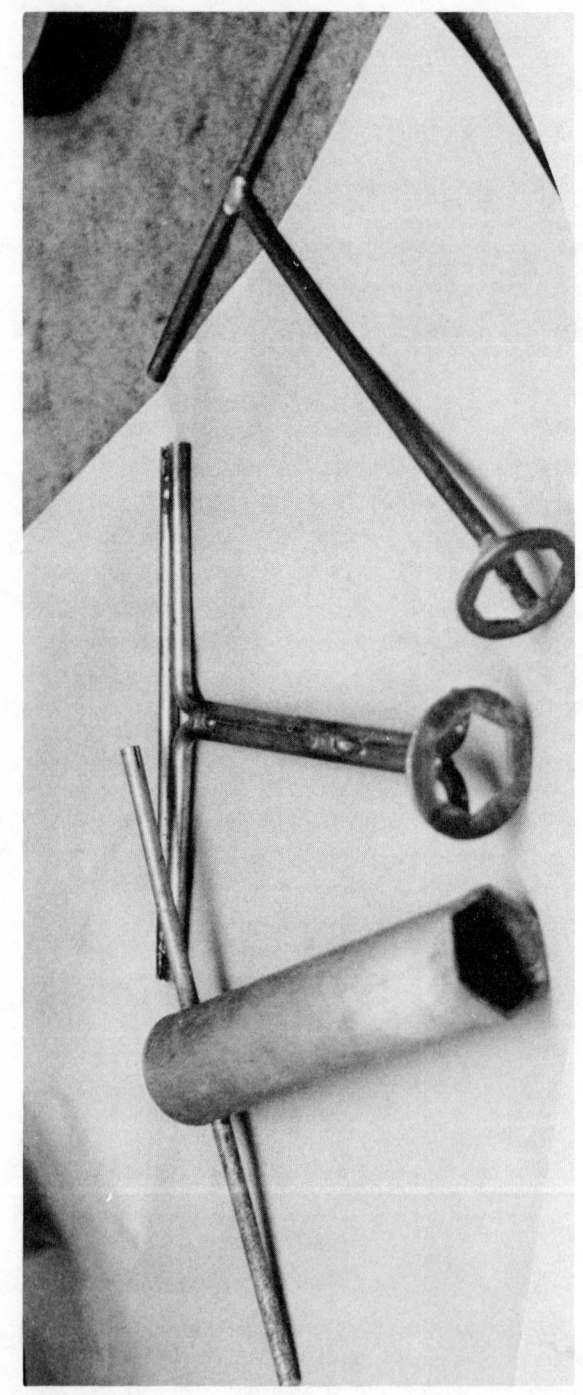

Fig. 6-12. Special wrenches used to tighten the heating element in percolators.

it also. Be sure to tighten the element securely, using an extra deep socket or special wrench as shown in Fig. 6-12. In Fig. 6-13 the repairman has the element clamped in the vise (firmly but not too tight) and is tightening the element nut inside the pot the special element wrench. In some cases it's better to place the wrench handle in the vise and turn the pot instead; experience will teach you the best way, depending on the type and brand of pot you're working on.

Replacing Warming Elements

Fig. 6-14 shows a number of warming elements used in various percolators. All except one can be replaced separately from the main element. With a combination unit, if either the warming or main element goes out, both must be replaced because they are built into a single unit.

Replacing Thermostats

In most cases adjustable thermostats are held in place by one or two screws, and replacement is simply a matter of getting the correct replacement part and installing it. In a few cases the replacement thermostat may be a universal type that is a near-fit for several different models. On these you'll find you sometimes have to ream out a mounting hole or perhaps bend a mounting bracket slightly so the replacement will fit.

Fixed - heat thermostats are often held in place by a simple pressure clamp, probably a piece of aluminum. The aluminum is simply bent up slightly to remove the old thermostat (Fig. 6-9). Then it should be bent down slightly so that the new one is held firmly (again not too firmly but snug). Be sure to position the new thermostat as near as possible to the original, and if there are heat shields around the thermostat be sure they are replaced in exactly the same manner as they were taken off; otherwise, you can be almost sure that the temperature setting will be off.

Temperature Settings

Due to design, there must of necessity be some latitude in the settings of percolator thermostat temperatures, but the

Fig. 6-13. This technician is tightening a heating element nut with a special wrench.

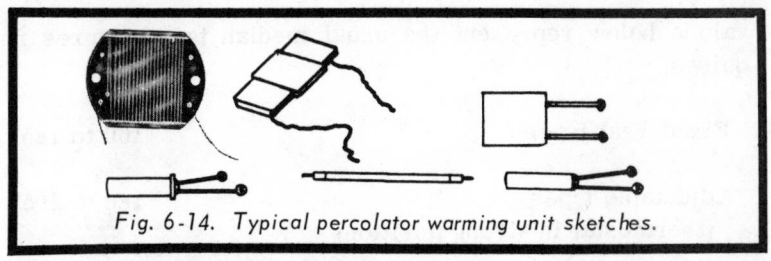

Fig. 6-14. Typical percolator warming unit sketches.

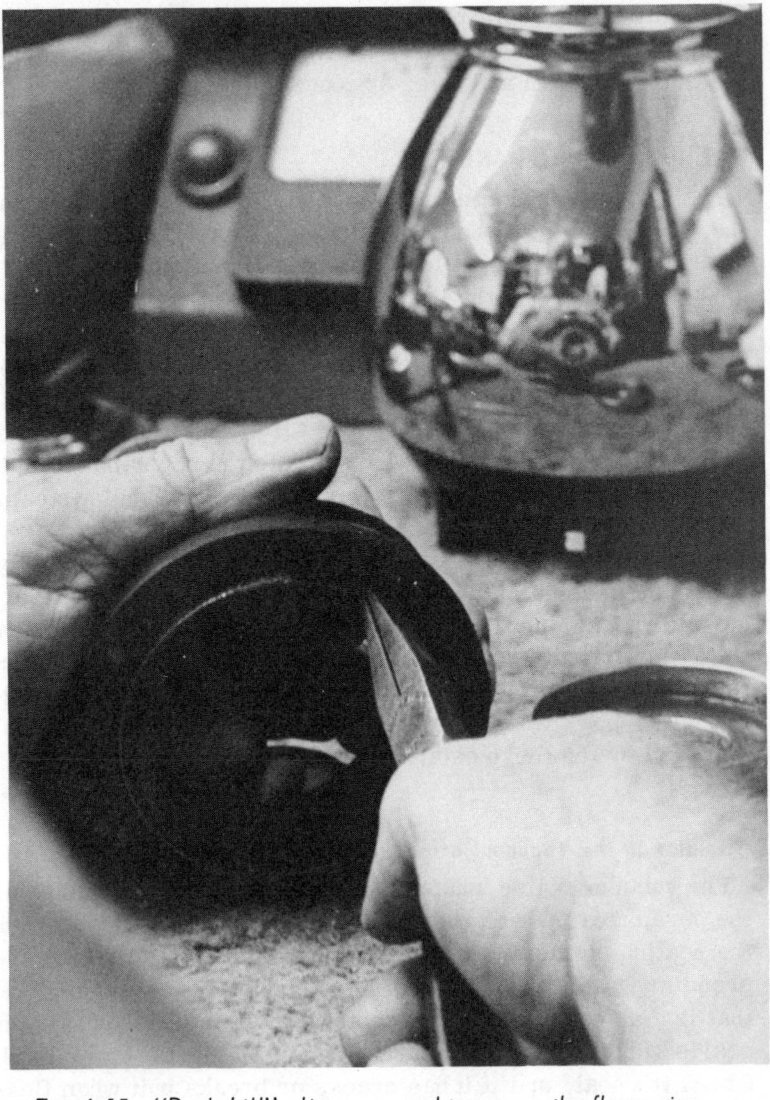

Fig. 6-15. "Duck-bill" pliers are used to remove the flange ring.

values below represent the usual median temperatures required:

Fixed-heat types	160 to 185°
Adjustable types (thermostat in strong position)	180 to 205°

Certainly no percolator should be allowed to reach a temperature above 205°, since only a slight discrepancy will bring the water to a boil and this, of course, is not desirable.

VACUUM COFFEE MAKER

The vacuum coffee maker was once extremely popular and there are still thousands in use today, many of which, though several years old, still look and work like new.

Water is placed in the lower bowl and the thermostat turned on. The top bowl, with the coffee inside, has a nozzle attached which extends down into the lower bowl. A large rubber seal on the bottom of the upper bowl holds pressure inside the lower bowl as the water heats. All except a small amount of the water in the lower bowl rises into the upper bowl. This small amount of water in the lower bowl boils, causing steam, which agitates the coffee and water in the upper bowl.

When all the water is boiled away, the heat in the lower bowl increases quickly and in about 25 to 40 seconds the thermostat will automatically switch to low. As the temperature in the lower bowl drops, a vacuum is formed and the coffee is drawn down through a filter (to remove the grounds) into the lower bowl where the temperature is kept between 165° and 185° by the thermostat.

Troubles in the Vacuum Coffee Maker

The vacuum coffee maker has the same heating troubles as the percolator. Check the cord and plug, the thermostat, and the heating element. In addition, vacuum coffee makers are prone to a rather common trouble, especially as it ages, and that is a defective seal on the bottom of the upper bowl. If the seal is bad the coffee will not run back down into the lower bowl. Check the seal, and if it has cracks or breaks in it when flexed, you should replace it with a new one.

Use only hand pressure to screw out the nozzle, because tools may damage the nozzle. Remove the old seal; then remove the metal ring and flange and install the new seal. Fig. 6-15 shows how the flange ring is removed with a pair of duckbill pliers, and Fig. 6-16 shows the flange being installed in the new seal.

Sometimes even a new seal will not correct the leakage problem if the lower bowl has been dropped and the top of the bowl so distorted that the seal does not fit snugly. A special tool is available for use in reforming the top so that the seal will work properly again.

FUSES

Most of the coffee pots made today are not fused, but there are many in use, made some years ago, that do have fuses in the AC line. The fuses were used to protect the pot should it be turned on with no water in the pot, or perhaps boiled dry for some reason. If the pot gets too hot the fuse opens and turns off the current to the heating element. The fuse could be a screw-in type or strip type. Fig. 6-17 shows some typical coffee maker fuses.

LARGER COFFEE PERCOLATORS

Larger coffee percolators, the 20- to 40-cup sizes used at parties, for meetings, etc., operate in essentially the same manner as their small counterparts. The principal difference is size. Fig. 6-18 shows a cutaway view of a 12- to 30-cup percolator. This particular model uses a fixed "bump" type thermostat, but others of the same general type use an adjustable one.

A neon lamp is connected across the thermostat points. When the points open the neon will light. (The neon lamp draws a very tiny current and even though it is in series with the heating element there is not enough current to produce any heat.) Because the lamp comes on when the thermostat goes off, it is often referred to as a "serve" or "ready" lamp.

For coffee makers without an adjustable thermostat, to check temperature:

1. Fill about 4/5 full of water.

Fig. 6-16. The technician is installing the flange ring in the new seal.

2. Plug in and allow to heat until "serve" or "ready" lamp comes on.

3. Water temperature should be between 175° and 195° F when the thermostat opens and the "serve" lamp comes on. If not, thermostat will have to be replaced.

SERVICE NOTES FOR AUTOMATIC PERCOLATORS

Be certain that the percolator operating instructions are being followed. Often, these instructions are imprinted on the bottom of the coffee pot.

Slow to Perk
Pump jacket may be loose on the stem

Stem may be partially closed by corrosion

Element coated with coffee stains and lime deposits

Thermostat defective

Weak Coffee, or Coffee Not Hot Enough
Bad thermostat

Pump jacket loose on the stem

Pump doesn't seat as it should

Percolator Does Not Heat
Loose connection

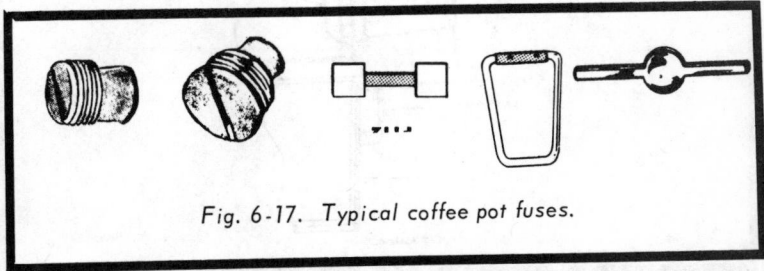

Fig. 6-17. Typical coffee pot fuses.

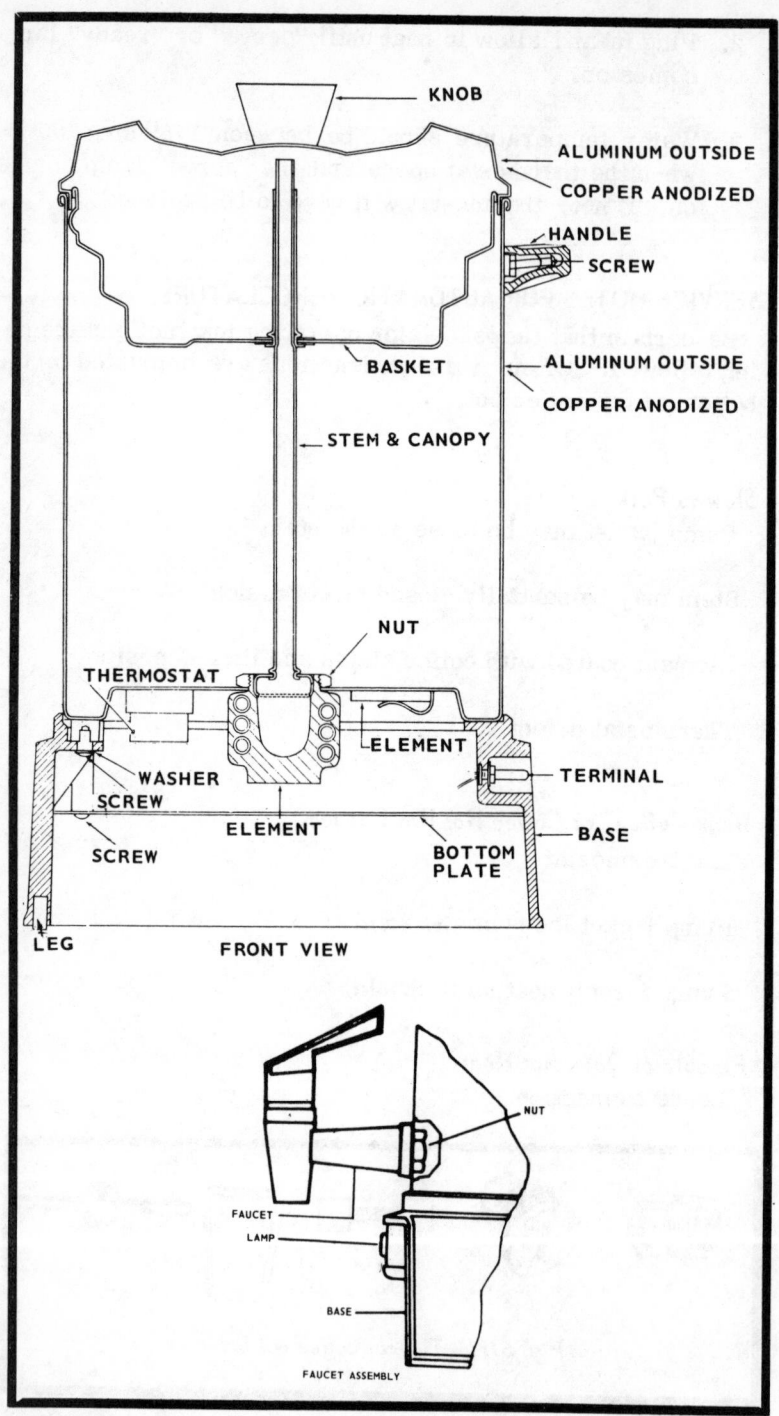

KNOB

ALUMINUM OUTSIDE

COPPER ANODIZED

HANDLE

SCREW

BASKET

ALUMINUM OUTSIDE

COPPER ANODIZED

STEM & CANOPY

NUT

THERMOSTAT

ELEMENT

TERMINAL

WASHER

SCREW

ELEMENT

BASE

SCREW

BOTTOM
PLATE

LEG

FRONT VIEW

NUT

FAUCET

LAMP

BASE

FAUCET ASSEMBLY

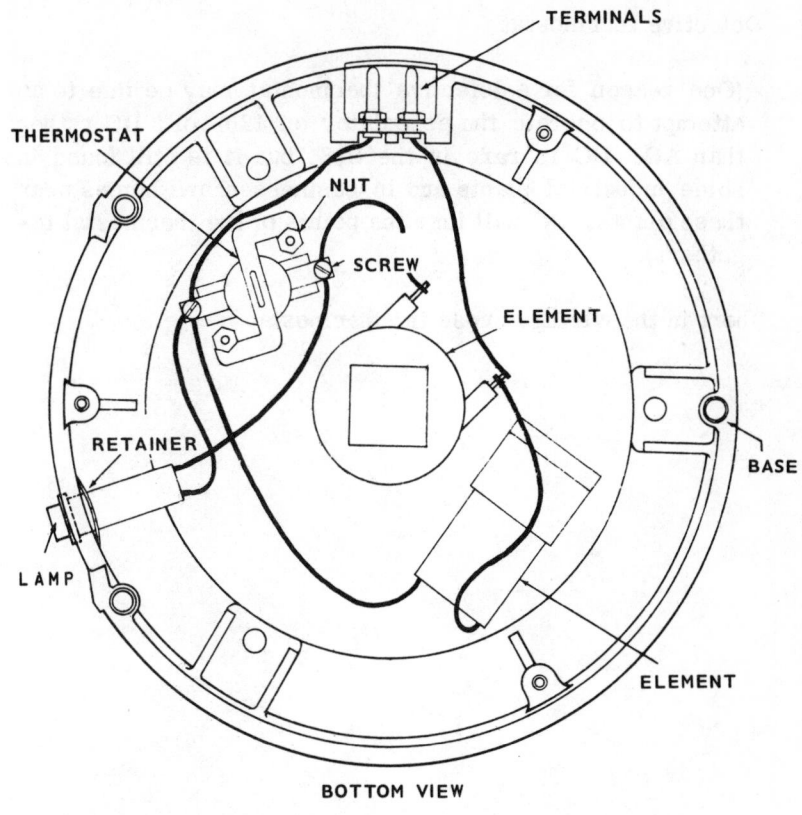

Fig. 6-18. A 12-to 30-cup coffee percolator. Courtesy West Bend

Bad cord or plug

Heating element burned out, which may have been caused by:

1. Plugged in without water in the pot

2. Used with too little water in the pot

3. Corrosion may have accumulated because of a lack of proper cleaning

4. Water leak may have corroded or shorted connections

Won't Stop Percolating

Defective thermostat

(One reason for a defective thermostat may be due to an attempt to operate the percolator on 120-volts DC rather than AC. DC is rare in the U.S. but it is still found in some industrial plants and in businesses and homes near these plants. DC will fuse the points of the thermostat together.)

Short in the wiring across the thermostat

CHAPTER 7

Blankets

Electric blankets are a necessity in many households now, and as such are a common appliance that the repairman is asked to fix. Many shops will not tackle blanket repair and recommend either that the customer buy a new one or return the old one to the factory for service.

Some shops, though, have been quite successful in repairing blankets, especially those that use several thermostats sewn inside. All except a few "electronically-controlled" blankets use the internal thermostat arrangement. The thermostats are connected in series and control a portion of the heating element.

Fig. 7-1 is an internal wiring diagram of a typical electric blanket. Notice there are two circuits (this is pretty well a standard procedure) inside the blanket. The blanket has a three-pin connector and the common terminal is the offset pin. Other blankets may use the center pin as common but most seem to use the arrangement in Fig. 7-1. If the blanket is OK, the two "hot" pins will have the highest resistance between them when measured with an ohmmeter or test lamp. The same resistance should exist between the common pin and each of the hot pins.

TESTING BLANKETS

The most common trouble in the blanket itself is a broken connecting wire, heater element, or open thermostat. Use a test lamp or ohmmeter to find out whether the blanket wiring is OK. Look at Fig. 7-1 again. You should have continuity between all three of the pins on the blanket plug; however, there should be more resistance between pins 1 and 2. If there is continuity between pins 1 and 2 but not to pin 3, the problem is in the common line inside the blanket. It may be

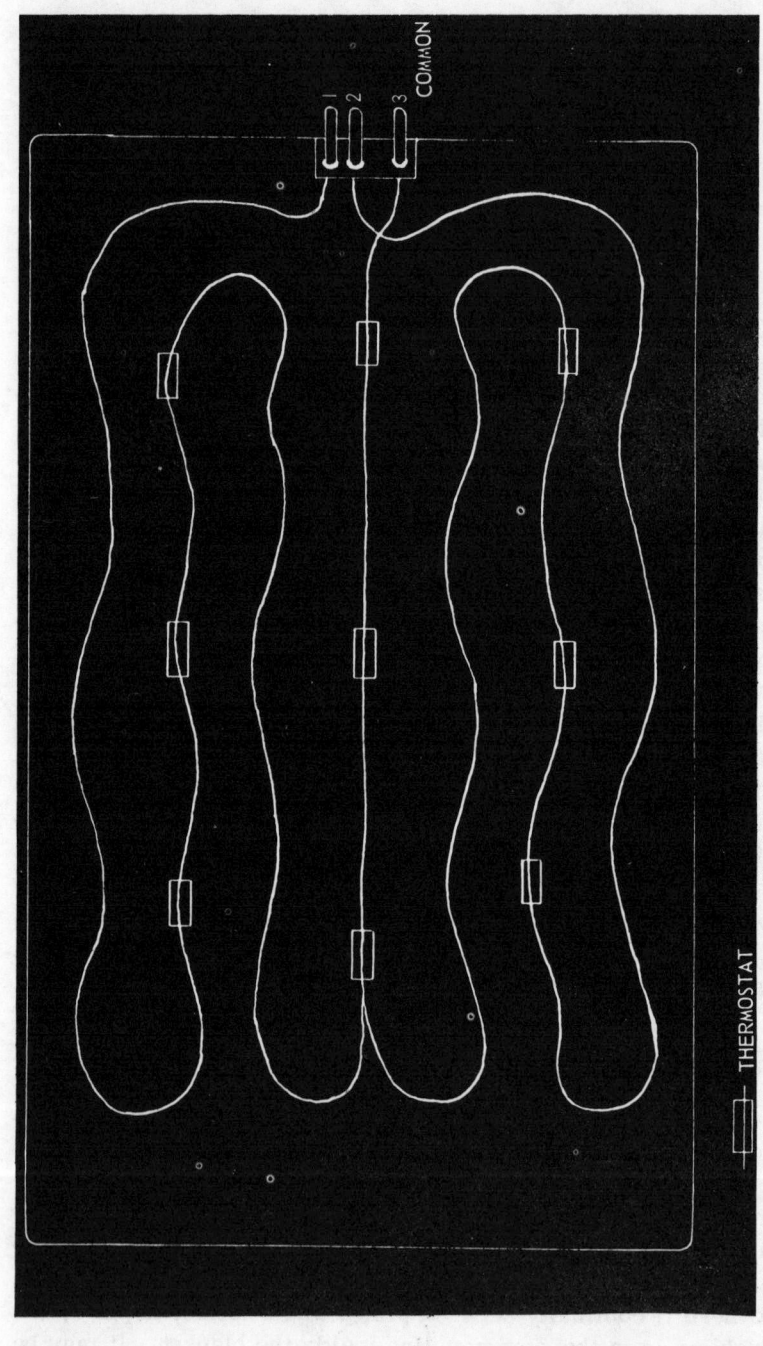

THERMOSTAT

COMMON

1
2
3

Fig. 7-1. Electric blanket wiring diagram. This blanket uses nine thermostats, three in each side and three in the common lead.

an open wire or thermostat, but you have localized the trouble
to the three center thermostats or the connecting wires. If,
on the other hand, you have continuity between pins 1 and 3
but not between 2 and 3 you know that the upper and common
circuits are all right but something is open in the lower half
of the blanket.

This preliminary testing tells you which portion of the blanket
the trouble is in but not exactly where. Next, feel through
the blanket and find the internal thermostats that could be
causing the trouble. Plug the control unit into a wattmeter
or wattage indicator (a wattage indicator should read 200 watts
or less) and move the thermostats around one at a time. See
if you can get at least a momentary contact, in which case you
can distort the thermostat enough to get the blanket to draw
current momentarily. If this fails, hold the thermostat in the
palm of your hand and tap each one with a rubber or plastic
mallet. This may "bounce" the points together long enough
for you to localize the trouble.

The High-Voltage Method

If the above methods do not produce results, the high-voltage
"arc" method will in many cases. Hang the blanket so that all
the surface can be seen from both sides. Two or three snap-

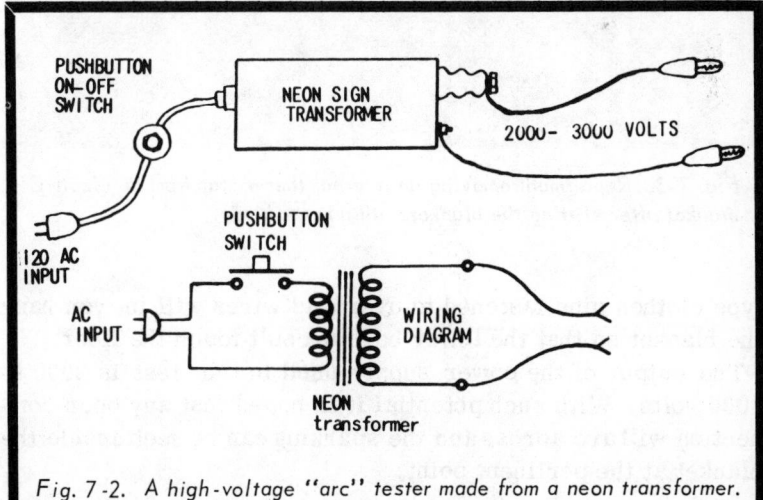

*Fig. 7-2. A high-voltage "arc" tester made from a neon transformer.
Notice the push-on switch in the primary circuit so the operator does
not have to touch the high-voltage leads while testing.*

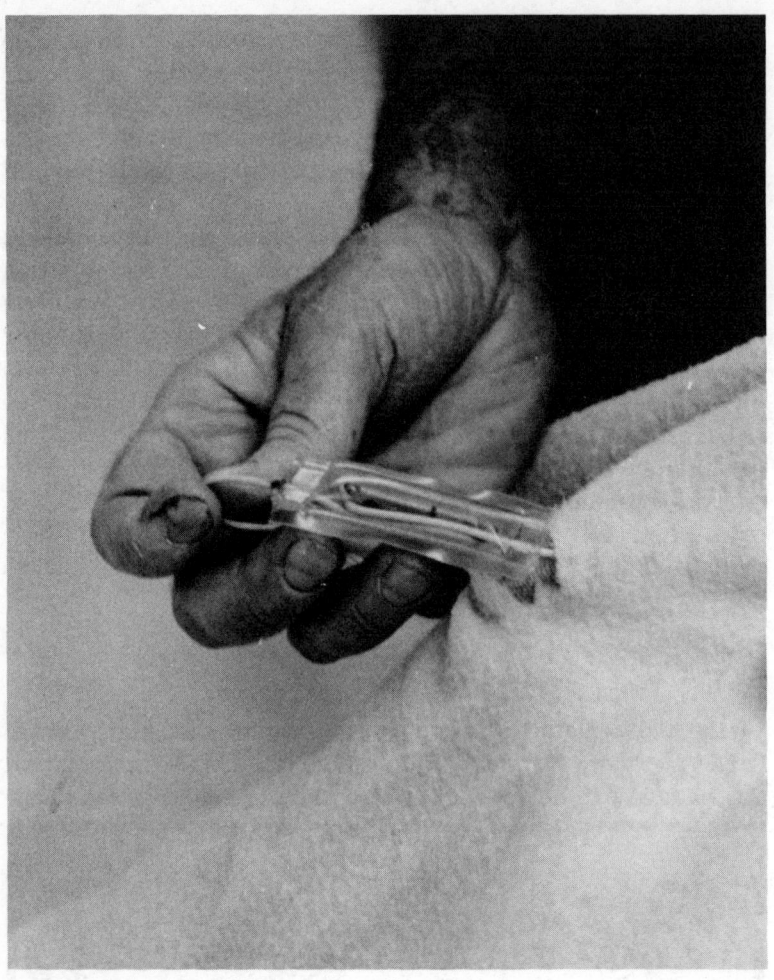

Fig. 7-3. Repairman removing an internal thermostat from an electric blanket after slitting the blanket with a razor blade.

type clothes pins fastened to overhead wires will let you hang the blanket so that the lower edge doesn't touch the floor.

The output of the power supply used in this test is 2000 to 3000 volts. With such potential it is hoped that any open connection will arc across and the sparking can be seen inside the blanket at the pertinent point.

WARNING: THE VOLTAGE USED IN THIS TEST IS DEFINITELY LETHAL. ALL NECESSARY PRECAUTIONS MUST

BE TAKEN TO PREVENT ANY POSSIBLE BODY CONTACT
WITH THE TEST CIRCUIT.

We recommend the setup in Fig. 7-2, since you need not touch
either of the high-voltage wires while the test is made. In addition, it is easy to stop and start the test while watching for
tell-tale sparks.

If possible, have at least one other person around to watch
for arcs so that both sides can be monitored at the same time.
"Bump" the on-off switch on the high-voltage transformer for
about a one-second "on" cycle. If no arcs show up, have

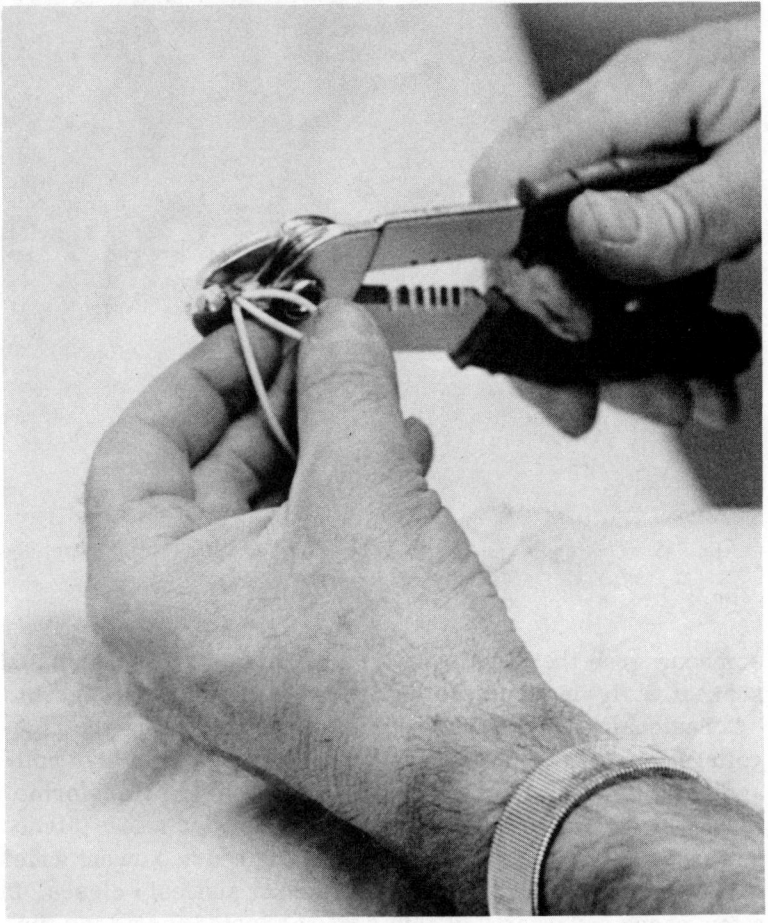

Fig. 7-4. A repair sleeve and crimping tool are used to connect wires
together after the defective thermostat is removed.

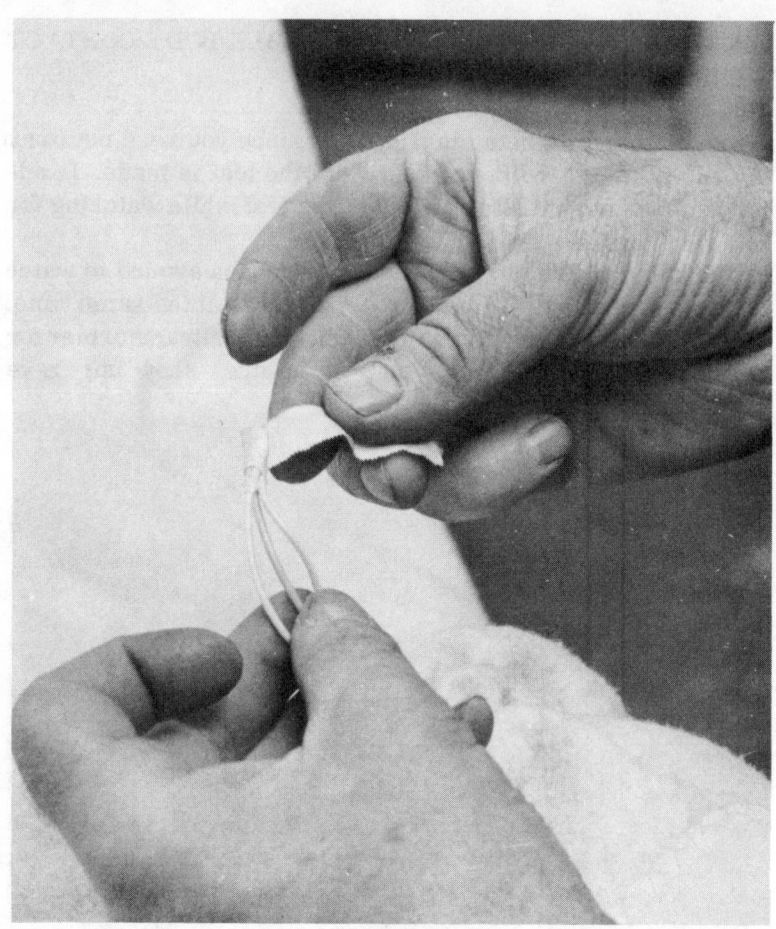

Fig. 7-5. The repair sleeve should be insulated with "glass" tape.

someone grab the corner of the blanket (with one hand) and shake it while you apply the high-voltage again in short bursts.

Occasionally, you may "repair" a blanket using the high-voltage test. If two open leads come together while high voltage is applied they may spot weld. If you hear the transformer (a neon-sign transformer is often used) develop a low-pitched hum it is an indication that it is drawing heavy current which will occur if the circuit inside the blanket suddenly closes. In a few cases a "repair" of this sort has lasted for a long time but usually a vigorous shaking of the blanket will open it again. Caution: An arc inside a blanket can cause the blanket to catch fire so watch the blanket carefully while applying the high-voltage test.

REPAIRING THE BLANKET

Once you have spotted the trouble, use a razor blade and cut a small slit just large enough to pull out the defective section of wiring. In Fig. 7-3 you see a repairman removing a defective thermostat. In Fig. 7-4 he has removed the defective thermostat and is using a splicing sleeve and tool to connect the wires together. This particular circuit has three

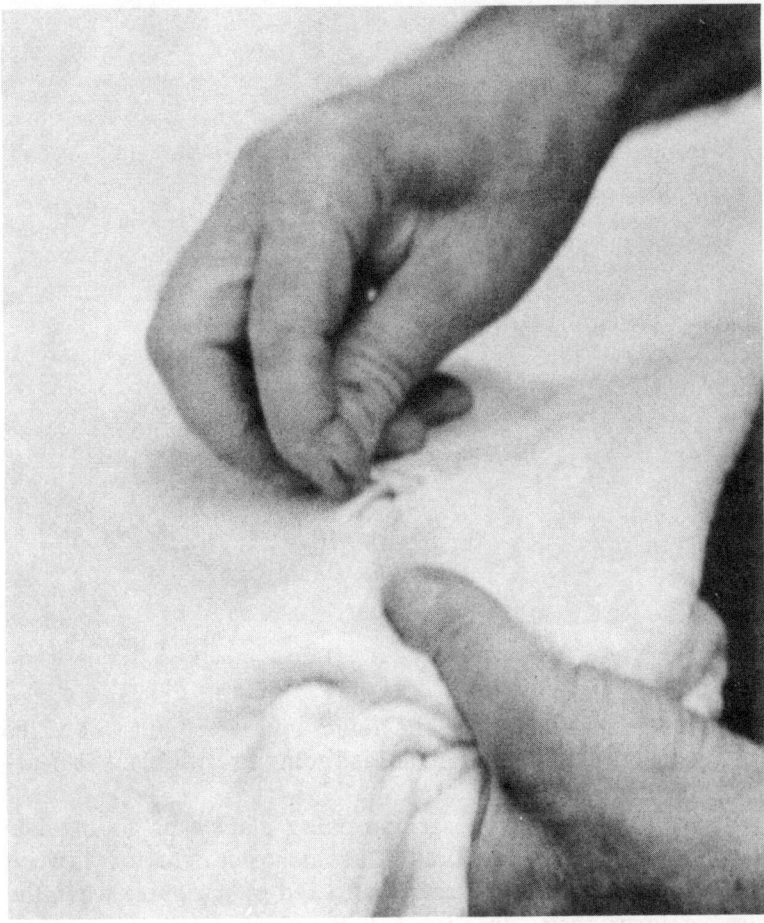

Fig. 7-6. Sewing up the repair slit using thread the same color as the blanket.

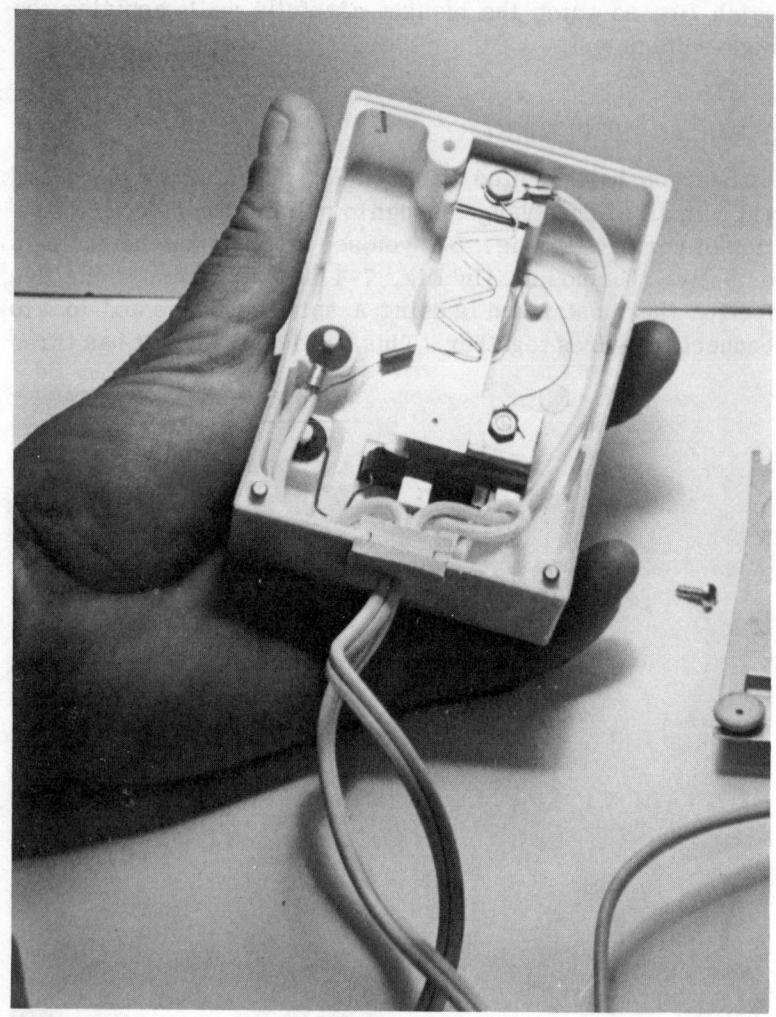

Fig. 7-7. The inside view of a blanket control box.

wires to tie together since the defective thermostat was at the
"Y" connection in the common lead going to both blanket heating elements.

Fig. 7-5 shows the repairman using glass tape to insulate
the wires and the connection. Glass does not deteriorate when
warm and it also is not greatly affected by moisture when the
blanket is washed. In Fig. 7-6 the blanket slit is sewn up,
using thread the same color as the blanket.

Although one thermostat was removed in the above repair

this is not considered to be too unsafe since there are still eight thermostats left to protect the user in the event of overheating; however, when more than one thermostat on a side or on the common line would have to be removed, it may be best to suggest to the customer that he buy a new blanket or send it in to the factory for repair. To our knowledge, blanket

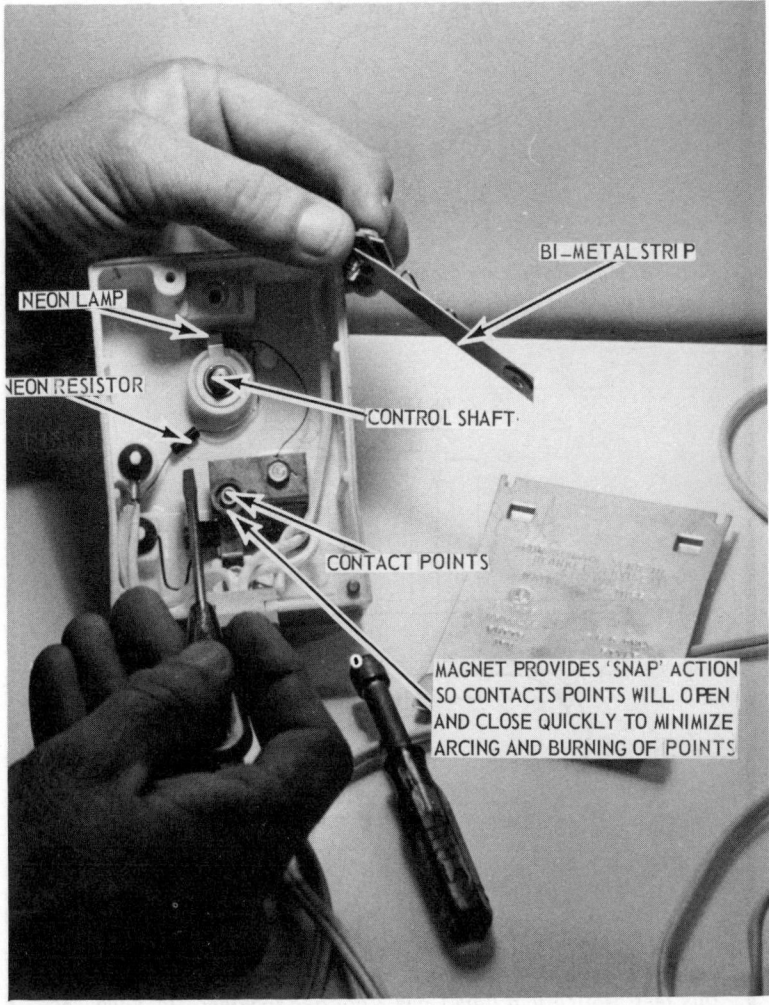

Fig. 7-8. The bi-metal strip has been removed to show the contact points, neon lamp and resistor, and control knob shaft. Notice the circular magnet that provides the snap action for the thermostat switch.

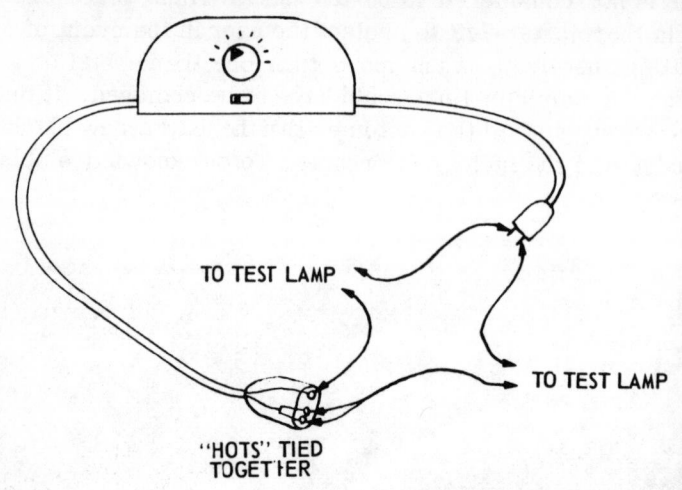

TO TEST LAMP

TO TEST LAMP

"HOTS" TIED
TOGETHER

Fig. 7-9. Pictorial wiring diagram of a typical blanket control. The resistor in series with the neon should be around 33,000 ohms. The neon lamp is an NE-2.

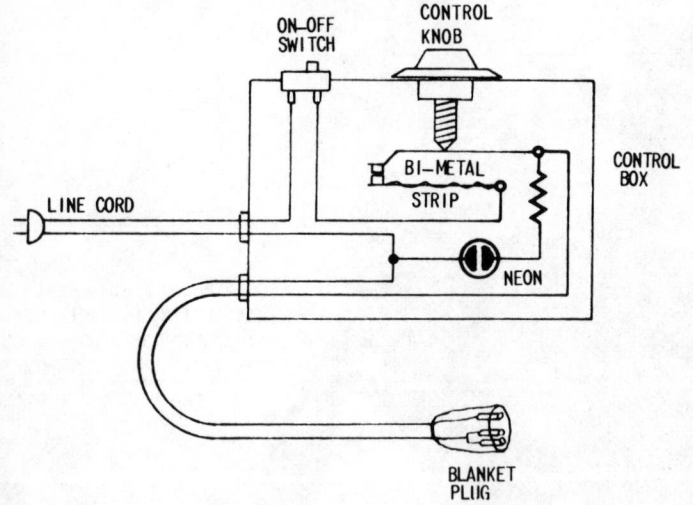

ON–OFF
SWITCH

CONTROL
KNOB

CONTROL
BOX

BI–METAL
STRIP

LINE CORD

NEON

BLANKET
PLUG

Fig. 7-10. Method of testing a control box with a test lamp. Be sure that the thermostat is on "high" heat and the on-off switch "on" for this test. Notice that pins 1 and 2 are tied together. In a dual control blanket, one control will energize pin 1 and the other pin 2 so in this case pins 1 and 2 will NOT be internally connected.

thermostats are not available from any source of supply. In some cases you may be able to salvage a thermostat from a discarded blanket.

TESTING AND REPAIRING CONTROL BOXES

With the exception of electronic controls and the controls for blankets with internal "sensing" wires around the heating element, a typical blanket control is basically a simple thermostat adjustable with an external knob, an on-off switch, and often a neon pilot lamp. Fig. 7-7 is a view of the inside of a blanket control box. Fig. 7-8 shows the same box with the bi-metal thermostat strip removed. The screwdriver is pointing to the resistor in series with the neon lamp which is at the top behind the control shaft. Fig. 7-9 shows a typical control box circuit. The resistor in series with the neon is often not marked but it can be replaced with a 33,000-ohm 1/2-watt resistor or even a larger value, but the neon will be dimmer as the resistance is increased.

To check the control box and cord for continuity, use a test lamp or ohmmeter as shown in Fig. 7-10. The two "hot" leads are normally tied together inside the blanket plug as shown; however, in some cases the wires are tied together inside the control box, in which case there will be three wires running to the blanket plug from the control box.

Make sure the thermostat is working by plugging the blanket into a wattage indicator and allow the blanket to heat. (Blanket thermostats work on <u>room</u> temperature and, except for those types which have special sensing wires, have no correlation with blanket heat. Blankets with a special sensing wire wrapped around the heating element cannot be serviced with normal equipment or the procedures suggested in this Chapter. If the thermostat turns off and on automatically when set at its lowest heat range you can be reasonably sure that it is working properly. At high heat settings the thermostat will not likely turn off and on unless room heat is high.

CHAPTER 8

Mixers

Upright or "self-standing" mixers once dominated the mixer field. Today portable mixers similar to the one in Fig. 8-1 probably make up the bulk of sales.

Upright mixers have larger motors and most have variable speed controls with a regulator to maintain the same speed whether mixing light liquids or heavy batter. The speed controls may have as many as 10 or 12 positions, ranging from very slow to full speed. The regulator is usually a set of points that are actuated by weights mounted on the armature. In some cases the armature has an actuating rod that opens and closes a set of stationary points.

Portable mixers generally have just three speeds, usually selected by a thumb switch on the handle, and have no speed regulation. Speed control in most portable mixers is attained by various taps on the motor windings.

THE SPEED REGULATOR

Fig. 8-2 is a simplified schematic diagram of a regulator-controlled universal mixer motor. This is a series motor (that is, the armature and field coils are in series) with the addition of a set of contact points that turn the motor off and on at a rapid rate once the armature comes up to a preset speed. This fast on and off switching holds the speed at a constant rate even though mixing light or heavy loads.

Turning a motor off and on, though, results in a considerable current surge each time the contacts open and close. Without some relief such arcing would burn the contact points rather quickly. To reduce the wear and tear on the points a resistor and capacitor are connected directly across them. When the points open, the resistor still allows some of the motor current to pass—not enough to run the motor except at very low speed but enough to bypass a considerable amount of the surge current around the points. The capacitor, which is shorted out when the points are closed, starts to charge as soon as the points open and so absorbs a great deal of the arcing and sparking that would reduce the life of the points.

Excessive arcing at the regulator contact points (heavy blue fire) may be caused by either an open capacitor or resistor or by an abnormally heavy load on the motor. Fig. 8-3 shows a breakdown drawing of a motor that has variable speed control and a regulator.

TROUBLES IN UPRIGHT MODELS

For motor testing and troubles refer to Chapter 9. For speed regulator troubles, first get a description of the symptoms

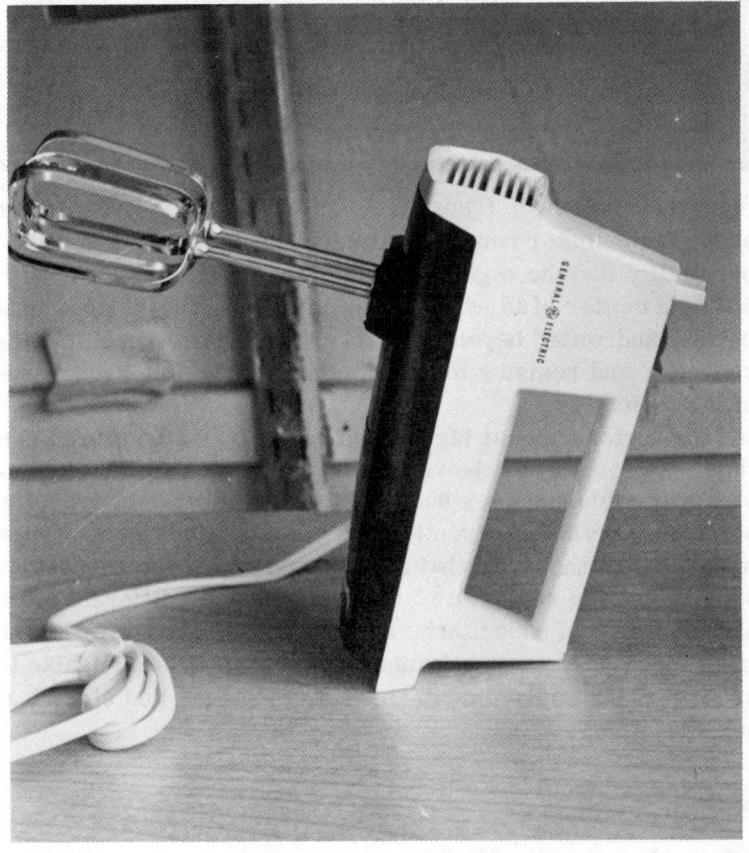

Fig. 8-1. A typical portable mixer.

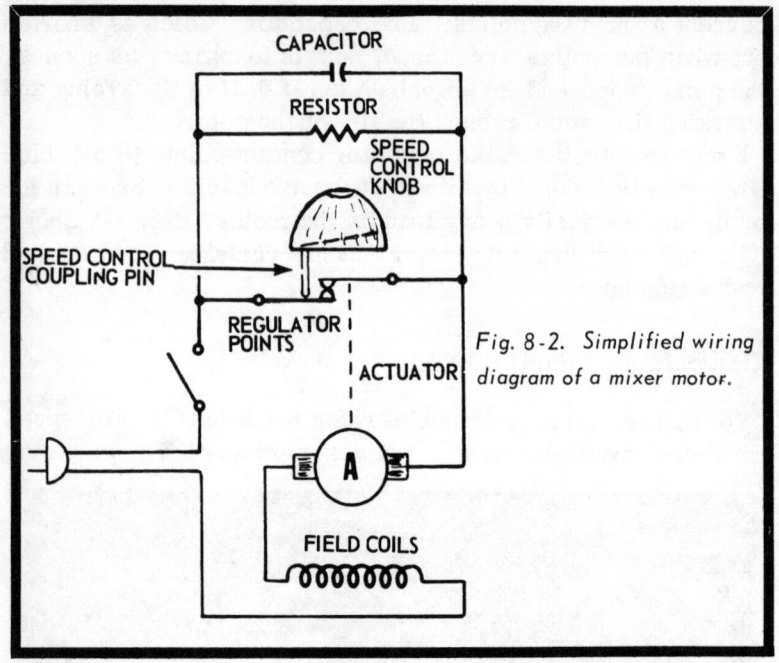

CAPACITOR

RESISTOR

SPEED CONTROL KNOB

SPEED CONTROL COUPLING PIN

REGULATOR POINTS

ACTUATOR

FIELD COILS

A

Fig. 8-2. Simplified wiring diagram of a mixer motor.

from the customer if possible, or check it carefully in the shop. If the motor runs only at very low speed there's a good possibility that the regulator points are not closing. It may be a simple matter of adjustment, but often you will find the points burned and pitted beyond repair. This means replacing the capacitor and resistor to guard against a possible recurrence of the fault.

If the motor runs at high speed only, it is a good sign that the capacitor across the regulator points is shorted. Resistors will seldom if ever short internally but capacitors quite often do. Both the capacitor and resistor in Fig. 8-4 have metal tips on the ends that snap in and out of the connectors provided on the regulators. Other mixers use different sorts of resistors and capacitors, sometimes soldered in and some with screw terminals. In nearly all cases it is advisable to use the exact replacement, both for physical and electrical considerations.

PORTABLE MIXERS

Portable mixers such as those in Figs. 8-1 and 8-5 are much simpler units, generally, than upright models. Because the

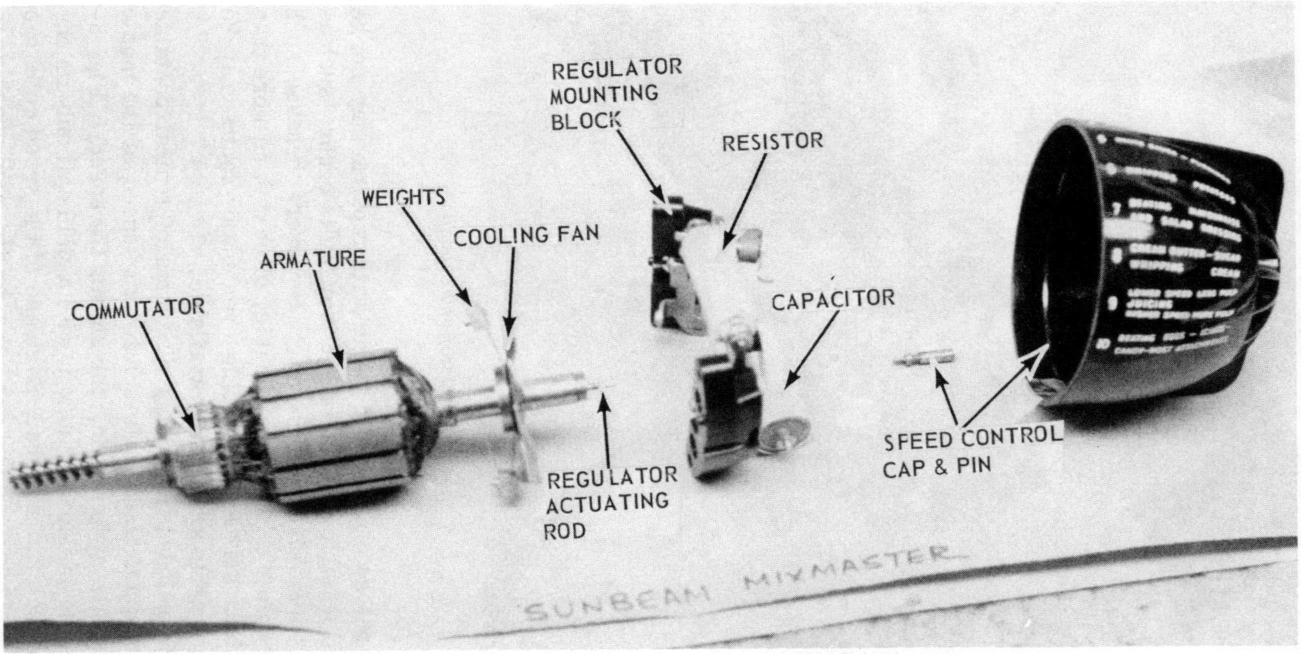

Fig. 8-3. Disassembled view of a motor with variable speed control.

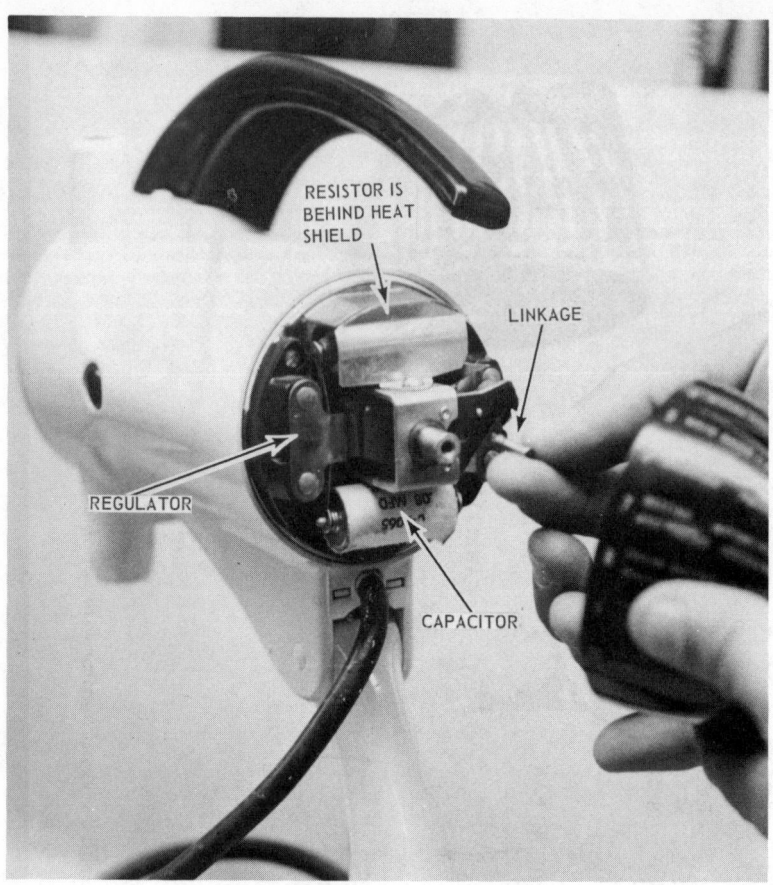

RESISTOR IS
BEHIND HEAT
SHIELD

LINKAGE

REGULATOR

CAPACITOR

Fig. 8-4. Snap-in resistor and capacitor.

units are not so expensive to begin with repairs may not be
considered feasible if more than minor faults occur, such as
a broken cord, dirty switch, etc. However, because such
mixers are often easy to disassemble, often with no more than
three or four screws, repairing even major faults may be
profitable if parts are readily available.

Fig. 8-6 includes the wiring diagrams of typical portable
mixers. Tapped field coils control the speed of the motor
(the more coils switched in, the slower the speed). Fig. 8-
7 pictures the inside of a mixer with a field coil only on one
side of the motor armature. Each one of the speed coils has
the same resistance so you can get a pretty good check as to
the condition of each coil by checking with the test lamp be-

tween adjacent taps on the motor coil. The lamp should glow with the same intensity across each coil. Fig. 8-8 shows the more conventional field coil arrangement. You can see the top coil; the other is on the opposite side of the armature.

With the cord unplugged, test from one brush through the field to the "high" terminal on the switch. The test lamp should be fairly bright. Now, check between the "med" terminal and the same brush; the lamp should be dimmer. The lamp will be dimmest when you check between the brush and the "low" speed terminal on the switch.

As Fig. 8-6 shows, not all the field windings are used except in the "low" speed position. Then, if the motor runs

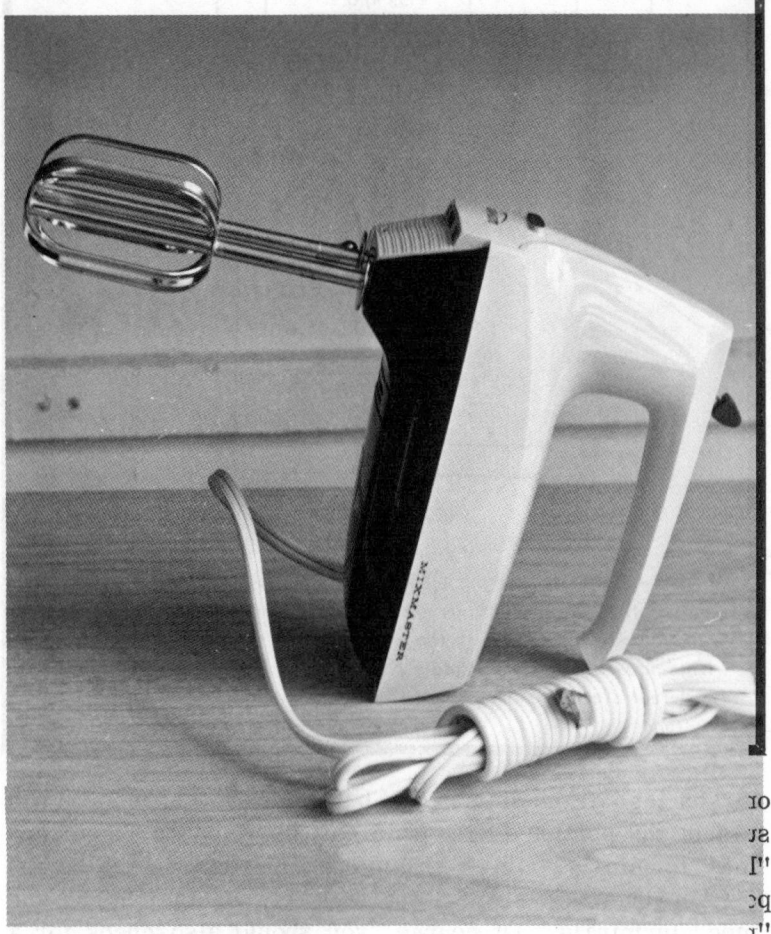

Fig. 8-5. Another popular portable mixer.

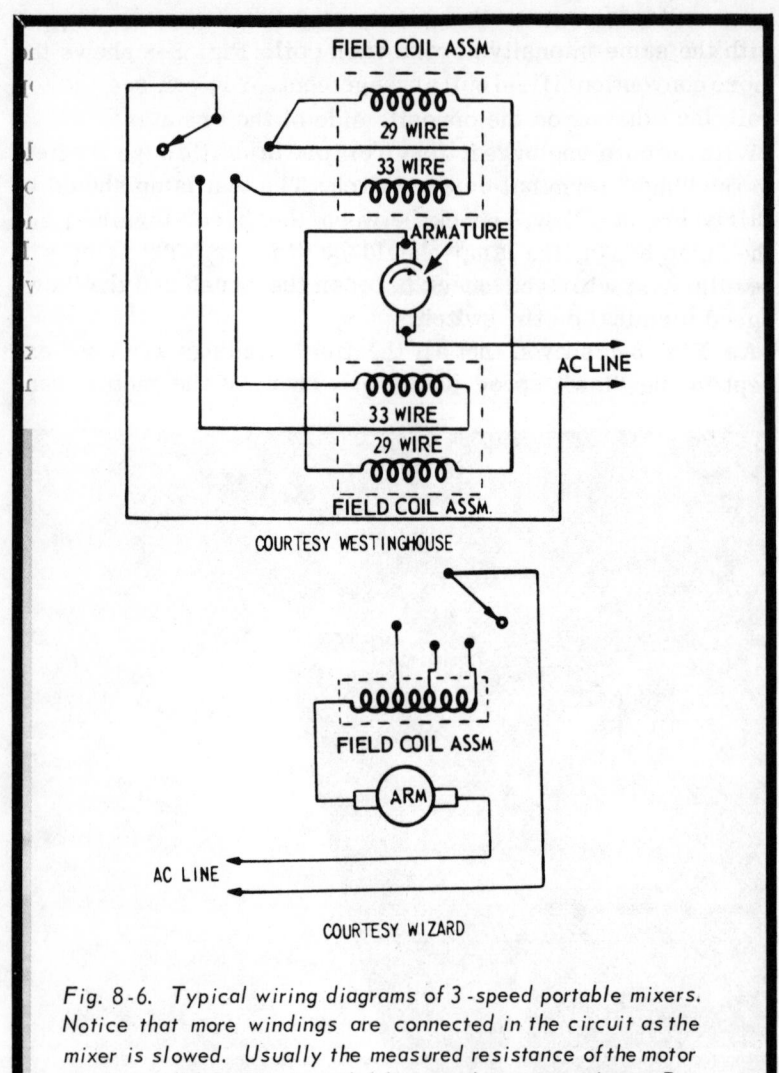

FIELD COIL ASSM

29 WIRE

33 WIRE

ARMATURE

AC LINE

33 WIRE

29 WIRE

FIELD COIL ASSM.

COURTESY WESTINGHOUSE

FIELD COIL ASSM

ARM

AC LINE

COURTESY WIZARD

Fig. 8-6. Typical wiring diagrams of 3-speed portable mixers. Notice that more windings are connected in the circuit as the mixer is slowed. Usually the measured resistance of the motor winding will be approximately the same between each tap. But different size wire used in coils will have some effect on resistance.

only on high or medium speed but not on low speed you can suspect the portion of the field coil between the "med" and "low" terminals. Or, if the motor runs only in the "high" position you would suspect the coil between the "high" and "med" terminals. Of course, you should also check for a dirty switch, a loose contact or wire, etc. Using the above deduction it is usually not too much trouble to find where to start checking if you have problems. For other motor troubles, refer to Chapter 9.

A complete exploded view of one portable mixer is shown in Fig. 8-9, along with a list of parts. Another popular portable appears in Fig. 8-10. As you can see, these mixers have much in common, and in general, repair hints for one will apply to another. Both mixers use permanently lubricated bearings, and clear silicone grease in the gear box. On slow speed the mixers run from about 400 to 700 RPM; on medium speed from about 600 to 900 RPM; and on high from about 900 to 1200 RPM. Sometimes these positions are called "Stir-Mix-Whip."

SOLID-STATE SPEED CONTROL

Fig. 8-11 shows a mixer with a solid-state speed control. It is almost the same as the three-speed mixer made by the same company, except for the solid-state control board which enables the user to select any one of 12 different speeds.

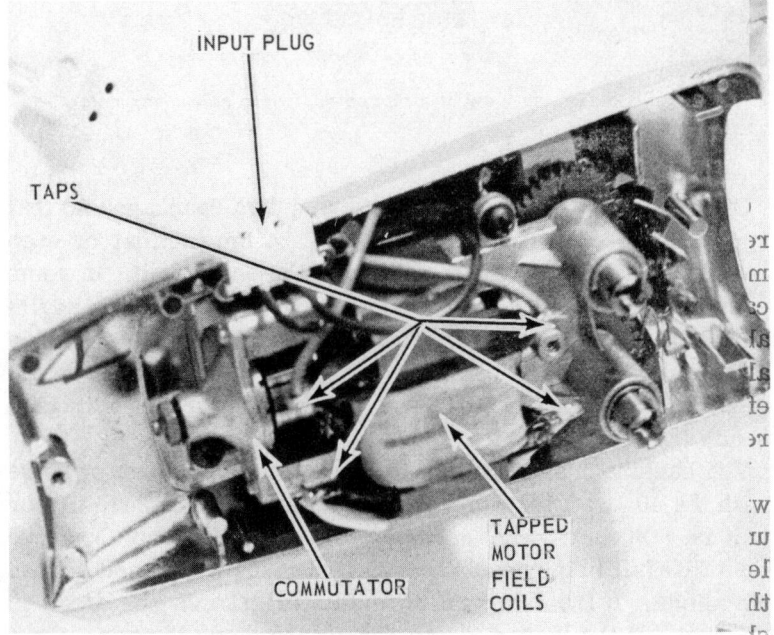

INPUT PLUG

TAPS

TAPPED MOTOR FIELD COILS

COMMUTATOR

Fig. 8-7. Inside view of a portable mixer. The field coil in this mixer is all on one side of the armature.

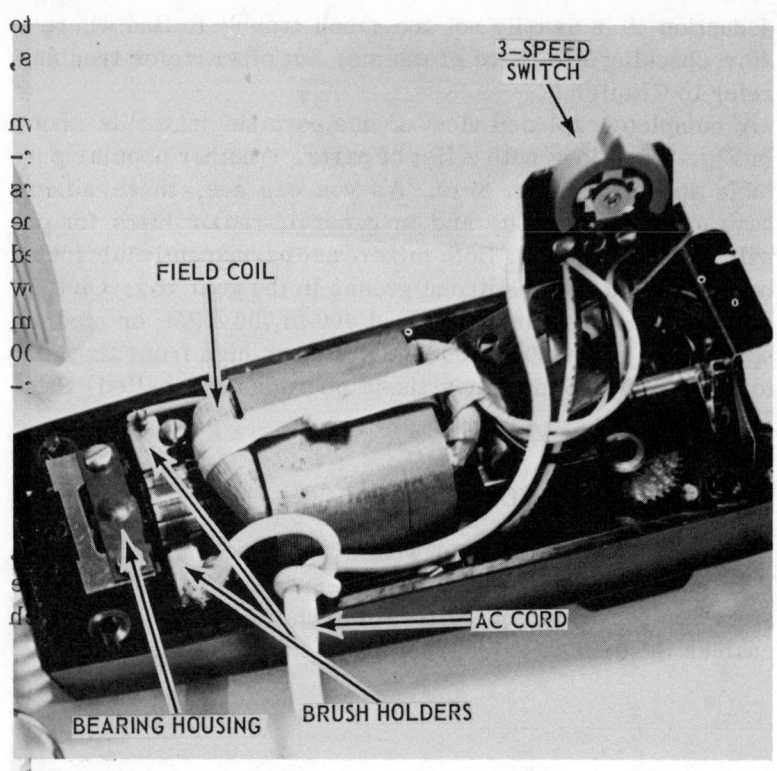

Fig. 8-8. Inside view of a tapped dual field coil mixer motor.

Often, solid-state control units are in a "package" so that replacement of individual parts may be impractical or even more expensive than the purchase of the entire unit. In some cases, though, you may find a defective diode which is available at either an appliance or radio supply house. Diodes allow current to pass in one direction only, thus they have the effect of allowing only half of the alternating current voltage to reach the other side.

You can check silicon diodes with ratings of 500 ma or more with the 40-watt lamp in the appliance tester (be sure heater unit is NOT on). Fig. 8-12 shows how. The lamp should be less than full brightness when the test leads are placed across the diode. If the lamp reaches full brightness the diode is shorted. If the lamp does not light, the diode is open.

CAUTION: Some small diodes used in speed controls are for control purposes only and could be burned out if checked with a test lamp. For these, use an ohmmeter on the R x 10 or R x 100 scale. You should get a low resistance reading when you place the test probes across the diode in one direction but not in the other, so you should get one high and one low reading by reversing the test probes. If the meter reads the same in both directions, the diode is defective.

TROUBLESHOOTING

Motor Won't Start

1. Check the line cord, using a test lamp or ohmmeter.

2. Remove the motor housing so other electrical connections can be inspected and tested.

3. If the mixer uses a governor switch (usually mounted on or at the end of the armature) check to see that points are closed.

4. If necessary, use a point file and clean the governor contacts. If badly pitted they should be replaced.

5. Check the carbon brushes, as well as the leads and springs. If brushes are worn short they should be replaced.

6. If the commutator is extremely dirty, clean with a soft cloth and spray cleaner. Use sandpaper (fine) to correct slight unevenness in the commutator. Never use emery paper.

7. Make sure that the armature will rotate freely. If it's binding, try lubrication. If that doesn't help, sometimes a tap on the case with a light plastic hammer will line up the bearing and the armature shaft. (This last case occurs most often when reassembly affects the position of the bearings in the housing.)

8. To check field coils individually it is often advantageous to slip a strip of narrow plastic between the brushes and the commutator (or if easier, remove the brushes, mark them as to right, left, and position). Check the field coil

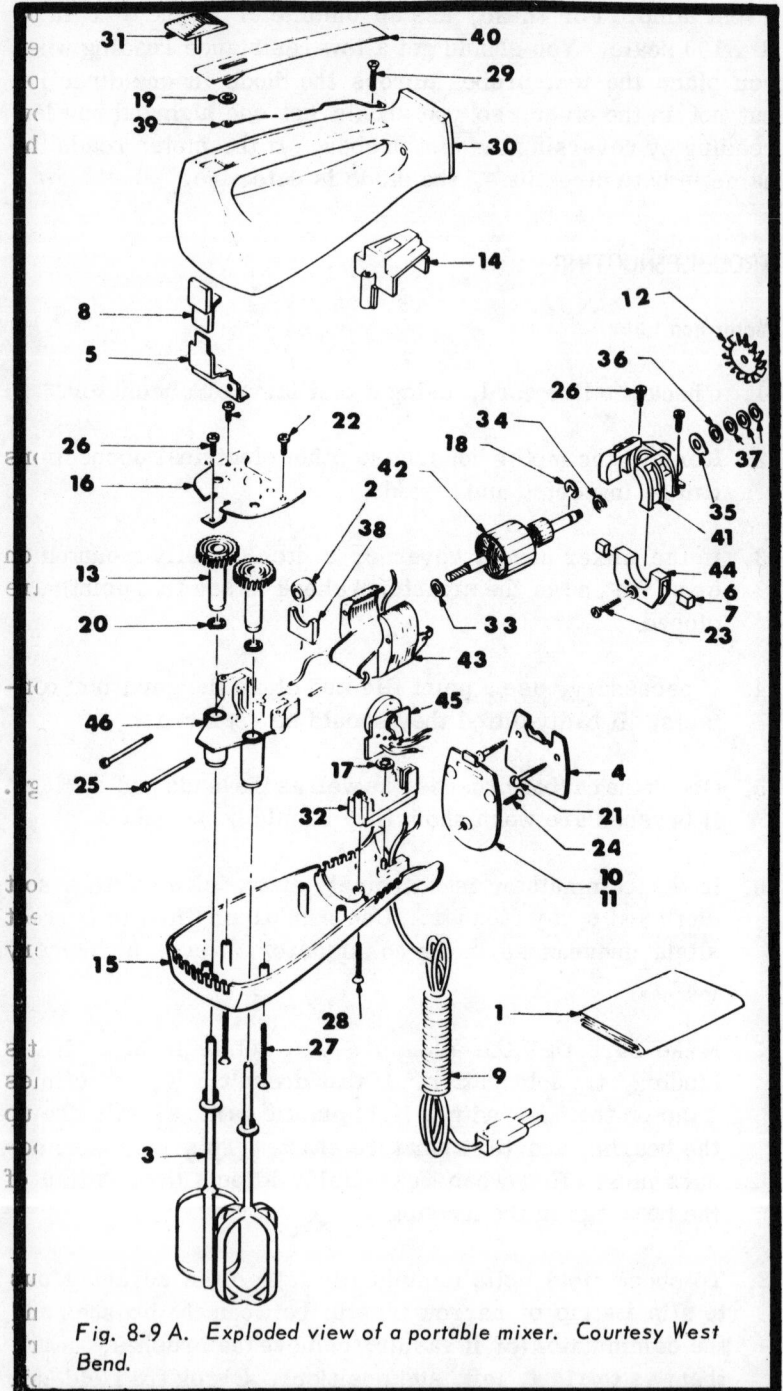

Fig. 8-9 A. *Exploded view of a portable mixer. Courtesy West Bend.*

NO	DESCRIPTION
1	Bag (Poly)
2	Bearing – Oilite (worm end)
3	Beater
4	Bracket (wall)
5	Bracket (ejector)
6	Brush
7	Brush
8	Button (ejector)
9	Cord set
10	Cover plate (inspection)
11	Cover plate (inspection)
12	Fan blade
13	Gear (beater)
14	Guide (beater storage)
15	Shell (lower)
16	Plate (bearing & gear cover)
17	Retainer ring (beater guide to lower shell)
18	Retainer ring (rotor shaft)
19	Retainer ring (switch button)
20	Retainer ring (beater gear)
21	Screw (wall bracket)
22	Screw (brg. & gear cover plate – rear)
23	Screw – brush holder to rear brkt. assy.
24	Screw (cover plate – rear inspection)
25	Screw (grear housing to stator)
26	Screw (motor housing to lower shell)
27	Screw (lower to upper shell – beater end)
28	Screw (lower to upper shell – cord end)
29	Screw (top shell to beater guide)
30	Shell (upper w./handle)
31	Slide (switch button)
32	Strain relief and switch housing (lower)
33	Washer (bearing & gear cover spacer)
34	Washer (thrust – commutator end)
35	Washer (bronze thrust w/lock tab)
36	Washer (nylatron)
37	Washer (spacer)
38	Wick (bearing and gear housing)
39	Wire – switch link (actuator)
40	Nameplate assy.
41	Rear bearing & bracket housing (w/brush holder)
42	Armature assy. (rotor)
43	Stator assy. (field coil)
44	Brush holder assy. (w/spring and term.)
45	Control board assy.
46	Bearing retainer and gear housing assy.

resistance; if two are used, both should have about identical resistances. (An ohmmeter is best for this, though a rough check can be made with a test lamp.)

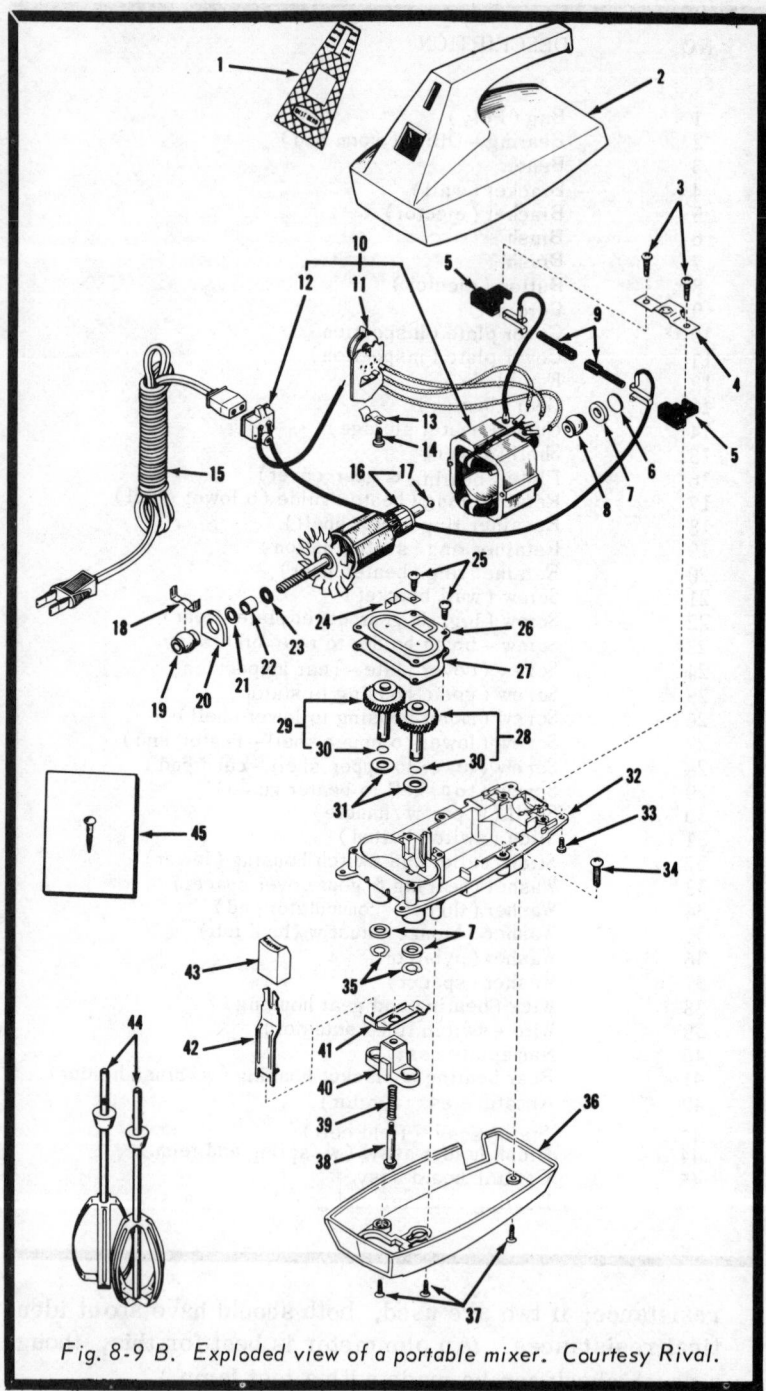

Fig. 8-9 B. Exploded view of a portable mixer. Courtesy Rival.

DESCRIPTION

1. Name plate
2. Motor cover
4. Rear bearing retaining strap
5. Brush holder housing
8. Gear bearing
9. Brush and springs
10. Field
11. Switch and leads
12. Plug receptacle
15. Cord
16. Armature
18. Front bearing retainer
19. Front bearing

24. Lead retaining clip
26. Gear box cover
27. Gear box gasket
28. Worm wheel shaft (left)
29. Worm wheel shaft (right)
30. Beater retaining rings
32. Motor frame
36. Lower motor cover
37. Cover to frame screws
39. Beater ejector spring
40. Beater ejector
44. Beaters
45. Wall—mount screw

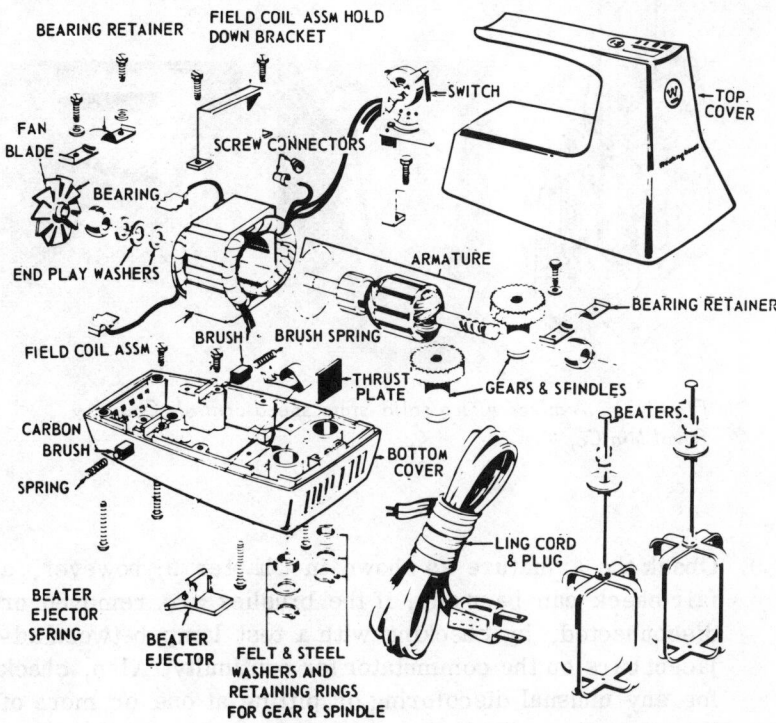

Fig. 8-10. Exploded view of another popular portable mixer. Courtesy Westinghouse

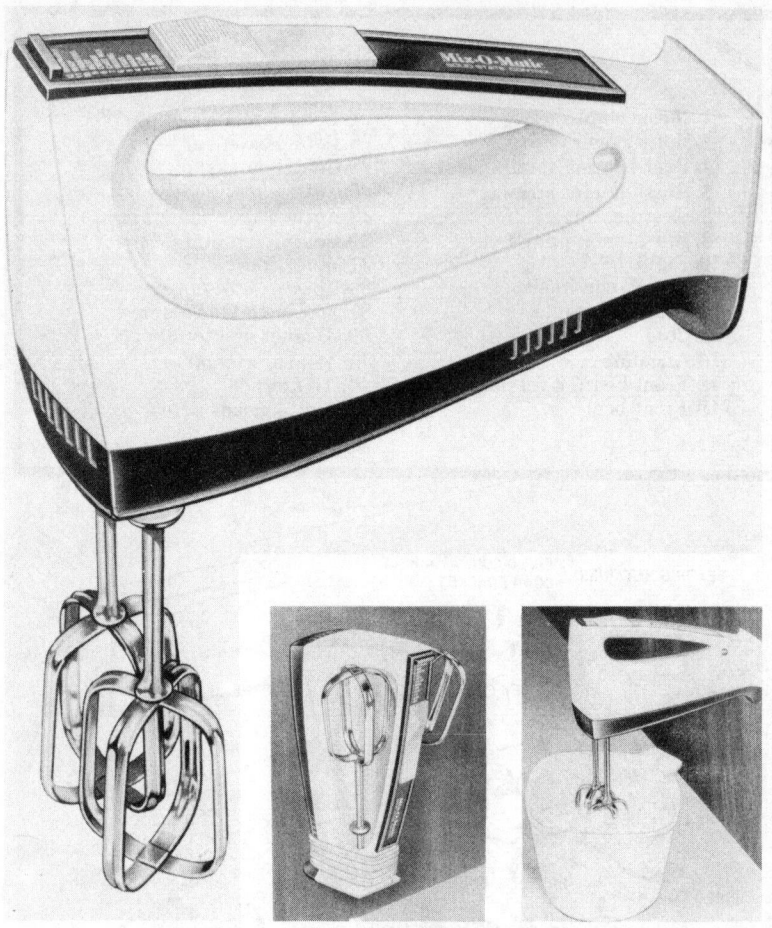

Fig. 8-11. A mixer with a solid-state speed control. Courtesy Rival Mfg.Co.

9. Check the armature as shown in Chapter 9; however, a fair check can be made, if the brushes are removed or disconnected, by checking with a test lamp between adjacent bars on the commutator for continuity. Also, check for any unusual discoloring or pitting at one or more of the commutator bars.

10. Test both armature and field coils for possible short circuits between the coils and the mixer case. In either case

there should be no electrical connection sufficient to light a 40-watt test lamp.

Mixer Runs At High Speed Only

1. In governor - controlled mixers this trouble is normally caused by a shorted capacitor across the governor contacts. It also can result if the governor contacts are bent or misadjusted, or fused together.

2. In portable mixers such trouble is more often caused by a defective switch or an open field winding in the slower speed positions.

Mixer Runs In Jerks

1. Check for loose connections, a broken line cord, defective brushes, etc.

2. If none of the above is the cause, check the governor points (if used).

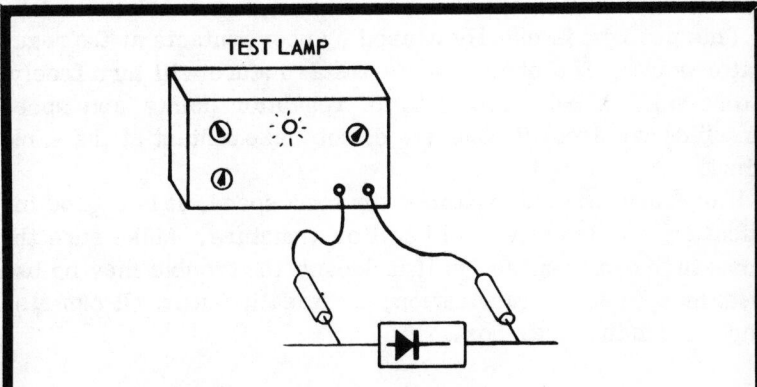

Fig. 8-12. Testing a silicon power diode with a test lamp. The lamp will be dim if the diode is ok. If the lamp doesn't light or lights with full brightness the diode is defective. Note: Unless you are completely familar with the circuit, it is a good idea to disconnect one lead of the diode from the circuit before making the test; otherwise, you may damage other parts, or other parts in shunt with the diode could give an erroneous reading.

3. Trouble may be mechanical. Check for binding bearings, bad gears, etc.

Mixer Won't Shut Off

1. Check for a defective switch.

2. Check inside the mixer for lead wires that may be shorting across the switch.

3. In governor-type mixers the on-off switch is sometimes part of the governor, and in the "off" position the governor points are opened. The linkage from the control arm may have been bent or is otherwise not correctly adjusted.

4. On any mixer using mechanical linkage between the internal switch and the customer's control, the linkage is often bent or not correctly aligned during reassembly. You'll find this most often as a result of "tinkering" by the do-it-yourself owner.

Motor Runs At Low Speed But Has No Power

This problem is usually caused by poor contacts at the regulator points, if a check shows the armature will turn freely. Some mixers have two sets of regulator points and speed troubles can occur if both sets do not make contact at the same time.

If overheating accompanies the slow speed, it is a good indication of a defective field coil or armature. Make sure the armature can turn freely; if it doesn't the trouble may be bad bearings, need of lubrication, or misalignment. It can also mean a binding gear box.

CHAPTER 9

Motors

Many small electrical appliances use motors—from the tiny motors in electric shavers up through the more powerful motors used on mixers, hedge trimmers, electric drills, and the like. Since most all appliance motors work in much the same way and are subject to similar faults, it seems fitting to consider motor troubles for all appliances at one time. Special features of particular appliance motors are included when necessary with the information on that appliance.

Motors used on most small appliances operate at a high speed and must have high starting torque. To provide the required starting torque, which is the ability to start even though under considerable load, most appliances use the "universal" series motors. These motors each have a commutator and an armature resembling one of those shown in Fig. 9-1.

REPLACING BRUSHES

Armature-type motors have carbon brushes that make contact with the armature commutator. The brushes come in various sizes, some with pigtail connections, some round, some square, and some rectangular. They may or may not have pressure springs attached; the springs hold the brush against the commutator to make a good connection. Just some of the many types of brushes in current use are shown in Fig. 9-2. Brush assortments are available from parts houses, as well as exact replacements. Brushes should be replaced if they are too short, chipped, or do not fit the brush holder properly.

If brushes are removed so the motor can be disassembled, it's a good idea to mark the brushes R and L and also their position. In other words, to insure good seating return the brushes to their holders exactly as they were taken out. When new brushes are installed there will normally be a little more sparking at the brush-commutator contact until the brush has

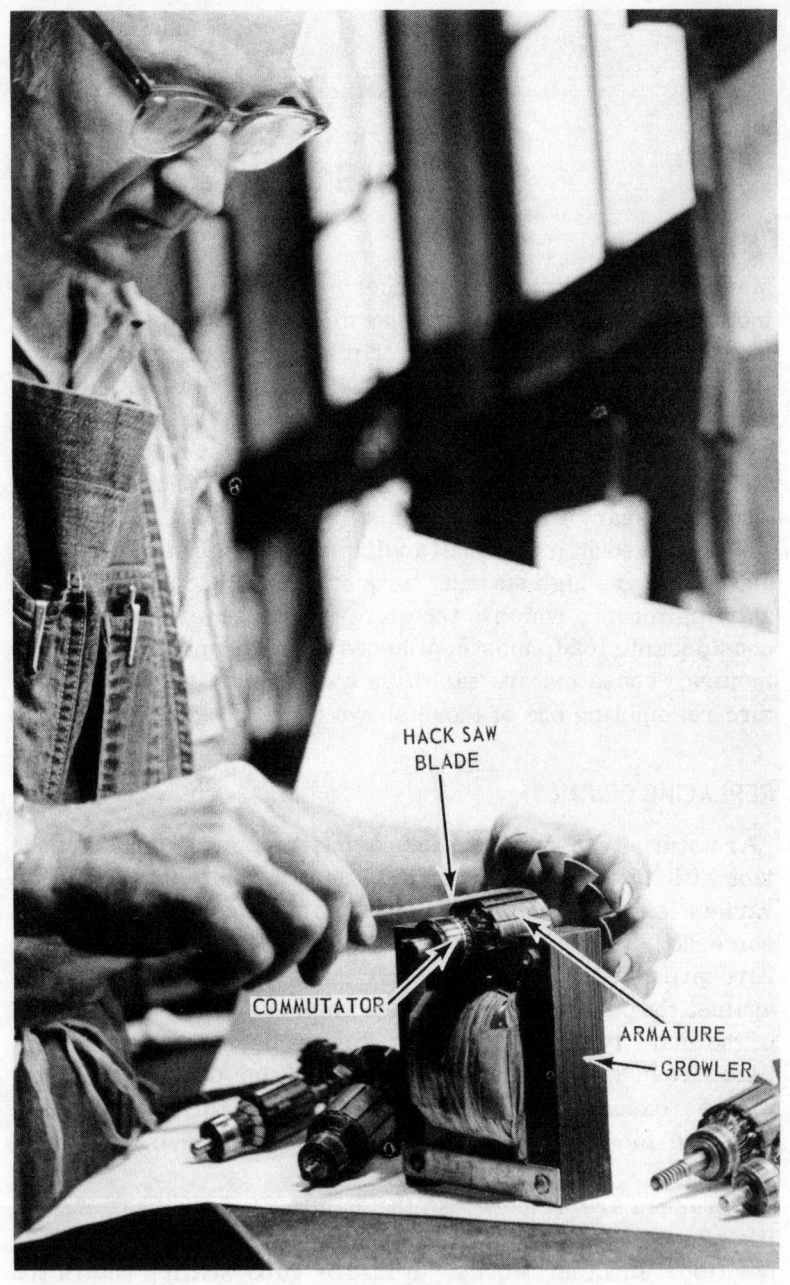

HACK SAW
BLADE

COMMUTATOR

ARMATURE

GROWLER

Fig. 9-1 Repairman checking an armature for an open coil using a ''growler''

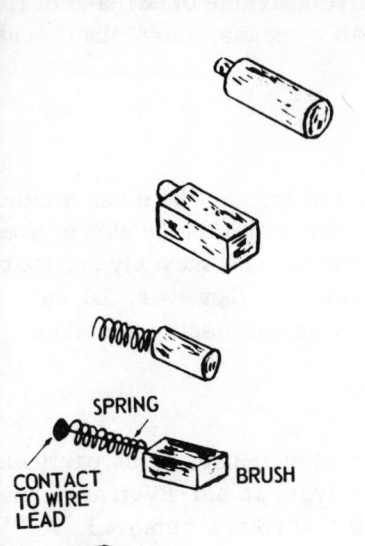

SPRING

CONTACT
TO WIRE
LEAD

BRUSH

Fig. 9-2. An assortment of
brushes of the type found in
small appliance motors.

"V" SHAPE CUT OUT
OF TRANSFORMER LAMINATIONS

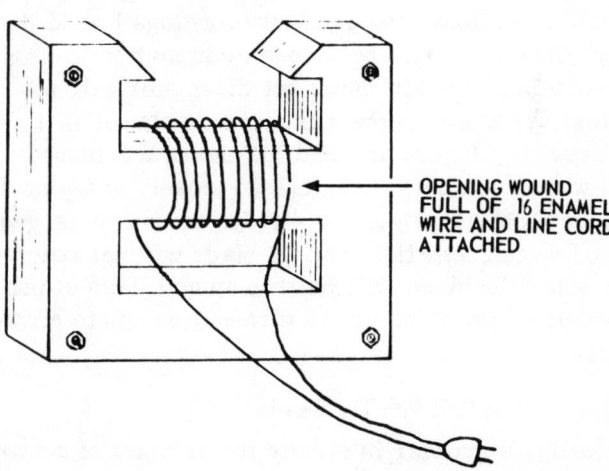

OPENING WOUND
FULL OF 16 ENAMEL
WIRE AND LINE CORD
ATTACHED

Fig. 9-3. This sketch shows how to build an armature growler from
a discarded power transformer.

time to seat; however, excessive sparking or streaks of fire around the commutator probably means more than brush troubles.

CHECKING THE ARMATURE

Aside from defective cords and switches, the most common motor fault is a bad armature. You may often be able to guess that the armature is bad if the motor runs unevenly and sparking trails all around the commutator; however, be sure of your diagnosis and prevent some embarrassing mistakes.

The Growler

Fig. 9-1 is a picture of a growler in use. This particular one was made by a shop owner from an old TV transformer which was disassembled and the windings removed. A "V" shape cut was made into the laminations on one side and a new coil, composed of #16 wire, wound on the center core and a line cord attached. See Fig. 9-3 for more details. Growlers are also available from supply houses.

Testing For Shorted Turns

If the insulation of the armature windings breaks down internally, the connections between the commutator bars and armature windings remain intact but the motor will not run right. To test for a short, the armature is placed in the growler, the growler plugged in, and the armature turned slowly by hand while a hacksaw blade is held loosely on top of the armature as shown in Fig. 9-4. If the armature is good, there will be no magnetic field and the blade will not react. If there is a short the blade will chatter up and down at one or more positions as the armature is turned a complete circle.

Finding An Open Coil With The Growler

Actually, a growler is simply the primary of a transformer and the armature becomes the secondary coils. This means that current is induced into the armature coils.

By taking the hacksaw blade and dragging it gently between two adjacent bars (Fig. 9-5) on the commutator you will find that at a certain relative position (may not be exactly on top) you can produce sparks as you short the two bars together with the hacksaw blade. You should see sparks between each of the adjacent bars in turn. If there are no sparks between two bars, the coil connecting the commutator bars is open (or there is a short between the bars).

Check between each two bars as you rotate the armature in the growler. Instead of the hacksaw blade, some repairmen have a 6-volt lamp attached to a couple of sharp-ended test prods. By connecting the text prods across adjacent bars the lamp should light. Once you find the spot where the lamp

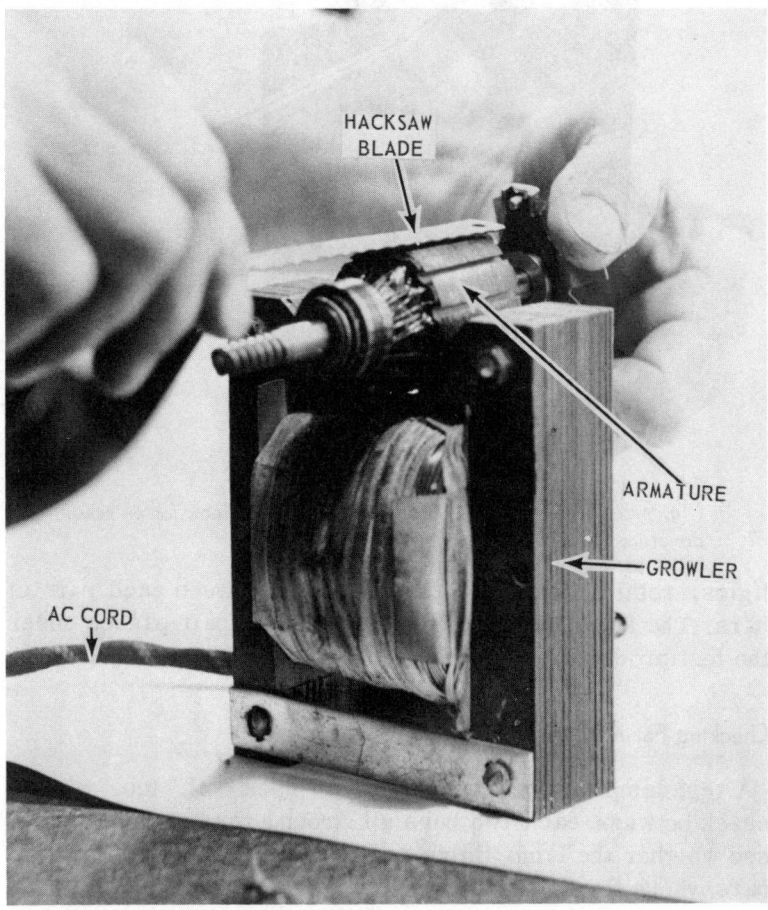

Fig. 9-4. The technician is checking an armature for shorted turns in the windings.

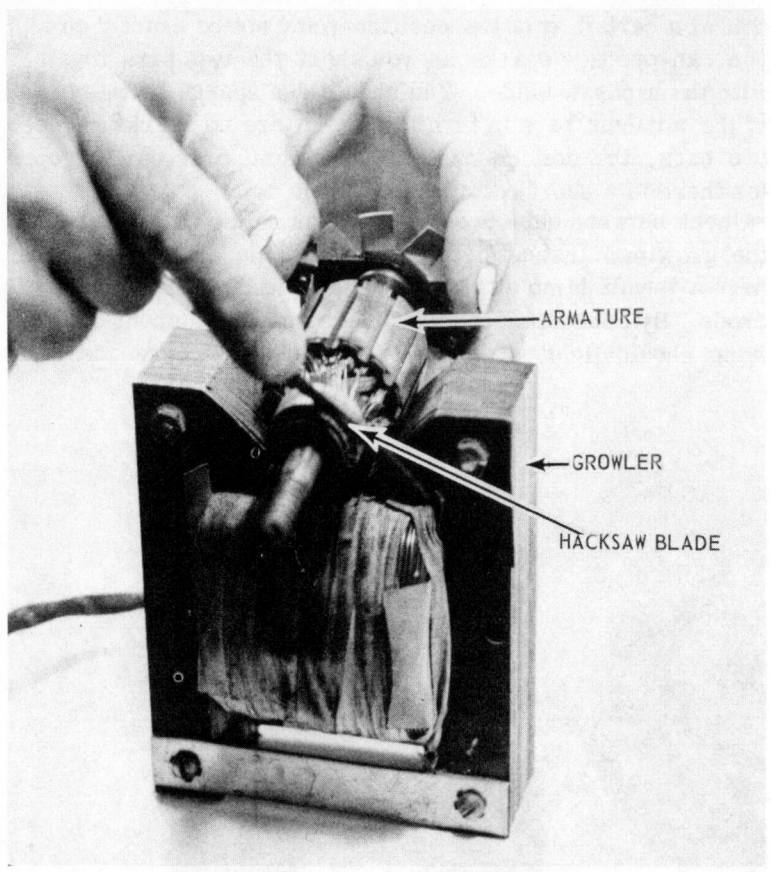

ARMATURE

GROWLER

HACKSAW BLADE

Fig. 9-5. The growler is being used here to check for an open armature coil.

lights, rotate the armature and check between each pair of bars. The lamp should light in turn as each pair passes under the test prods.

Checking For An Open Coil With a Test Lamp

A test lamp can be used to find an open coil, too. Simply check between each two bars all around the commutator and see whether the lamp lights in each position. If you find two bars where the lamp doesn't light, the coil is open, Fig. 9-6.

An open coil usually cannot be repaired but on occasion the break may be at or near where the lead connects to the commutator bar. If the break is visible you may be able to solder the two ends of the broken wire.

On many commutators today the leads, though, are crimped in or otherwise connected so that repairing the lead may be difficult. Manufacturers have gone to other methods of connection to speed up the manufacturing process and also because solder tends to melt and sling out if the motor runs hot for any length of time. If you do re-solder a lead, make sure that the lead and commutator connection are both clean and that the solder runs freely into the joint, producing a smooth, clean finish. Do not leave any globs of solder which can be thrown off and damage other parts of the motor.

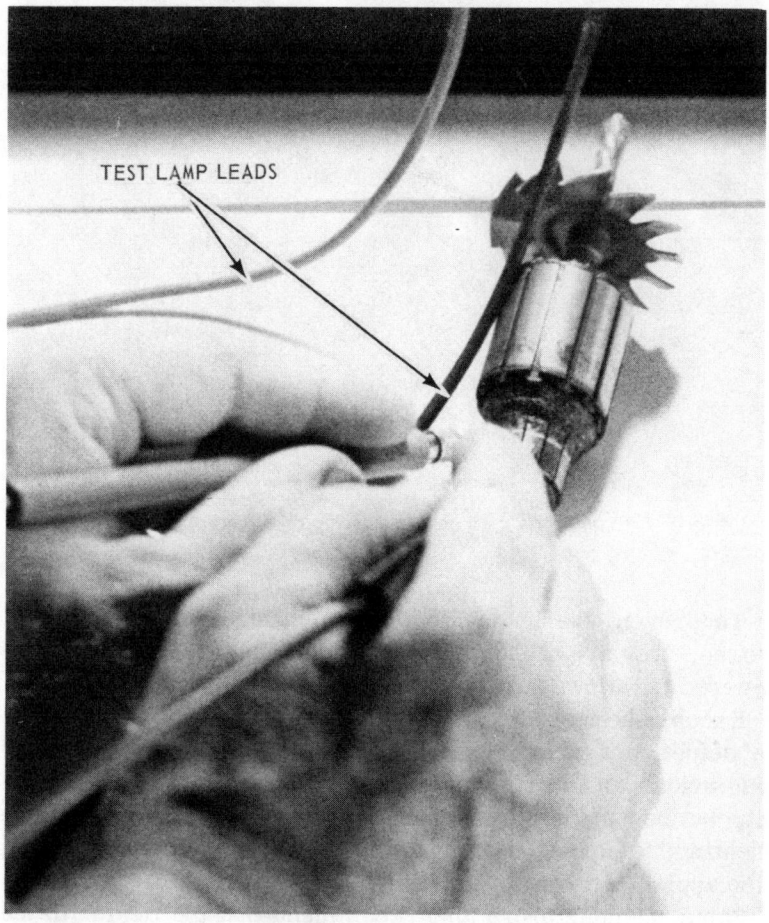

TEST LAMP LEADS

Fig. 9-6. A test lamp can be used to check an armature coil.

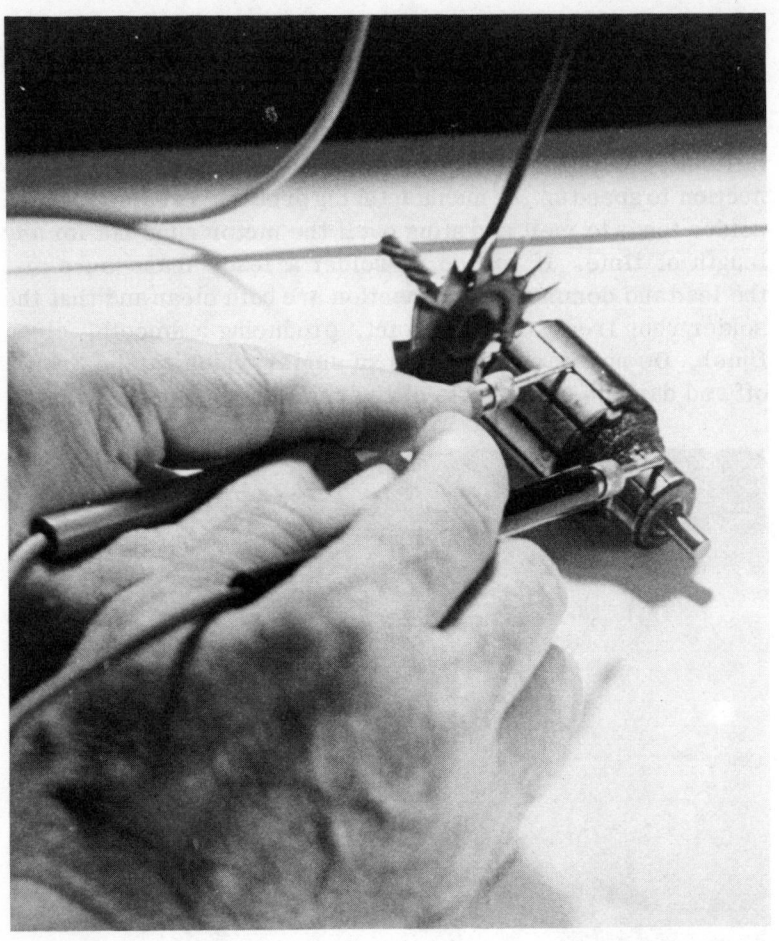

Fig. 9-7. The technician here is testing an armature for "grounds."

To prevent the leads from being pulled out by centrifugal force, they are often wrapped with a cord which is then lacquered and allowed to dry for several hours or baked in an oven.

Except when a new one is unavailable, we recommend that a defective armature be replaced. Of course, if the repair is obvious and can be made easily, then go ahead and make it, but be sure that you check the motor carefully for overheating, excessive brush sparking, etc., before returning the appliance to the customer.

Some manufacturers also recommend that the field coils be replaced in any motor which has a bad armature, on the theory that a bad armature may have caused the field coils to overheat or that bad field coils may have damaged the armature in the first place.

Testing For Grounds

The final test on an armature before pronouncing it good is a test to make sure there is no short between any of the coils and the metal shaft and frame. Fig. 9-7 shows a technician making this check between the commutator and the metal laminations of the armature. The armature need not be turned during this test, since if any coil is shorted it will show up at every commutator bar.

Sometimes when intermittent grounding is suspected, the armature can be placed in a jig or vise and tapped with a plastic mallet and turned as the tests for ground are made. If the test lamp comes on even intermittently while tapping the armature, the armature must be replaced. Often, grounds of this sort will show up only when the armature is turning at high speed, and on occasion this sort of trouble will respond to no stationary test.

CHECKING FIELD COILS

The field coils are generally arranged in pairs, though a few motors (see mixers) may have a field coil on only one side. Test the field coils for continuity with a test lamp. Since the coils are identical pairs, normally they should have the same resistance (be careful when making tests that you are not fooled by taps on the windings). This means that a test lamp across each one should light at the same brightness. A better way is with an ohmmeter so you can read the exact resistance of each coil. If either of the readings is significantly different, it is a good sign that one of the coils is defective.

If the coils are cloth wrapped, you can often tell if they have been overheated by the condition of the wrapping. For enameled wire coils any flaking or cracking of the enamel is a good sign that the fields will have to be replaced.

MOTOR BEARINGS

Motors that have been in use for any length of time may develop dry or worn bearings. For bearings that just haven't been lubricated you may be able to get some additional service by oiling them with a mixture of 10-weight motor oil and a friction-proofing oil such as Bardahl, STP, or Wynn's. Mix the two about half and half and flush the bearing. Try to get the motor running so the oil will spread throughout the bearing surface before running off.

If the motor shaft is frozen into a bearing, try to get some oil to soak into the bearing for an hour or so until it frees enough to be turned by hand. Keep flushing with oil until the shaft runs freely. If the motor will start now, keep putting oil on the tight bearings until the motor comes up to speed and holds.

If oiling doesn't free a frozen bearing, the motor will have to be disassembled. Pull the bearing from the shaft; if it's a ball-bearing type, replace it; if it's a sleeve-type bearing, the freezing may have been caused by a lack of oil, or in some cases by the owner's use of a household oil, such as often comes in small cans from the variety store. Such oil frequently breaks down into a gummy substance when subjected to the heat generated in a high-speed motor. Use a solvent to clean out the gummy deposits and then re-lubricate with fresh oil.

End-Play

Nearly all motors use washers on the armature shaft to control or limit the amount of "end-play." End-play is known as armature "travel" from end to end. Obviously, too much end-play could allow the brushes to ride off the commutator, or the armature might move partially out from under the fields. Too little end-play can cause binding which will slow down the motor and cause overheating after being in use a short while.

Because of end-play it is important when disassembling a motor that you check the order of washer placement on the armature shaft. Placing all the washers at one end, for example, might mean that the brushes would no longer be contacting fully the surface of the commutator, or it could mean that the gear train coupled to the armature would not mesh correctly or adequately. Most any motor should have some end-play to ensure against binding, but it should not have so much that the armature may not line up with its corresponding parts.

MOTOR RUNS ROUGH

If the motor on any appliance runs in "spurts" or if it will not start every time it is turned on, the trouble is either defective brushes or brush holder, an intermittently open cord, or a defective armature. If the brushes can be taken out without disassembly, do so. If they are burned down to a short "nub," then replacement may be all that is necessary to get the motor back into operation again. But before you replace the brushes use a flashlight and look at the commutator, turning it if possible so you can check for burned spots. If the commutator coloring is not uniform all the way round, if there is a blackened spot between segments, or if the segments seem to be farther apart at one spot (usually with black spots at the point where the brushes pass over), brush replacement will not likely cure the trouble, since in all likelihood the armature is defective. A "ring of fire" around the commutator as the motor runs is also a good indication of possible armature trouble, though in rare cases this may be caused by a poor brush fit or even a defective field coil. When new brushes are first installed there will be somewhat more arcing at the brushes than there will be after the brushes have seated. But new brushes will seldom be the cause of a virtually continuous ring of arcing all around the commutator.

MOTOR RUNS SLOW

If the motor runs slow but runs at a fairly steady rate, it may be caused by insufficient lubrication in either the motor bearings or in any gear box driven directly by the motor. Motor bearings should be oiled with #10-weight non-detergent motor oil mixed about half and half with special friction-proofing oil such as Bardahl, STP, or Wynn's. Never use any of the special household oils such as can be purchased in variety stores. Many of these oils, as mentioned earlier, will break down under heat and leave a waxy gum that will eventually cause the bearings of the motor to freeze. Special grease is available for use in gear boxes. Newer type silicone greases work well and withstand higher temperatures than regular oil.

If the motor has been disassembled (or even sometimes if dropped) the motor may run slow because of misalignment of the bearings. Usually, misalignment can be cured by simply turning the motor on and tapping near the bearings with a small hammer. Keep tapping around the bearing location until the motor is turning normally, and if you're using an ammeter or wattmeter in the line, until the least amount of current is drawn.

DIRECT CURRENT MOTORS

With the advent of small rechargeable batteries, some appliances, such as carving knives, tooth brushes, and the like use a direct current (DC) motor. The main difference between these motors and the types we have been discussing is that they operate on much lower voltage and in many cases have permanent magnets instead of wound fields.

Repairing DC motors often is not practical; however, you should check for adequate lubrication, absence of binding, discharged batteries, etc. Many of these appliances have a charging diode built into the appliance, while other times the charging device is external. In nearly all cases the motor operates on the batteries whether or not the unit is plugged into the AC outlet. However, the motor may run when plugged into the power line and refuse to run when not plugged in. This problem is normally due to the fact that the batteries are discharged and the charging current from the power line is supplying the motor current.

If the batteries refuse to hold a charge, they should be replaced. Usually, they are sold as a package of four or five cells connected together to form a 5- to 7-volt battery. Although they are similar in size, such batteries are NOT the same as the dry cells used in flashlights. Typical dry cells cannot be charged successfully. Most rechargeable batteries are nickel-cadmium (ni-kad) cells.

CHAPTER 10

Other Small Appliances

In addition to those covered in previous Chapters various other appliances are in common use today. Most have much in common with other motor-driven or heating appliances; therefore, similar repair techniques are suitable.

ELECTRIC KNIVES

Fig. 10-1 is an exploded view of an electric knife that operates from the power line. Repairing the knife calls for essentially the same procedures you have been using—checking the continuity of the cord and internal electrical parts. Check the brushes to be sure they are making contact and are not burned too short. Check for binding in the motor, gears, or blades. Use lubrication sparingly, but moving parts must have some lubrication.

Fig. 10-2 is an electric knife made by the same company (Hamilton Beach), but this knife is battery-operated. The principle difference is in the motor. The motor operates on about 5 volts or less, and to save battery power uses a permanent magnet field rather than a wirewound field. Permanent magnet fields can be used only in direct current motors. Some knives are "convertible"; that is they can be operated from the AC power line, too. However, a transformer and rectifiers are used to drop the voltage and change it to direct current. Fig. 10-3 shows the power unit and Fig. 10-4 is the wiring diagram. Notice that there are two outputs. One output is used when operating the knife on the AC line. When the knife is stored, however, two contacts provide a "trickle" charge for the batteries to keep them ready for use. The resistor in series with the DC voltage prevents the batteries from being charged too quickly or overcharged.

ELECTRIC FRENCH FRYER

Fig. 10-5 is a functional drawing of a french fryer. Notice

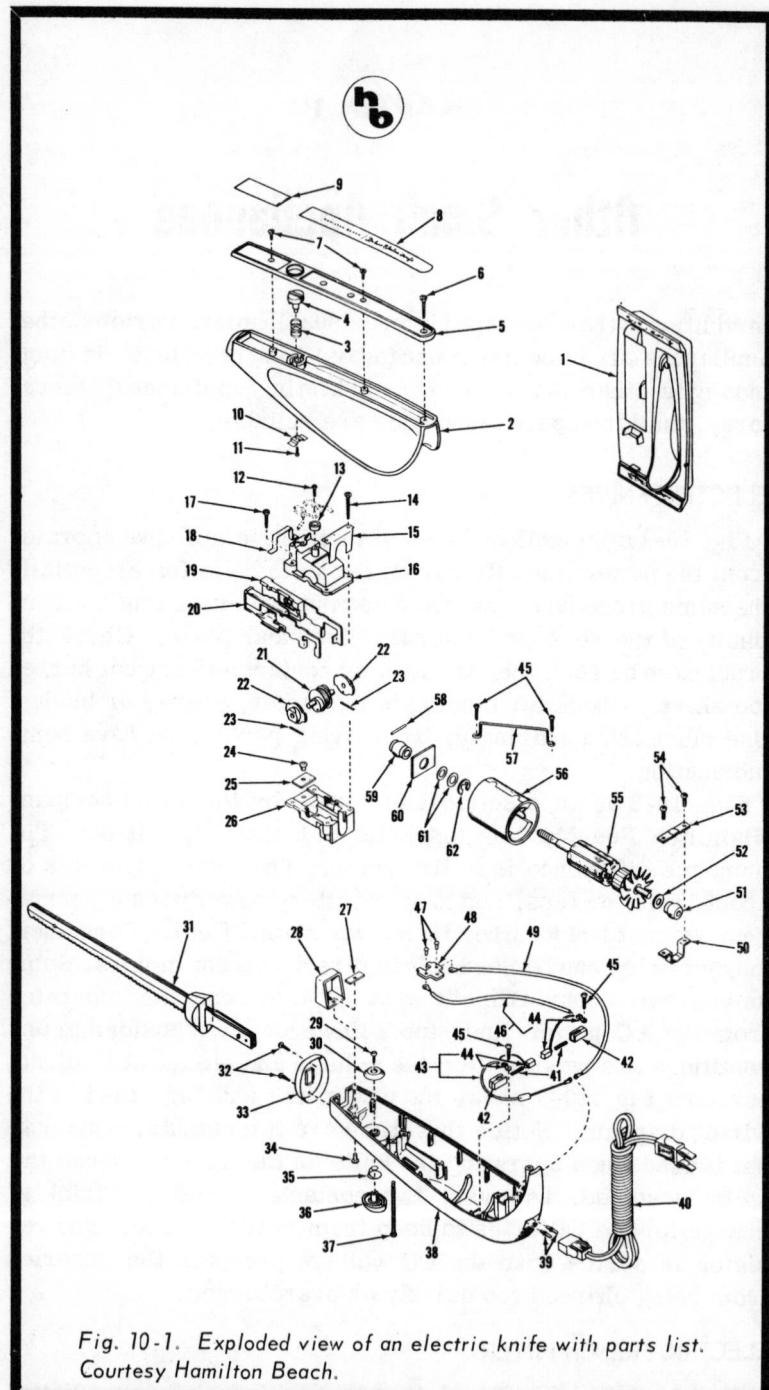

Fig. 10-1. Exploded view of an electric knife with parts list.
Courtesy Hamilton Beach.

DESCRIPTION

1	Storage tray	32	Screw (2 used)
2	Upper housing	33	Decorative plate
3	Spring	34	Rivet
4	Switch knob	35	Spring
5	Handle cover	36	Blade release button
6	Screw	37	Screw
7	Screw (2 used)	38	Lower housing (items 27, 28, 34)
8	Name plate	39	Contact (2 used)
9	Name plate	40	Cord
10	Switch contact plate	41	Brush spring
11	Drive screw	42	Brush holder
12	Screw	43	Rectifier assembly (item 44)
13	Tube	44	Brush and terminal (2 used)
14	Screw (2 used)	45	Screw (4 used)
15	Seal retainer	46	Lead complete (item 44)
16	Gear box cover	47	Contact (2 used)
17	Screw (2 used)	48	Switch plate
18	Sealer tape	49	Lead complete
19	Driver assembly	50	Bearing support
20	Driver assembly	51	Rear bearing
21	Crank assembly	52	Fiber washer
22	Crank bearing (2 used)	53	Bearing strap
23	Bearing spring (2 used)	54	Screw (2 used)
24	Eyelet	55	Armature
25	Gear box plate	56	Field complete
26	Gear box	57	Field strap
27	Front plate	58	Bearing spring
28	Front guide	59	Front bearing
29	Screw	60	Bearing seal
30	Release wedge	61	Shim washer (2 used)
31	Blades	62	Snap ring

again the similarity between this unit and other electrical appliances such as a skillet.

Fig. 10-6 is the wiring diagram. Notice that the neon lamp is connected across the thermostat points. When the fryer heats to the preset temperature the thermostat opens and the neon lamp lights, indicating that the fryer is ready to use. While the fryer is preheating the thermostat is closed and the neon cannot light because it is shorted out.

HAIR DRYER

Fig. 10-7 is an exploded view of a hair dryer, one of the easier appliances to service. This particular model uses a pre-wound heating element; others use heating element wire wrapped around a ceramic form. In this model it is usually

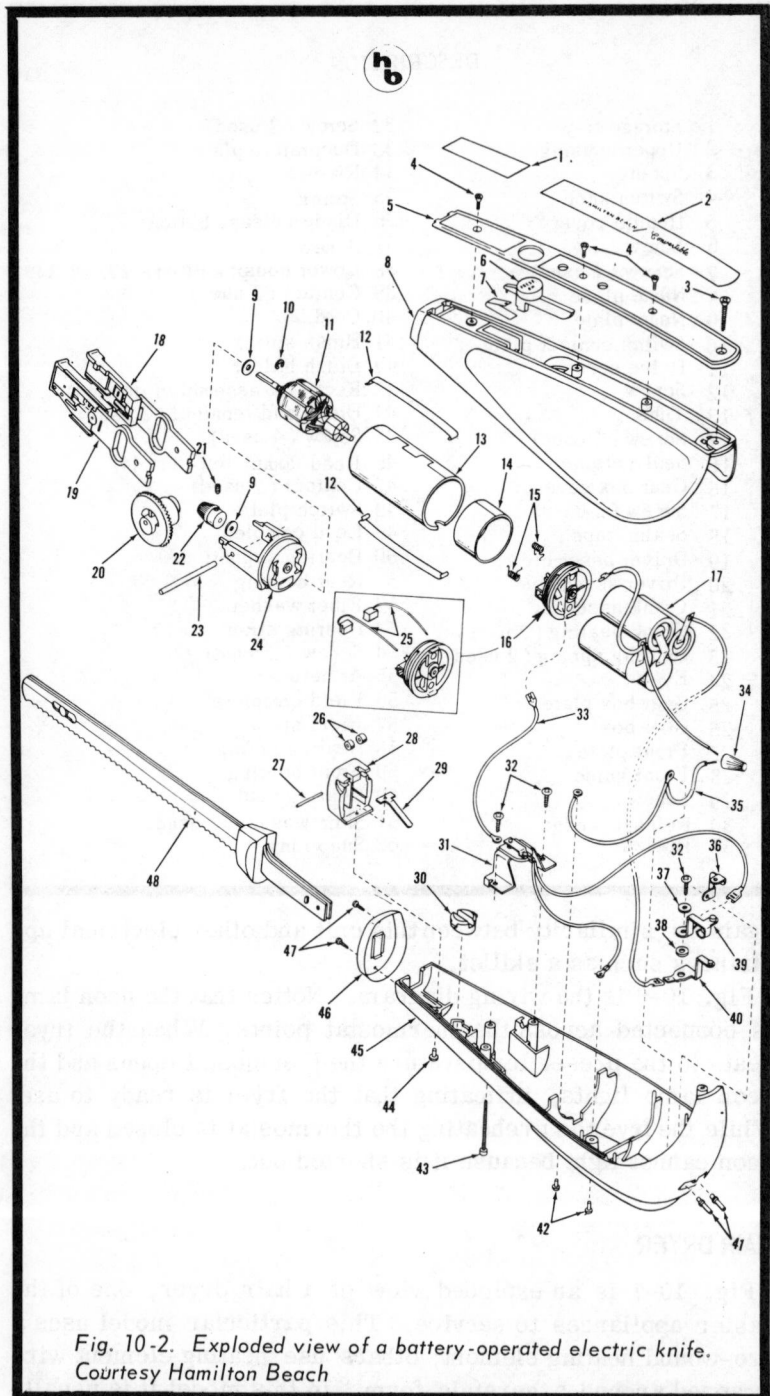

Fig. 10-2. Exploded view of a battery-operated electric knife.
Courtesy Hamilton Beach

DESCRIPTION

1	Decorative plate	39	Contact spring assembly
2	Name plate	40	Contact & support lower
3	Screw	41	Contact (2 used)
4	Screw (3 used)	42	Rivet (2 used)
5	Handle cover	43	Screw
6	Switch button	44	Rivet
7	Switch spring	45	Housing & contacts
8	Upper Housing	46	Decorative plate
9	Thrust washer (2 used)	47	Screw (2 used)
10	Retaining ring	48	Blades complete
11	Armature complete	49	Case cover assembly
12	Motor clamp (2 used)	50	Cover lid retaining knob
13	Field complete	51	Screw
14	Insulator	52	Cord
15	Brush spring (2 used)	53	Case
16	End housing complete	54	Contact assembly
17	Battery pack complete	55	Screw (10 used)
18	Driver & retainer	56	Lead & resistor
19	Driver & retainer	57	Screw (4 used)
20	Gear & crank	58	Receptacle support
21	Set screw	59	Lead complete
22	Pinion	60	Lead
23	Gear shaft	61	Cord
24	Gear bracket complete	62	Strain relief
25	Brush (Set of 2 ea.)	63	Transformer
26	Roller (2 used)	64	Nut (4 used)
27	Shaft	65	Lead
28	Front guide complete	66	Rectifier (2 used)
29	Spring	67	Lead complete
30	Release button	68	Nut (2 used)
31	Clamp & contact assembly	69	Insulator (4 used)
32	Screw (2 used)	70	Screw
33	Lead complete	71	Heat sink
34	Wire nut	72	Base
35	Lead complete	73	Screw (4 used)
36	Contact & support— upper	74	Screw (2 used)
37	Washer	75	Felt Pad (4 used)
38	Insulator		

necessary to replace the complete heating unit, but in others you may be able to fix it with a repair sleeve.

Besides the heating elements, a hair dryer has a motorized blower to push warmed air through a flexible hose to a hood. Should the motor burn out it is often more practical for the customer to replace the entire unit, especially if it has been in use for three or four years.

The flexible hose and the hood may develop leaks. Replacements are available at a reasonable price from any parts distributor, but be sure you include the dryer make and model

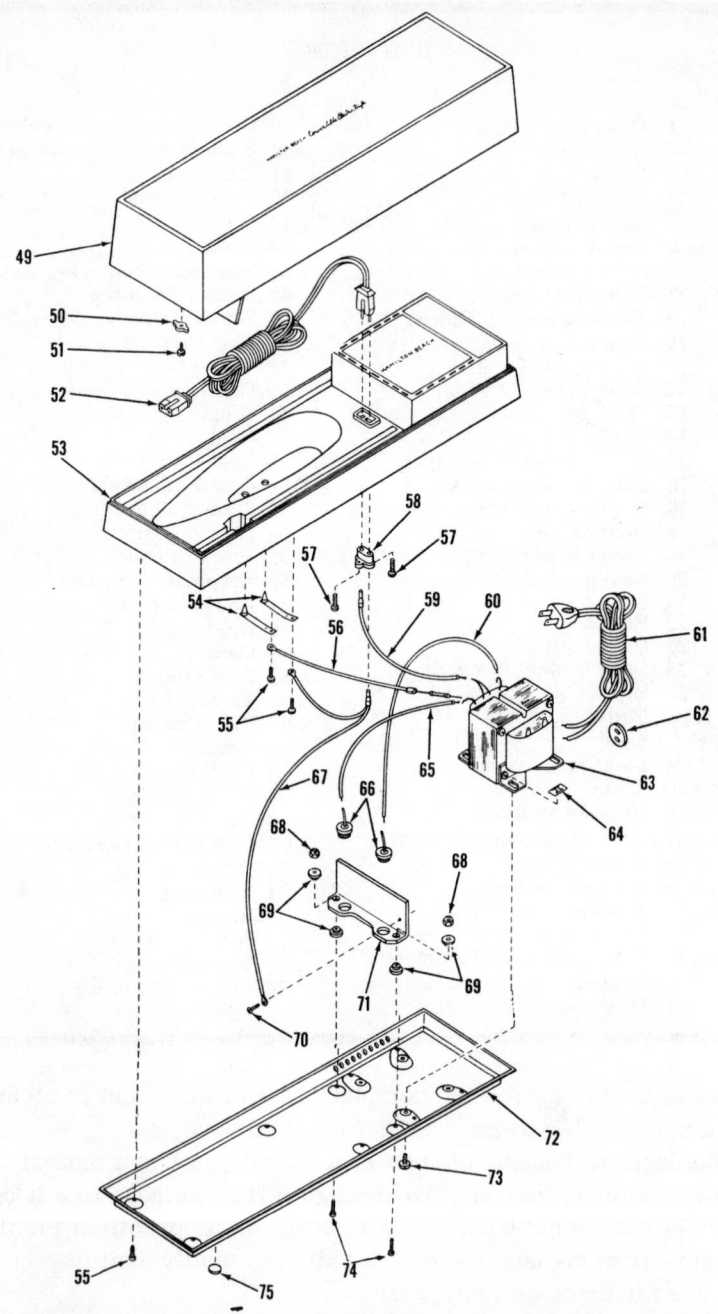

Fig. 10-3. Power pack and trickle charger used for operating the battery powered knife from the power line and to keep internal batteries charged during storage. (See parts list, Fig. 10-2.)

when you order. Be careful during reassembly of the dryer that the fan or impeller blades on the motor do not rub against the frame, and make sure that the heating element is rigidly mounted.

Because the fan or impeller blades move air quickly over the heating element, the element will not normally glow red so long as the fan is pushing air across it. If you check the element while the dryer is disassembled, it is best not to keep the heating element on too long without the air moving across it. In some dryers the element would not be damaged, perhaps, but nearby plastic parts could be. Use the series test positions on the appliance tester to reduce the current to the element if it is necessary to operate it while disassembled.

SHAVERS

Often, certain model electric shavers can be repaired if care is used in disassembly. Some manufacturers will not supply replacement parts; they prefer to have the shaver returned to them for repair. In such cases a thorough cleaning and gentle lubrication may help.

Fig. 10-8 shows a Remington Rollectric using a point-contact motor. Thousands upon thousands of shavers use this same kind of motor. Service instructions for this particular model are applicable to most other similar types.

Fig. 10-9 shows how to adjust for equal balance, tension

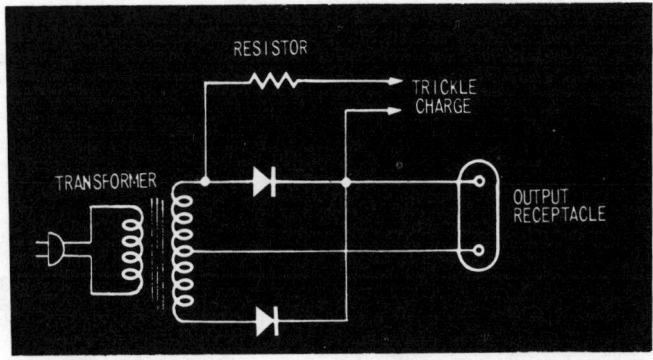

Fig. 10-4. Wiring diagram of the power pack shown in Fig. 10-3.

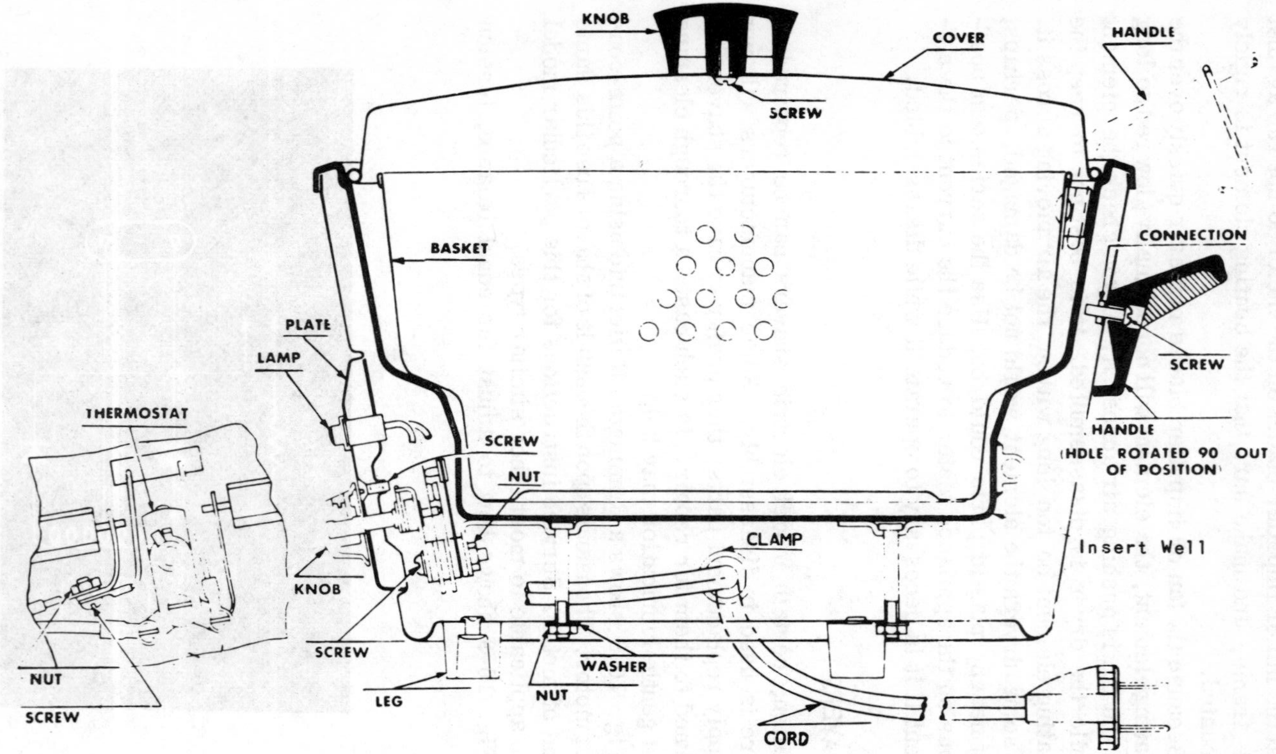
KNOB
COVER
HANDLE
SCREW
BASKET
CONNECTION
SCREW
PLATE
LAMP
THERMOSTAT
SCREW
NUT
HANDLE
(HDLE ROTATED 90 OUT
OF POSITION)
CLAMP
Insert Well
KNOB
SCREW
WASHER
NUT
NUT
LEG
SCREW
CORD

Fig. 10-5. Functional drawing of a french fryer. Courtesy West Bend.

and point gap. If tension, gap, and balance are not correctly set the shaver will not run fast enough and may draw excessive current. The shaver should run a minimum of 8000 RPM and draw about 135 milliamperes or about 15 watts.

TROUBLESHOOTING CHART

Fault	Cause	Remedy
Runs erratically	Poor adjustment	Readjust
	Burnt or worn contact points	Replace contact points
	Open capacitor	Replace capacitor
	Loose wire	Resolder
	Intermittent line cord	Replace line cord
Noisy	Worn oscillator	Replace
	Weak cutter spring	Replace springs
Slow	Tight inner cutters	Replace
	Poor adjustment	Readjust
	Burnt or worn contacts	Replace
	Dirty heads	Clean and oil

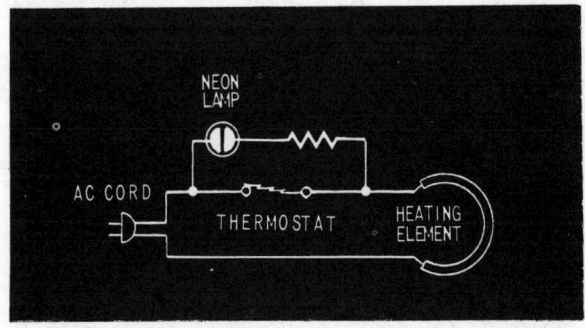

Fig. 10-6. Wiring diagram of the power pack shown in Fig. 10-3.

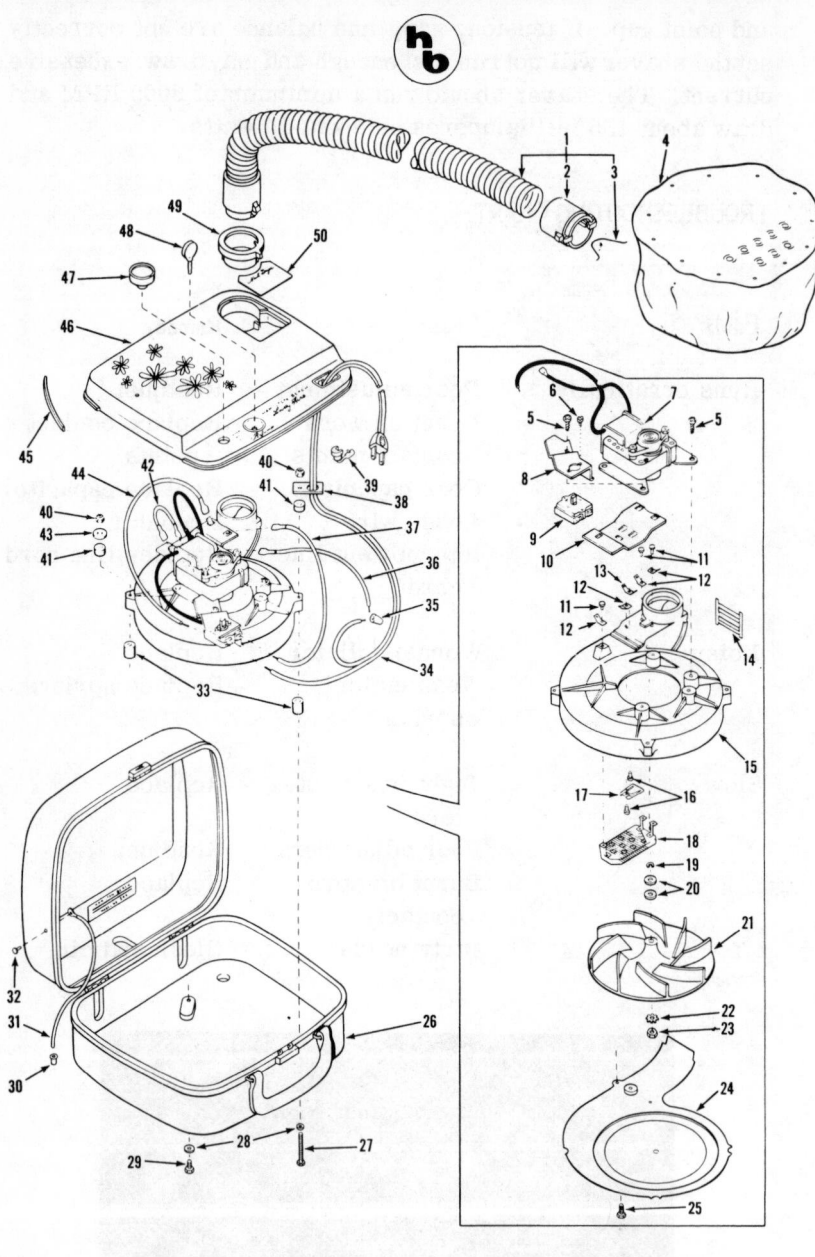

Fig. 10-7 Exploded view of a hair dryer with parts list. Courtesy
Hamilton Beach.

DESCRIPTION

1	Hose assembly (includes items 2 and 3)	27	Screw (3 used)
2	Connector (2 used)	28	Washer (4 used)
3	Spring (2 used)	29	Screw
4	Bonnet	30	Eyelet
5	Screw (3 used)	31	Nylon cord assembly
6	Switch screw (2 used)	32	Rivet
7	Motor complete	33	Rubber spacer (3 used)
8	Switch bracket	34	Cord complete
9	Switch	35	Wire nut
10	Terminal shield	36	Lead complete (White)
11	Rivet (3 used)	37	Lead complete (Red)
12	Terminal tab (4 used)	38	Strain relief bracket
13	Terminal tab	39	Strain relief
14	Screen	40	Nut (3 used)
15	Scroll	41	Rubber bushing (3 used)
16	Rivet (2 used)	42	Lead complete (White)
17	Thermostat	43	Washer (2 used)
18	Heating element complete	44	Lead complete (Green)
19	Retaining ring	45	Fastener (2 used)
20	Washer (2 used)	46	Cover plate with decorative plate (Includes Item 50)
21	Impeller	47	Switch knob
22	Lockwasher	48	Perfume stick assembly
23	Nut	49	Vent tube
24	Scroll cover plate	50	Cover plate
25	Screw (2 used)		
26	Case assembly (includes 30, 31, and 32)		

Poor shave	Worn oscillator	Replace oscillator
	Weak cutter springs	Replace springs
	Defective heads or inner cutters	Replace heads
	Motor running slow	See above
High current drawn by shaver	Poor adjustment	Readjust
	Tight heads	Replace inner cutters
	Dirty heads	Clean and oil heads
Shaver doesn't operate	Defective cord	Replace cord
	Shorted capacitor	Replace capacitor
	Broken wire	Resolder
	Defective coil	Replace motor

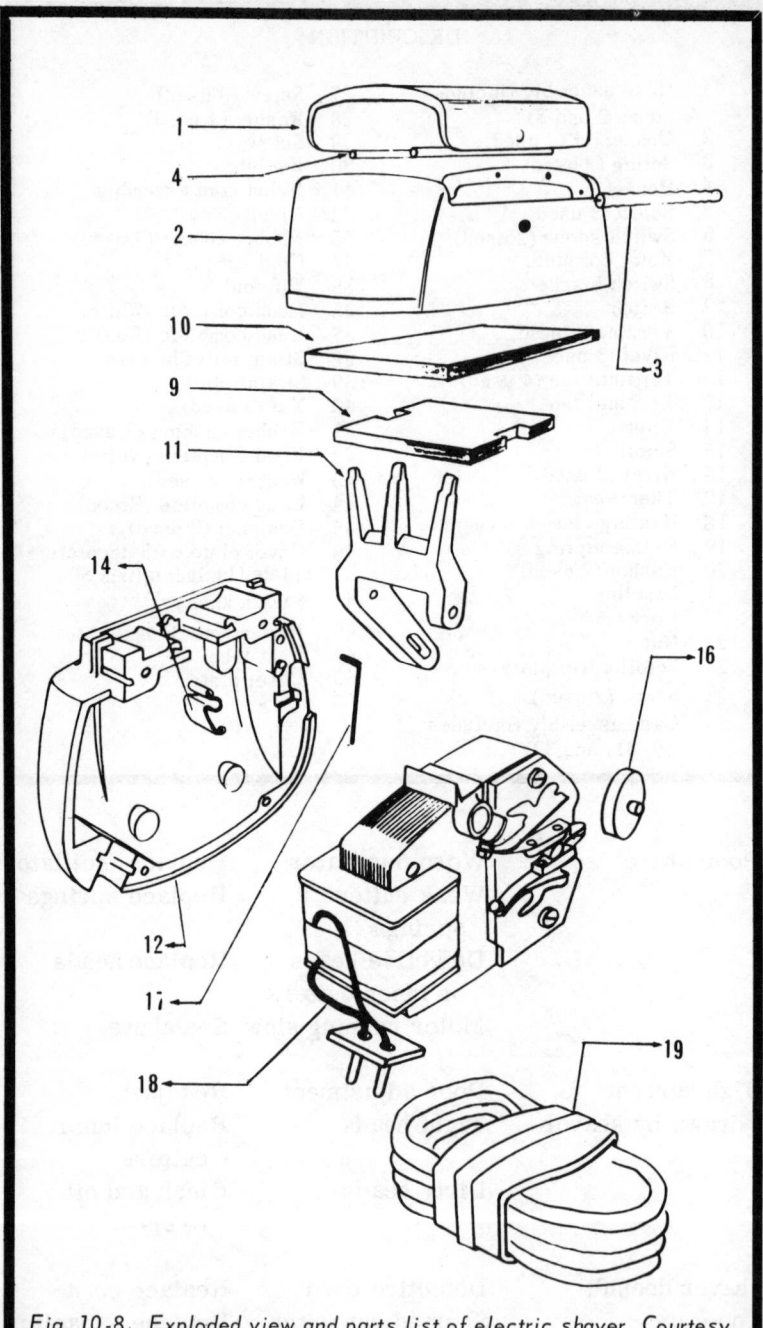

Fig. 10-8. Exploded view and parts list of electric shaver. Courtesy Remington.

1.	Head guard
2.	Hair pocket shell
3.	Roller comb
4.	Roller comb, thin
9.	Hairstopper, lower
10.	Hairstopper, upper
11.	Oscillator (molded)
12.	Case base
14.	Clip head
16.	Starting wheel assembly
17.	Starting wheel tension spring
18.	Motor assembly complete
19.	Cord & ring assembly

Note: When adjusting a shaver motor be sure to set the points at no closer than .012 inch. The shaver motor may run faster with a closer spacing but will stop running within a few weeks because the nylon cam will have worn out. The points should not be spaced wider than .016 inch, however.

Some shaver motors are much like the universal motors used in mixers except, of course, much smaller. Cleaning and lubrication may be all that is necessary to get the shaver back in working order again. Some shavers have dual voltage motors so that the razor may be operated on either the power line or from an automobile power supply. Still others have built-in battery power supplies that are rechargeable in much the same manner as those discussed previously.

Troubleshooting Chart For Internal Battery-Operated Units
(Courtesy Remington) Fig. 10-10.

Fault	Cause	Remedy
Runs erratically	Sticking brushes	Form brush leads
		Replace brushes
		Replace motor
	Loose wires	Resolder and tighten
	Dirty switch	Clean contacts
Noisy	Bad bearing	Replace motor
	Oscillator	Replace oscillator
	Weak cutter spring	Replace springs

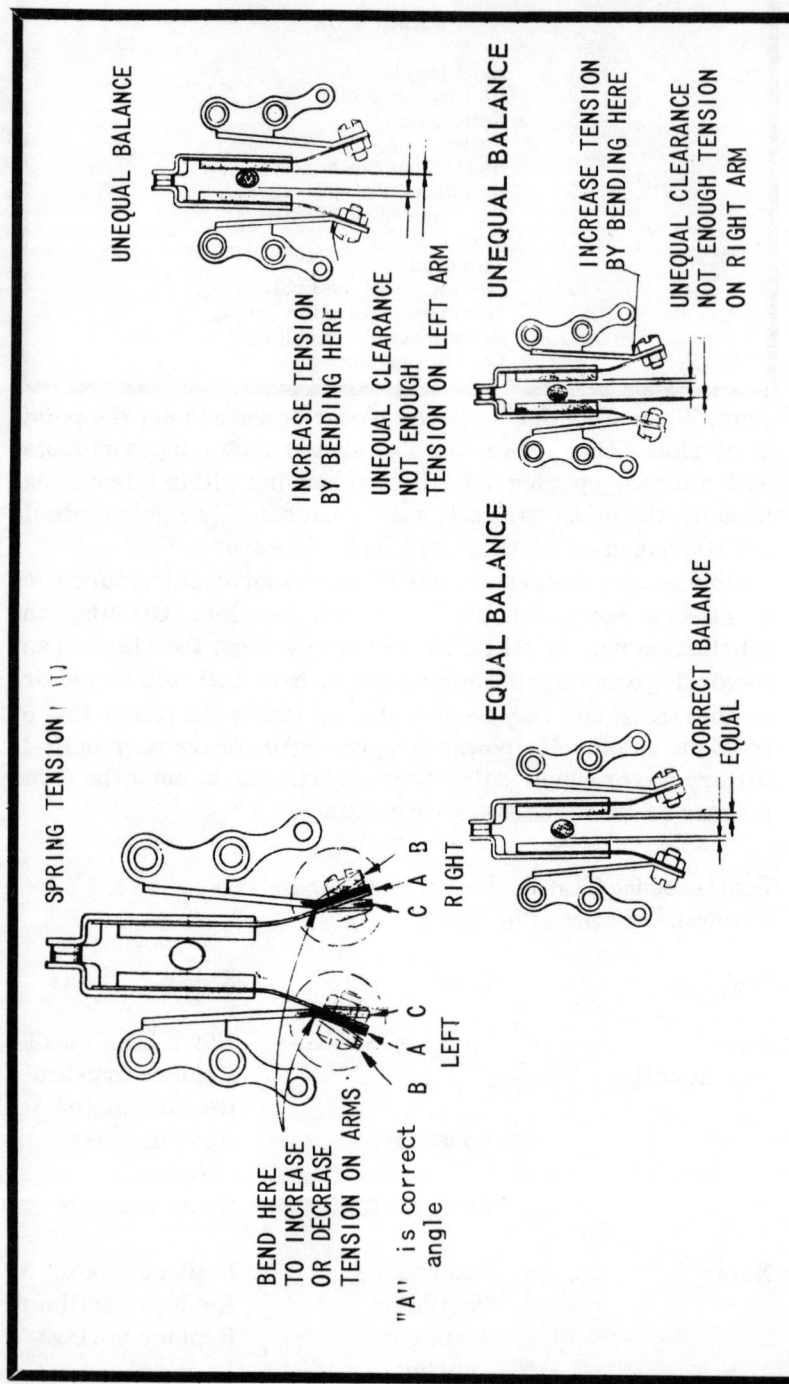

SPRING TENSION (1)

BEND HERE
TO INCREASE
OR DECREASE
TENSION ON ARMS

"A" is correct angle

B A C   C A B
LEFT   RIGHT

UNEQUAL BALANCE

INCREASE TENSION
BY BENDING HERE

UNEQUAL CLEARANCE
NOT ENOUGH
TENSION ON LEFT ARM

UNEQUAL BALANCE

INCREASE TENSION
BY BENDING HERE

UNEQUAL CLEARANCE
NOT ENOUGH TENSION
ON RIGHT ARM

EQUAL BALANCE

CORRECT BALANCE
EQUAL

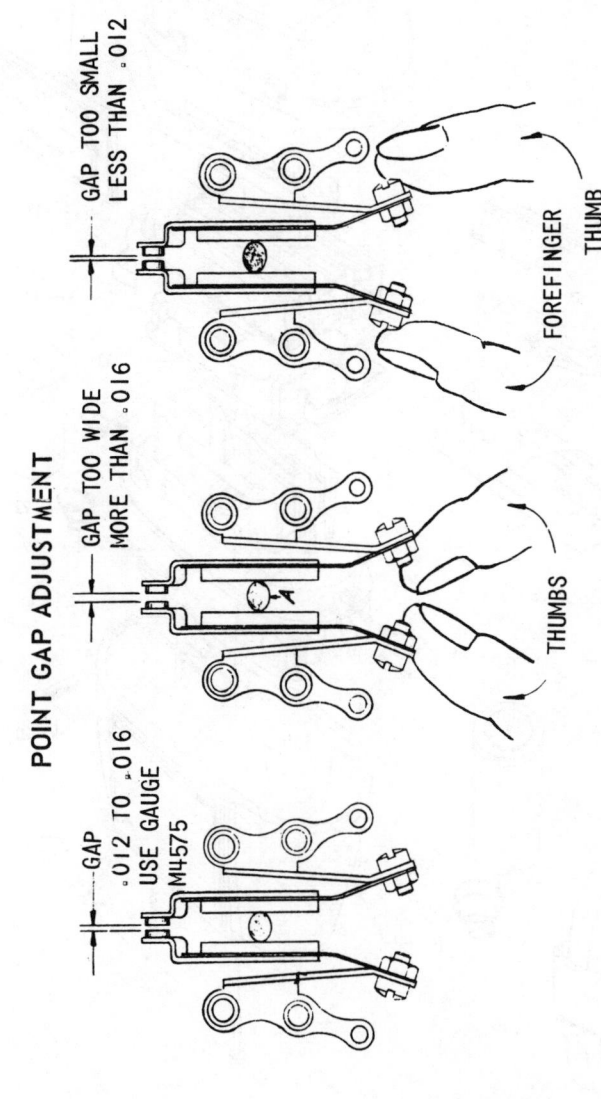

POINT GAP ADJUSTMENT

GAP .012 TO .016
USE GAUGE
M4575

GAP TOO WIDE
MORE THAN .016

GAP TOO SMALL
LESS THAN .012

FOREFINGER
THUMB

THUMBS

Fig. 10-9. Method of adjusting balance, tension, and point gaps on a Remington shaver motor.

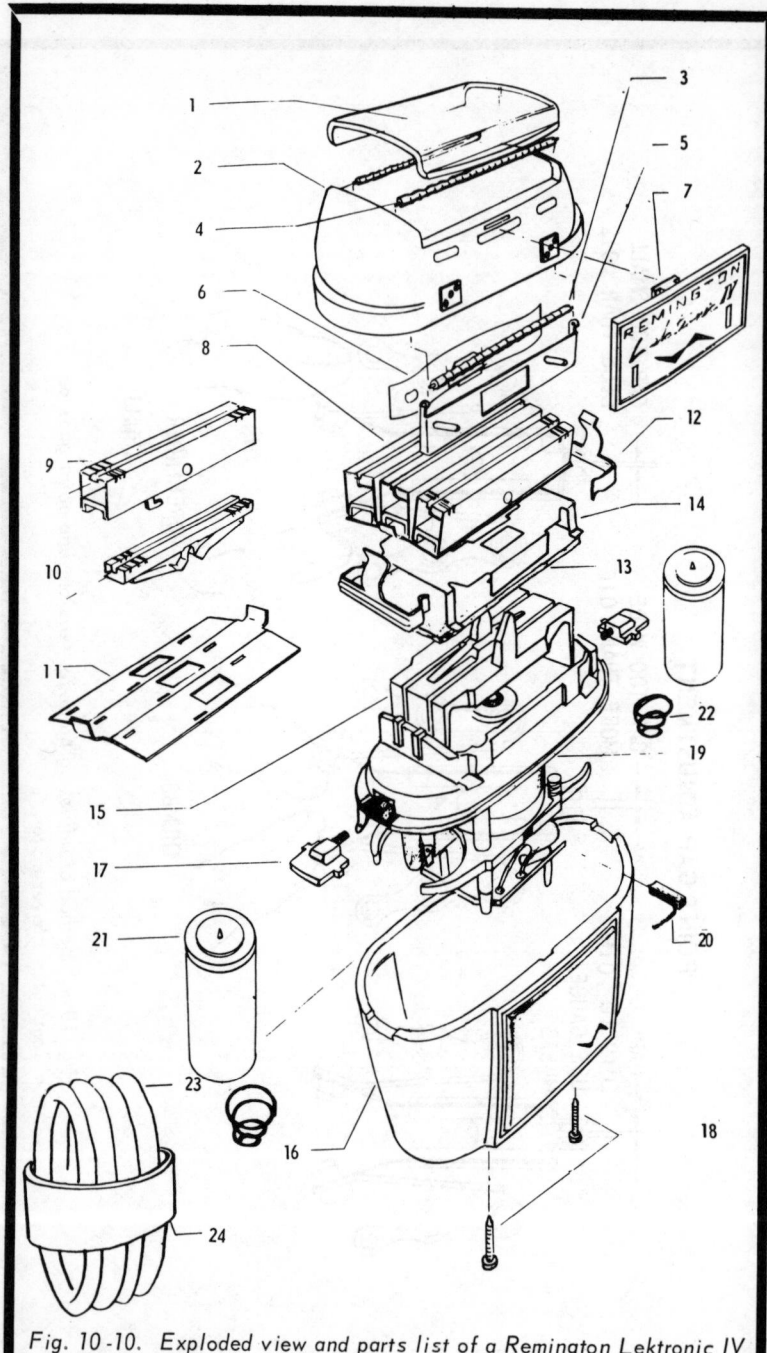

Fig. 10-10. Exploded view and parts list of a Remington Lektronic IV electric battery-operated shaver.

DESCRIPTION

1	Head guard
2	Hairpocket shell
3	Roller comb
4	Roller assembly-thin
5	Roller lift
6	Spring actuator
7	Actuator medallion
8	Head cutter & plate assembly
9	Head & cutter assembly
10	Inner cutter & spring assembly
11	Head plate
12	Head plate retainer clamp
13	Hairstopper
14	Oscillator cover
15	Oscillator, molded
16	Enclosure complete
17	Release button & spring assembly
18	Screws (enclosure & housing)
19	Motor assembly complete
20	Brush
21	Cell
22	Spring cell
23	Cord & ring assembly
24	Cord ring

	Loose motor screw	Tighten screws
Slow	Binding	Clear the cause of binding
	Defective bearing	Replace motor
	Loose wire	Tighten wire
	Poor solder connection	Resolder
	Dirty switch	Clean contacts
	Battery voltage low	Recharge battery
	Worn brushes	Replace brushes
	One cell defective	Replace cell
Poor shave	Oscillator low or worn	Replace or shim
	Weak inner cutter	Replace inner cutters
	Defective heads	Replace
	Motor slow	See above

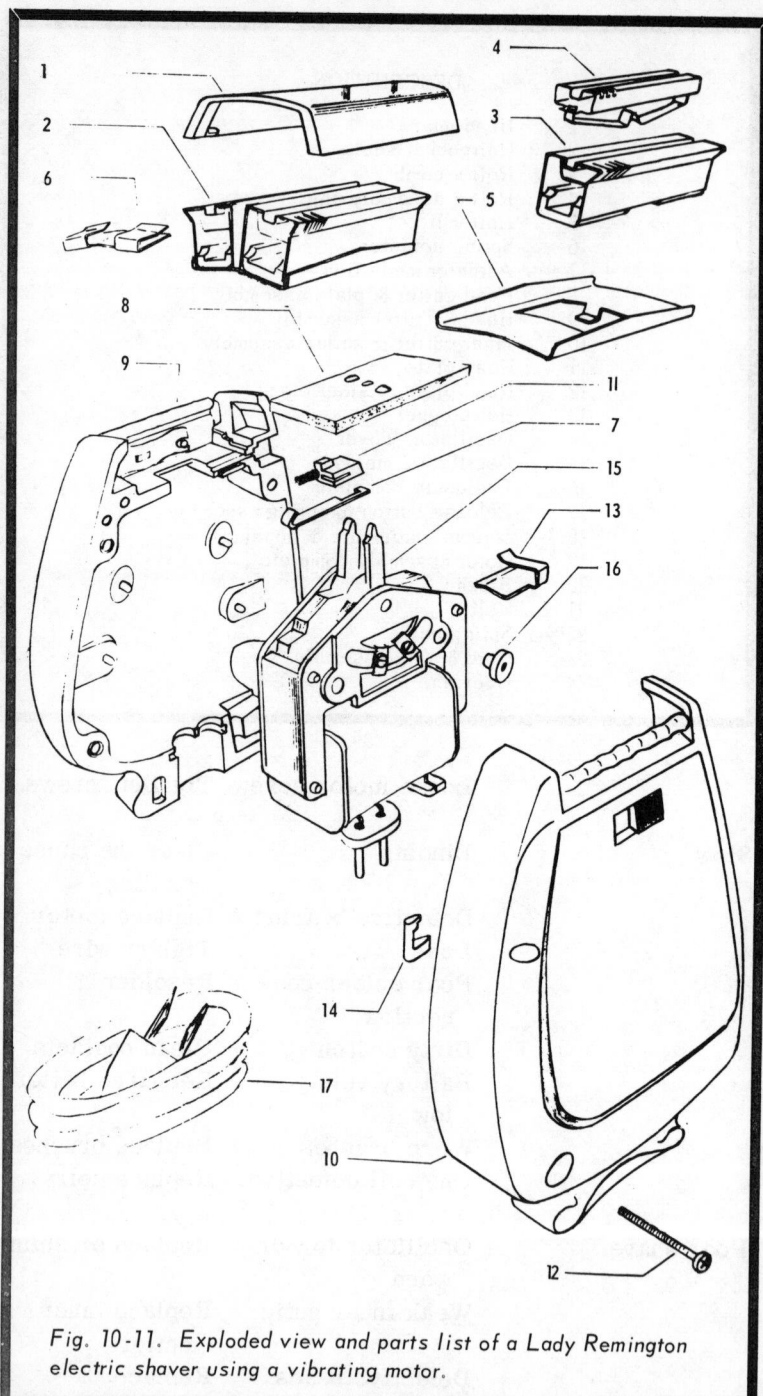

Fig. 10-11. Exploded view and parts list of a Lady Remington electric shaver using a vibrating motor.

DESCRIPTION

1. Head guard
2. Head, cutter & plate assembly
3. Head & cutter assembly
4. Inner cutter & spring assembly
5. Head plate
6. Clip head
7. Headplate latch
8. Hairstopper
9. Case base
10. Case cover
11. Release button & spring assembly
12. Screw cover
13. Latch clip
14. Arm switch
15. Motor assembly complete
16. Rubber mounts
17. Cord

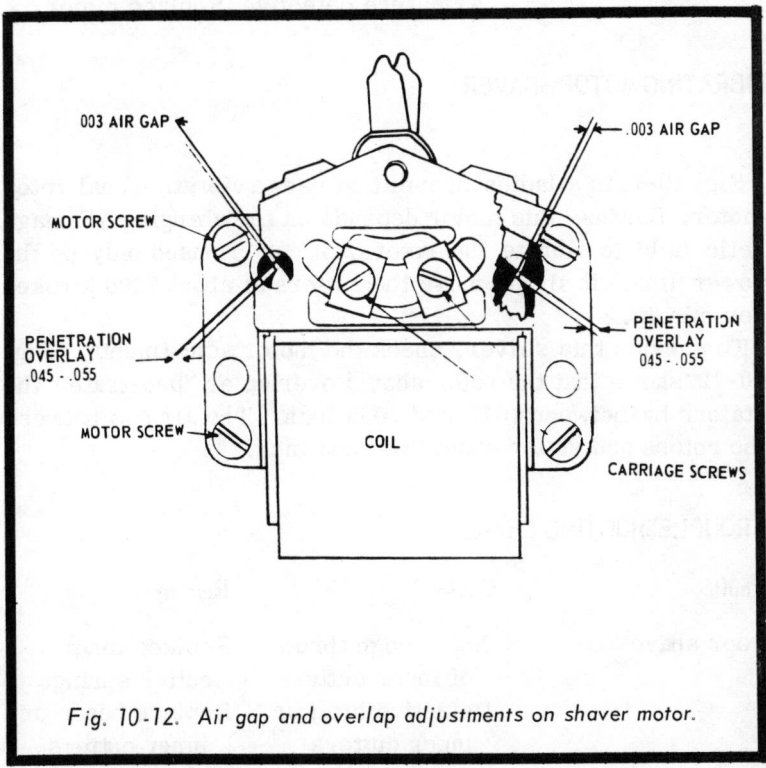

Fig. 10-12. Air gap and overlap adjustments on shaver motor.

Shaver runs slow	High shaver current	See below
	Defective cord	Replace cord
	Poor solder connections	Resolder
	Defective rectifier	Replace rectifier
Does not run on accessory transformer	Defective cord	Replace cord
	Open transformer winding	Replace charging stand
	Rectifier defective	Replace
	Blown fuse	Replace fuse-transformer
High current	Tight heads	Replace inner cutters
	Oscillator	Replace
	Bad bearing	Replace
	Bearing not seated properly	Replace motor
	Armature defective	Replace motor

VIBRATING MOTOR SHAVER

Fig. 10-11 is a ladies' shaver that uses a vibrating dual rotor motor. Because this motor depends on the changing AC magnetic field to vibrate the rotors, it can be used only on the power line. It should move the cutters at about 7200 strokes per minute.

To service this shaver, check the motor adjustments. Fig. 10-12 shows that the rotor should overlap or "penetrate" the stators by between .045 and .055 inch. The air gap between the rotors and stator should be .003 inch.

TROUBLESHOOTING CHART

Fault	Cause	Remedy
Poor shave	Not enough throw of inner cutters	Replace inner cutter springs
	Defective head or inner cutters	Replace heads or inner cutters

	Incorrect adjustment	Adjust motor
Does not run	Defective motor coil	Replace motor
	Defective switch	Replace motor
	Loose wire	Resolder
	Defective head or inner cutters	Replace heads or inner cutters
	Incorrect adjustment	Adjust motor
Does not run	Defective motor coil	Replace motor
	Defective switch	Replace motor
	Loose wire	Resolder
Draws high current (should draw 8 watts)	Incorrect adjustment	Readjust
	Shorted motor coil	Replace motor

183

CHAPTER 11

Appliance Tester

The portable tester pictured in Fig. 11-1 was built by the authors. You can build one like it, or one using the same ideas but, perhaps, in a different sort of box, or perhaps install it in the wall as shown in Fig. 11-2.

The tester will check any small appliance for open circuits, and for current consumption in the range of about 100 to 1200 watts. With the test leads plugged in, it will check between any two points for continuity, for shorts between the case and the electrical circuit, and the neon will indicate leakage (small current flow but not enough to light the 40-watt lamp).

The chime position is operated by a current relay in series with the line which trips the chime each time the current goes off and on. This feature is useful for checking appliances to see if the thermostat is working without having to continually watch it. The chime feautre is shown only on the wall model

Fig. 11-3 is a parts layout of the tester pictured in Fig. 11-1. All parts are available at almost any electrical supply house. The line cord and chassis are not shown in these pictures. The chassis can be purchased from a radio parts supply house. The shunt resistors, made of heater-element wire, are not shown but they can be seen in Fig. 11-4, which is also the physical layout used.

WHAT THE TESTER DOES AND HOW

Fig. 11-4 is a photograph of the underneath side of the finished tester. Fig. 11-5 is a wiring diagram so there is no mistaking the connections. Notice that the particular socket used for the neon lamp has a built-in 22,000-ohm 1/2-watt resistor. If you use a regular lamp socket you will have to install the 22K resistor in series with one lead of the socket. The type of neon lamp you use here is not too important. You

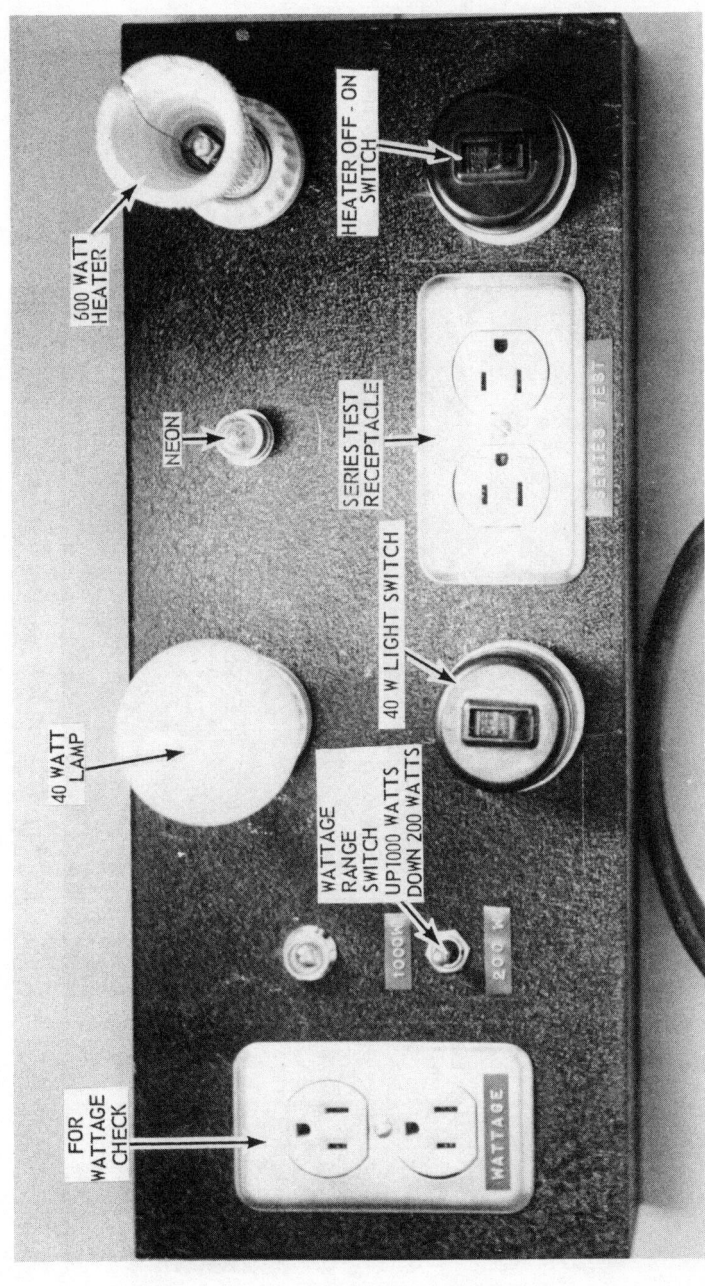

Fig. 11-1. This appliance tester is simple to build and quite useful. Test leads are plugged into the series test receptacle. For continuity tests, the lamp switch should be on and the heater switch off.

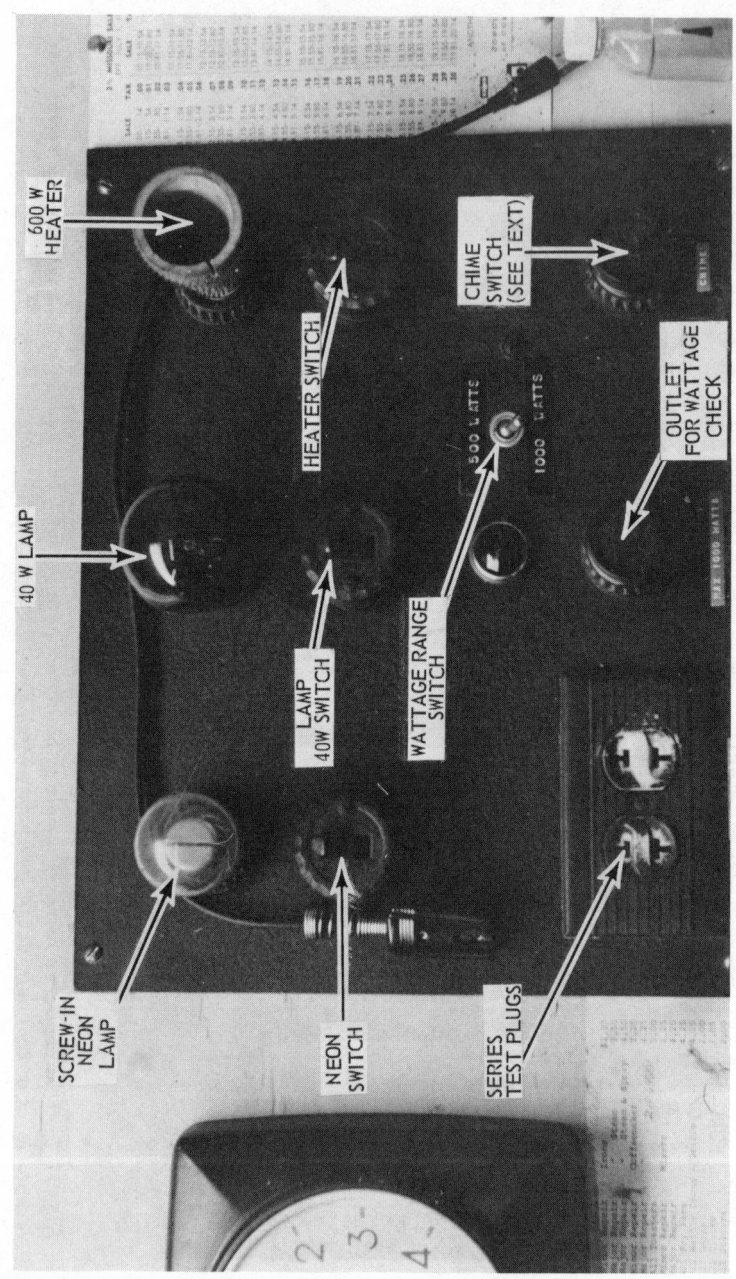

Fig. 11-2. A wall-mounted test panel.

may want to use the screw-in type as shown in Fig. 11-2. This and other type neons have the series resistor built into the lamp itself but the NE-51, NE-2, and some other small lamps

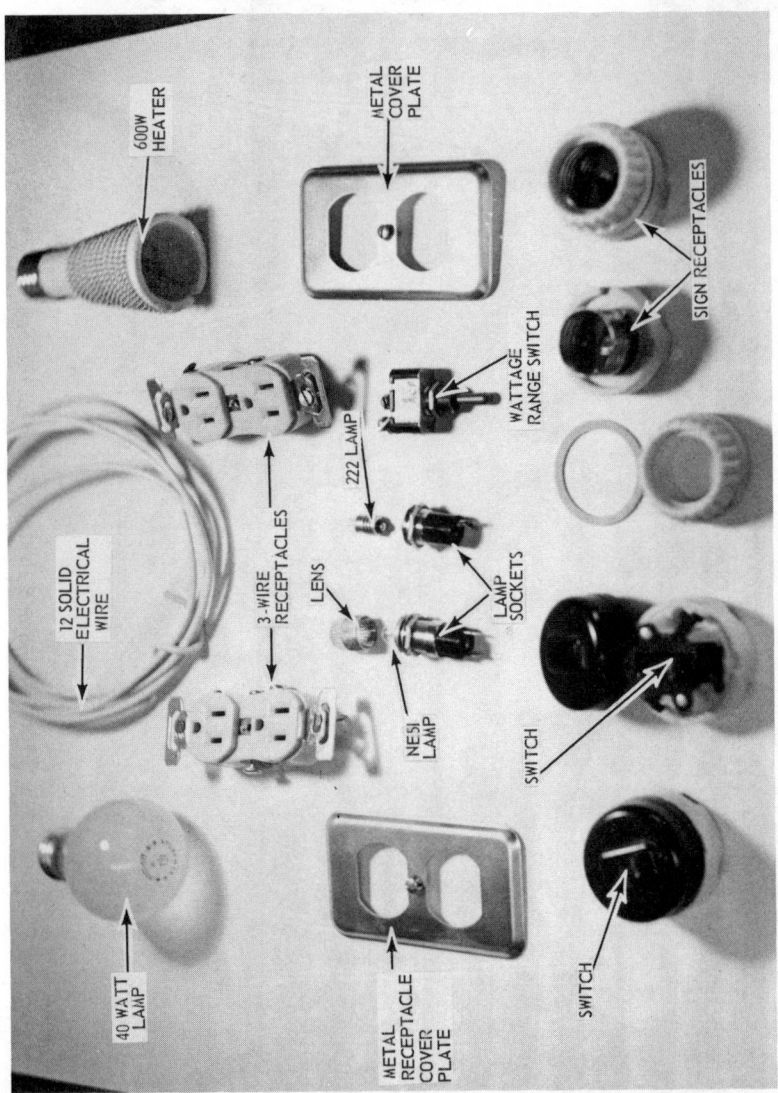

Fig. 11-3. Parts used in the appliance tester in Fig. 11-1. The AC cord, chassis, and nichrome wire shunts are not shown.

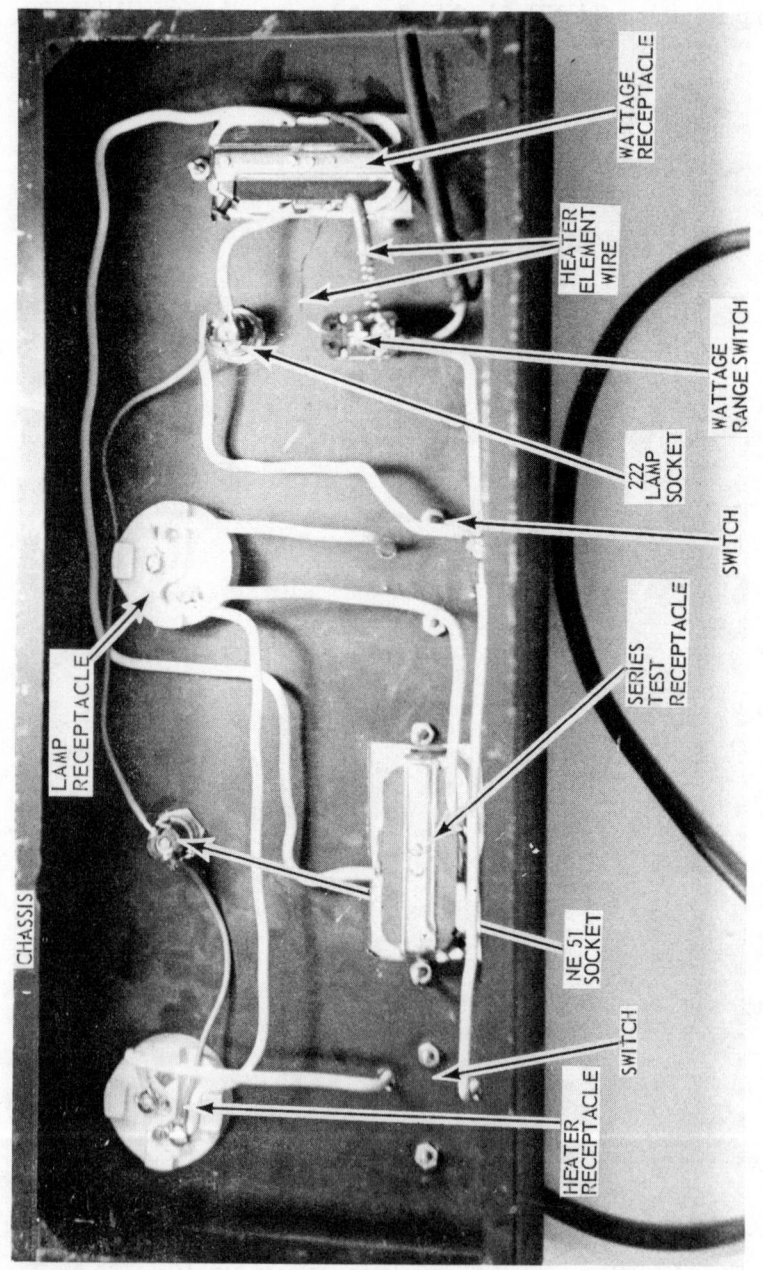

WATTAGE RECEPTACLE

HEATER ELEMENT WIRE

WATTAGE RANGE SWITCH

SWITCH

222 LAMP SOCKET

LAMP RECEPTACLE

SERIES TEST RECEPTACLE

NE 51 SOCKET

HEATER RECEPTACLE

SWITCH

CHASSIS

Fig. 11-4. Wiring and chassis layout for the appliance tester.

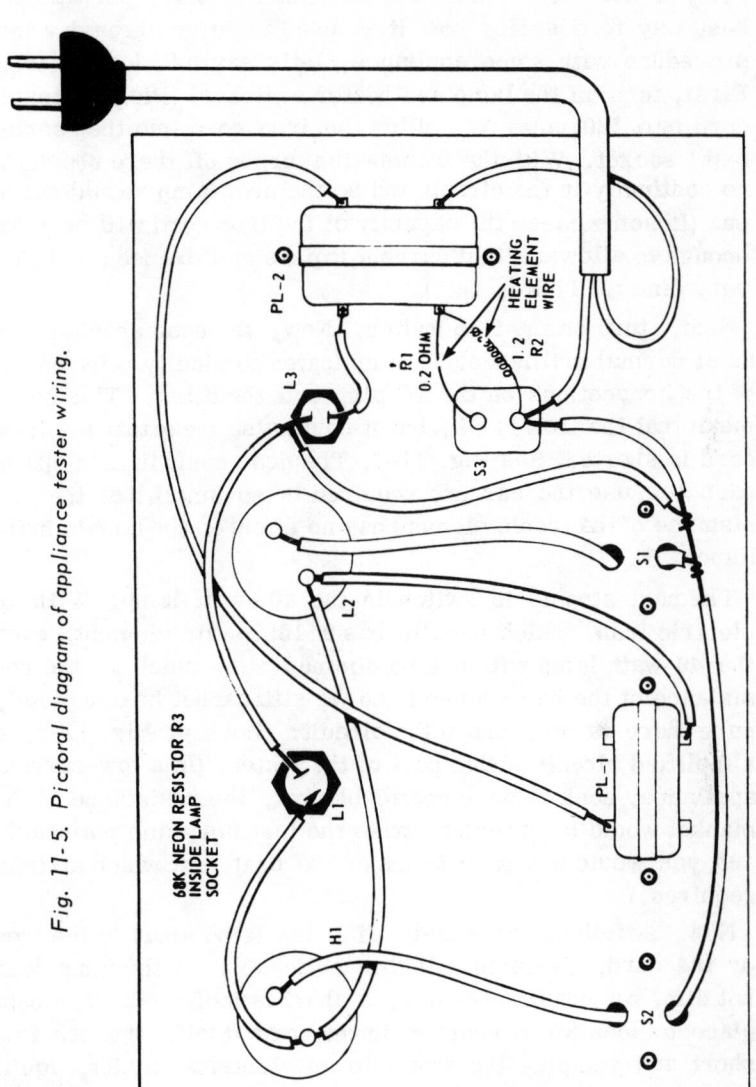

Fig. 11-5. Pictoral diagram of appliance tester wiring.

HEATING
ELEMENT
WIRE

PL-2

L3

R1
0.2 OHM

0.00000E-10

1. 2
R2

S3

S1

L2

68K NEON RESISTOR R3
INSIDE LAMP
SOCKET

L1

PL-1

H1

S2

do not. Fig. 11-6 is the schematic wiring diagram with the test probes connected to a male AC plug shown at the bottom. Their use will be discussed shortly.

If you have never used a tester such as this, perhaps the best way to describe how it is used is to go through a test procedure with some appliance, let's say an electric iron. First, turn off the lamp and heater switches. Plug the tester cord into 120 volts AC. Plug the iron cord into the "series test" socket. With the iron switch turned off there should be no continuity in the circuit and so the neon lamp should not be on. (In some cases the capacity of the iron cord will be great enough to allow a slight current to pass and the neon will glow very dimly. This is OK.)

Next, turn on the iron switch. Now, the neon should come on at normal brilliance. This indicates continuity between one of the connections on the AC plug and the other. This could mean that the iron is OK, but it could also mean that the iron cord is shorted. See Fig. 11-7. The neon could light in either case because the current required is so small that the resistance of the iron's element has no effect on the lamp's brilliance.

The next step is to switch in the 40-watt lamp. With an electric iron, which usually has a 1000-watt element, even the 40-watt lamp will not be dimmed very much by the resistance of the iron element, so we still cannot be completely sure there is no short in the circuit. Look at Fig. 11-8, a simplified circuit of this part of the tester. (In a low-current appliance, such as an electric blanket, the resistance of the blanket would be enough to make the test lamp dim noticeably and you would not have to make the next test which an iron requires.)

Now, switch on the heater. If there is no short in the iron or the cord, the lamp will dim noticeably. If the lamp does not dim, or just barely dims, a short is indicated. The best place to look for a short is in the cord itself. If there is a short and you plug the iron into an electrical outlet, you'll have fireworks until a fuse blows or a breaker in the mains is tripped. The tester lets you find out in advance whether such a short is present and if it is, you can use the test leads to find out just where.

Let's go back, now, and suppose that when we turned on the iron switch the neon lamp did not light—an indication of an

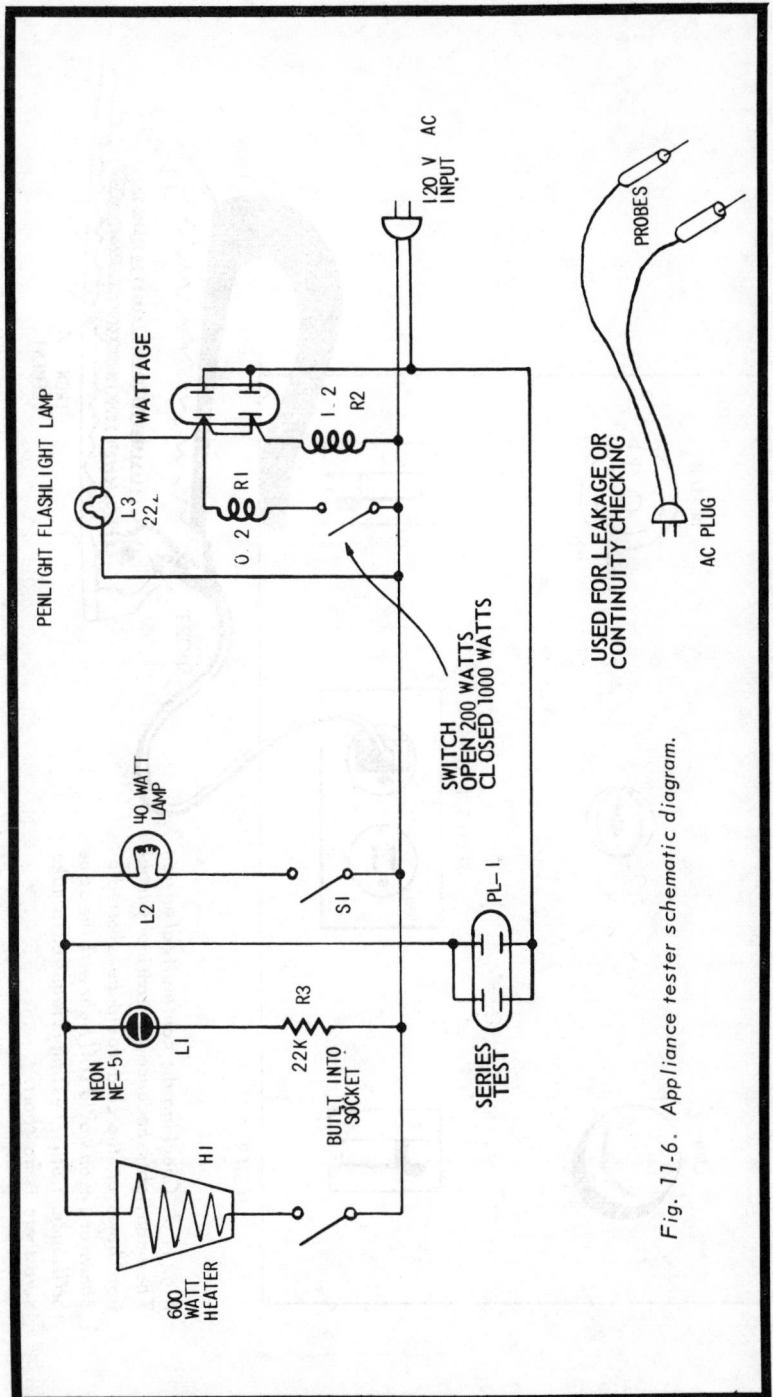

PENLIGHT FLASHLIGHT LAMP

WATTAGE

120 V AC INPUT

L3 22Ω

R2 I·2

R1 0·2

SWITCH
OPEN 200 WATTS
CLOSED 1000 WATTS

PROBES

AC PLUG

USED FOR LEAKAGE OR
CONTINUITY CHECKING

40 WATT LAMP

L2

S1

PL-1

SERIES TEST

NEON NE-51

L1

R3 22K

BUILT INTO SOCKET

H1

600 WATT HEATER

Fig. 11-6. Appliance tester schematic diagram.

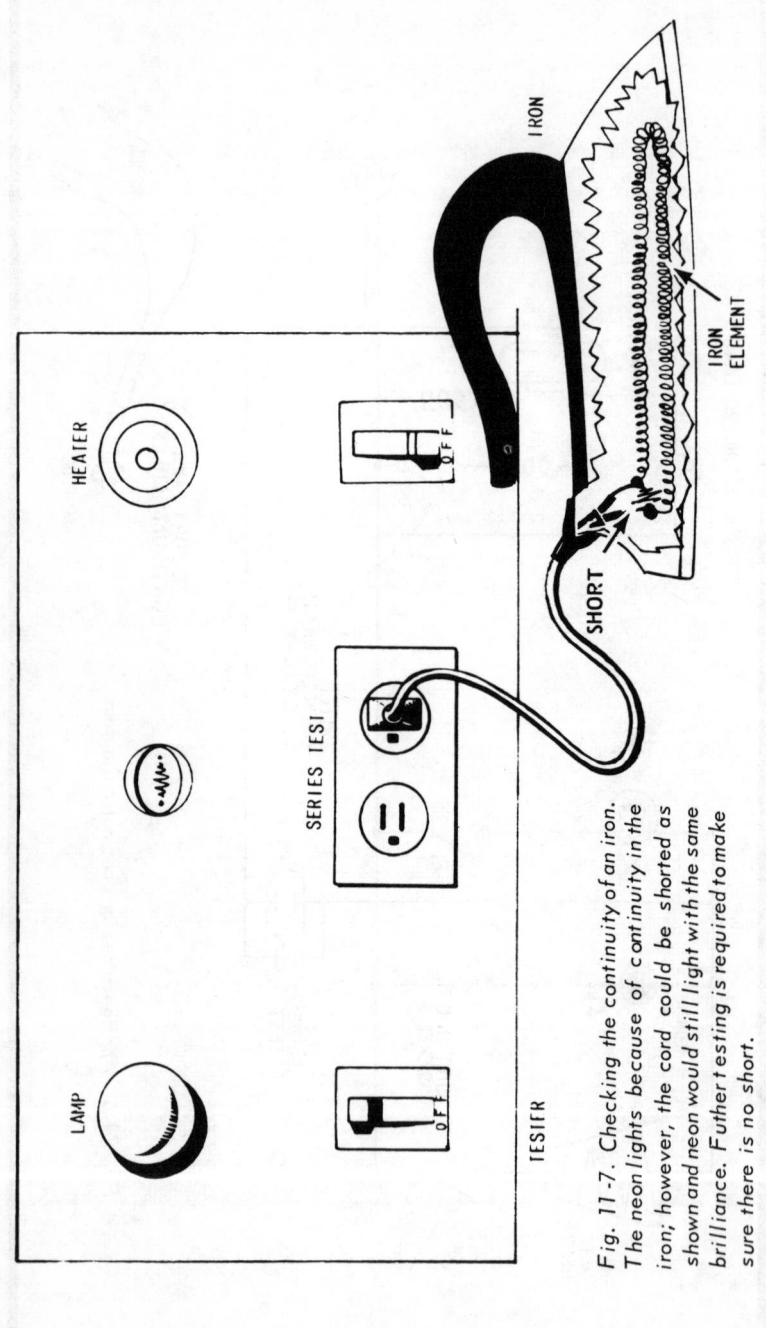

LAMP

SERIES TEST

HEATER

TESTER

IRON

IRON ELEMENT

SHORT

Fig. 11-7. Checking the continuity of an iron. The neon lights because of continuity in the iron; however, the cord could be shorted as shown and neon would still light with the same brilliance. Futher testing is required to make sure there is no short.

open circuit. In other words, no current is traveling through the iron and cord. The most common fault with any appliance is the cord. While watching the lamp, try wiggling and pulling on the line cord and see if you can get it to flicker on. If so you almost surely have a bad cord, in which case the entire cord should be replaced. (Repairing a line cord is seldom, if ever, a good practice, especially on an appliance that draws a lot of current such as an electric iron.) You can make the previous tests with only the neon lamp as an indicator; however, somewhat better results can be expected in most cases if you use the 40-watt lamp also. Starting out with the neon only and then switching in the 40-watt lamp is probably the best practice.

THE WATTAGE TEST

Once you have satisfied yourself that the appliance has a good cord, that it will switch on and off and there are no shorts, you are ready to make a "wattage" test. The wattage test on this tester is a relative indication. With the resistors used

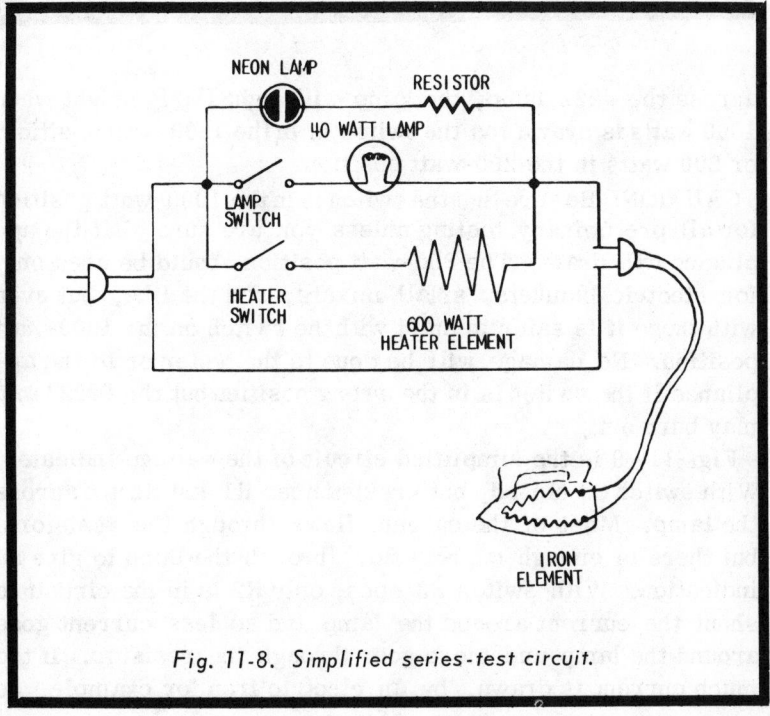

Fig. 11-8. Simplified series-test circuit.

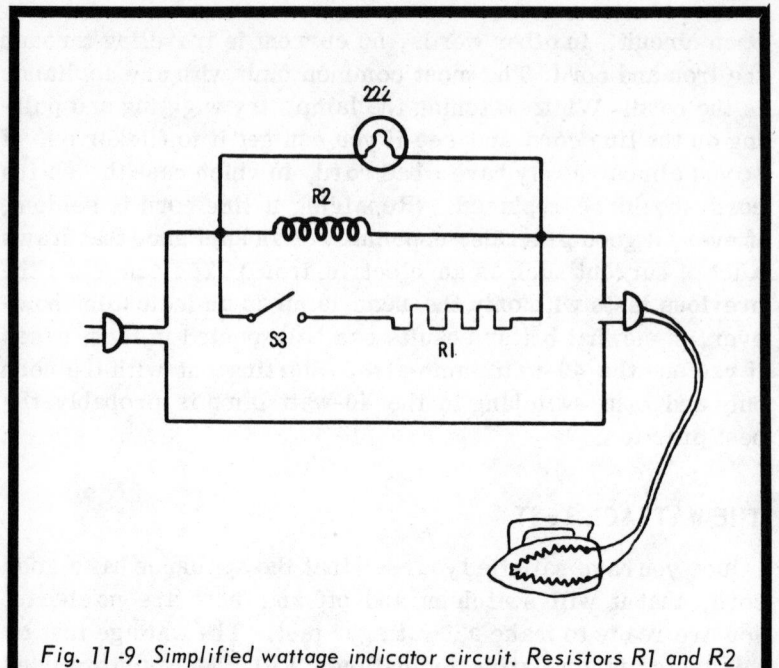

Fig. 11-9. Simplified wattage indicator circuit. Resistors R1 and R2 are made of short lengths of heating element wire.

across the #222 lamp, the lamp will light fairly bright when 1000 watts is drawn and the switch is in the 1000-watt position, or 200 watts in the 200-watt position.

CAUTION: Be sure that the switch is in the 1000-watt position for all preliminary testing unless you are sure what the appliance will draw. The 200-watt position should be used only for electric blankets, small mixers, and the like, but even with these it is safer to start with the switch on the 1000-watt position. No damage will be done to the tester or to the appliance if the switch is in the wrong position but the #222 lamp may burn out.

Fig. 11-9 is the simplified circuit of the wattage indicator. With switch S3 closed, both resistances R1 and R2 are across the lamp. Most of the current flows through the resistors, but there is enough current flow through the lamp to give an indication. With switch S3 open, only R2 is in the circuit to shunt the current around the lamp and so less current goes around the lamp and more goes through the resistor. If too much current is drawn, by an electric iron for example, so much current will go through the #222 lamp that it will likely burn out.

The #222 lamp is a penlight bulb which will light at almost full brilliance with only about 2.4 volts across it. This tester is designed to place about 1.7 volts across the lamp when the appliance is drawing 100 watts, so an appliance drawing about 1200 watts still will not burn out the lamp.

The shunt resistors (R1 and R2) were made from heating element wire which is available in spools of various lengths at appliance parts houses. The ohms-per-foot rating is normally specified so that you can get close to the correct ohmage by simply cutting to the right length; for example, if the specifications call for 20 ohms per foot, then the 1.2-ohm resistor would be about 3/4 inches. These measurements are made with the wire in coils. Cut off the 3/4 inch and uncoil a small amount from each end for the connecting leads.

The 0.2-ohm resistor (R1) may have to be found by trial and error if an ohmmeter is not available. Try a piece of uncoiled heater element wire about 2 inches long. If the lamp is not bright enough when an electric iron is plugged in to the wattage test socket, increase the length of the resistance wire, and vice versa.

USING THE TEST PROBES

The test probes can be plugged into the "series test" and used to make continuity checks on line cords, thermostats, heating elements, motor windings, etc. Fig. 11-10 shows a continuity check being made on an appliance cord and plug. For the continuity check use only the neon lamp and the 40-watt lamp. The neon lamp alone can be used but it will sometimes be misleading since it will show an indication even though the circuit has such high resistance that it cannot work properly.

The other purpose, and this is an important function, is to find whether there is any leakage between the electrical circuits and the metal parts of the appliance. An appliance with leakage to the metal case could be the cause of a lethal electrical shock for the user, so be sure you always make the leakage test.

Fig. 11-11 shows the leakage test being performed on an electric drill. Measure from both sides of the plug and make sure that the measurement is made with the switch in both the on and off positions.

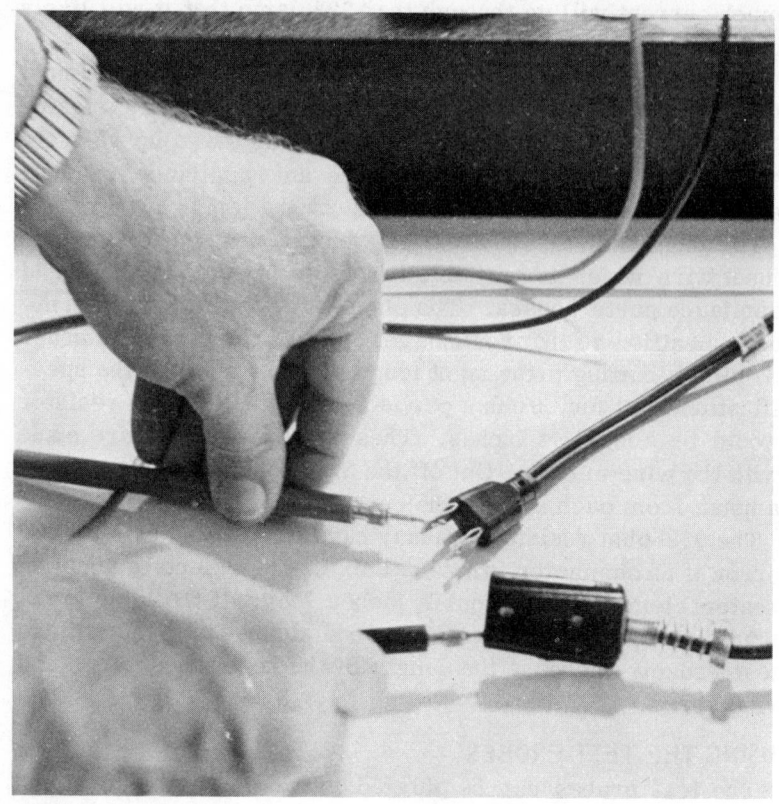

Fig. 11-10. Continuity test for cord and plug, using test probes.

Special Note: The above is often called checking for "grounds." This doesn't mean an actual earth ground; it means that the parts which are normally neutral (ground) should not in any way be connected to the electrical circuit. Leakage in electrical appliances can be extremely dangerous since one side of the power line is attached to an earth ground. If the side opposite from ground in some appliance should be leaking internally to the case, and you were holding that appliance while standing on the ground, or touching something else which was grounded such as a water pipe or faucet, you could receive a fatal electrical shock. This is why checking for grounds is so important.

For several years three-wire plugs have been used on all metal appliances. The third wire is a ground wire attached

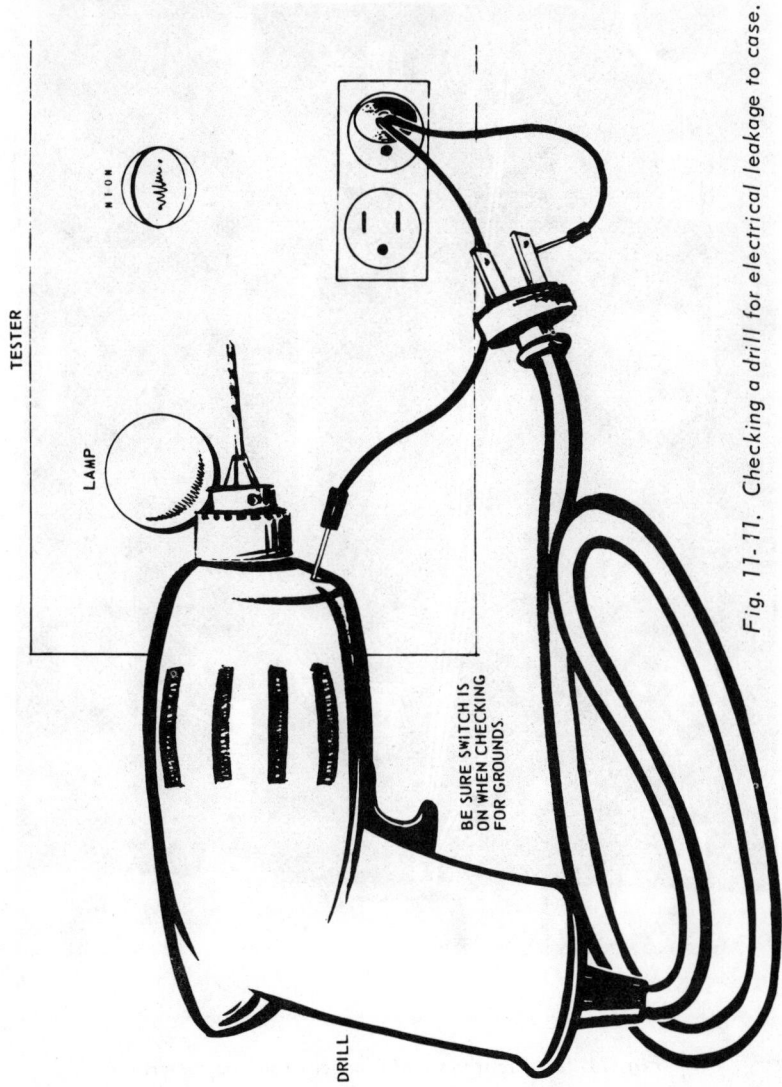

TESTER

NEON

LAMP

DRILL

BE SURE SWITCH IS
ON WHEN CHECKING
FOR GROUNDS.

Fig. 11-11. Checking a drill for electrical leakage to case.

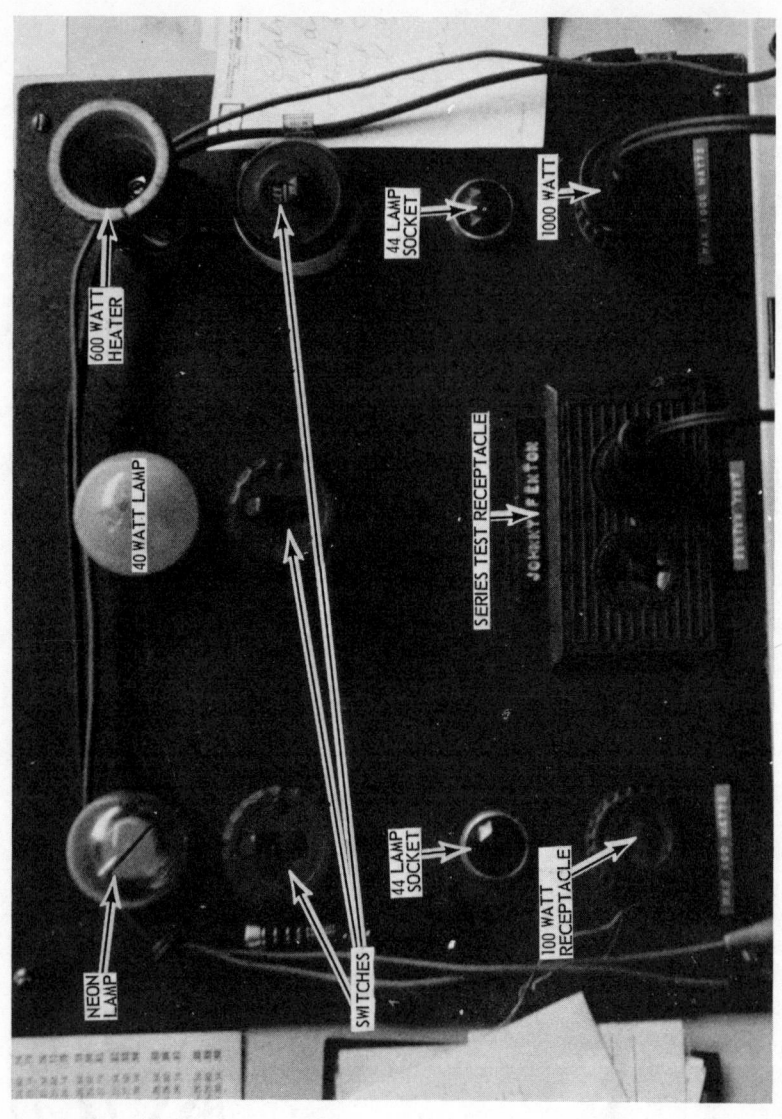

Fig. 11-12. Front view of a bench-mounted tester.

to the power line ground and the appliance housing or frame. Any short that occurs between the case and ground simply flows through the third wire rather than through you. Unfortunately, many homes are not wired for three-wire plugs so adapters are used instead, or the round third pin is simply broken off. So be sure you check for grounds every time you test an appliance. You could be saving someone's life!

The neon lamp is ideal for leakage checking since it will glow even though the leakage is not yet too severe. A very soft glow in the neon is sometimes due to the capacity of the cord and plug. It can be ignored when an appliance is plugged in, but normally you should not even see a soft glow when using the test leads for leakage tests, although there is a slight possibility with certain appliances. You should always investigate any sort of leakage to the case. Sometimes the neon will light because of moisture captured inside an appliance, such as a steam iron, coffee maker, and the like. Disassemble the appliance and you will likely find the telltale evidence of moisture. Clean thoroughly and dry out under a heat lamp or some other method and again check for leakage.

Like all testers, this device will become more valuable to you as you use it. You will soon have a good idea of just what to expect from it and from the various types of appliances you service. You'll find that a tester of this sort will save you many times its cost as a result of time saved in diagnosis alone, and it also is excellent for making operating and final tests. For example, with the tester on "wattage" it is easy to see when an iron or percolator thermostat turns off and on by just watching lamp L3. This tester, along with some sort of temperature tester, is about all the equipment that you absolutely need to start an appliance service business.

BENCH-MOUNTED TESTER

Fig. 11-12 is the front view of a tester that has been used every day for several years in a small appliance shop. This unit is similar to the one described, except that instead of switching the wattage ranges separate plugs are used. A switch is also provided to turn off the neon lamp. The back view is shown in Fig. 11-13 and the wiring diagram in Fig. 11-14.

The #44 lamps used in this unit are bayonet base (push-in turn) types. They light with full brilliance with about six to eight volts across them, so at full brightness there is about a 6- to 8-volt drop from the line to the appliance. In other words, the appliance being tested will receive six to eight

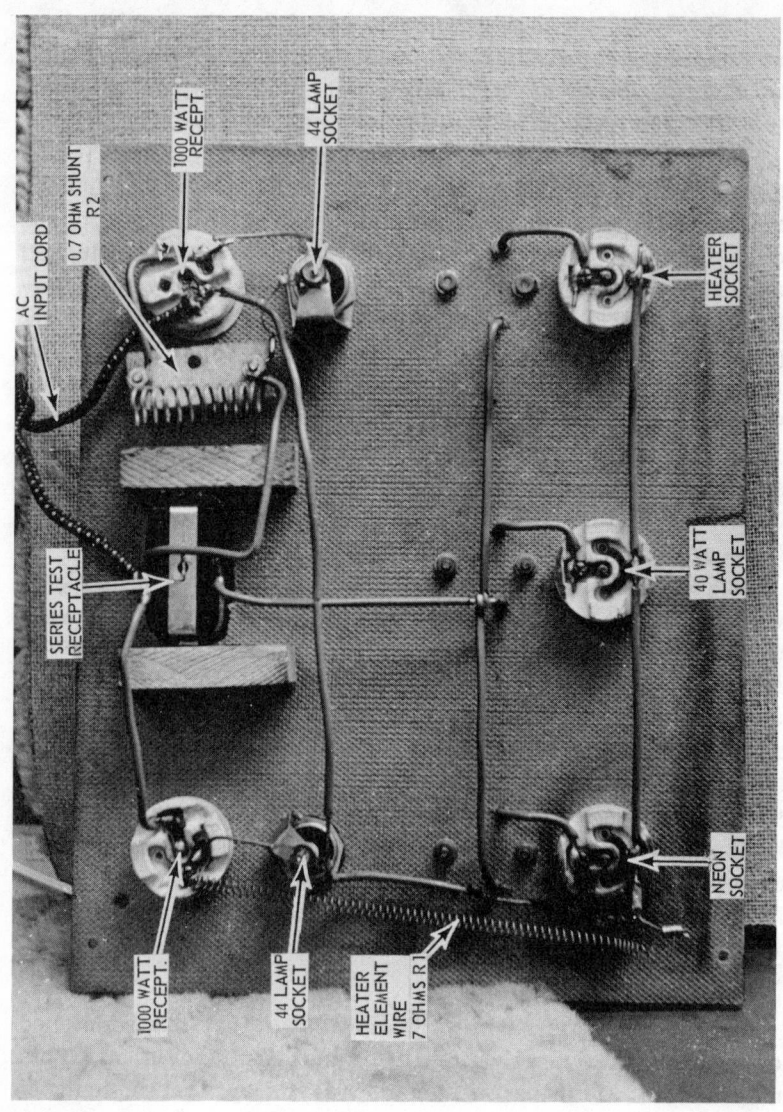

AC INPUT CORD

0.7 OHM SHUNT R2

1000 WATT RECEPT.

44 LAMP SOCKET

HEATER SOCKET

SERIES TEST RECEPTACLE

40 WATT LAMP SOCKET

NEON SOCKET

1000 WATT RECEPT.

44 LAMP SOCKET

HEATER ELEMENT WIRE 7 OHMS R1

Fig. 11-13. Rear view of a bench-mounted tester.

volts less than it would if plugged directly into the line. This normally is no problem, however. The #222 lamp used in the previously described tester could also be used here by changing the shunts to a lower value; in this case the drop from the line voltage would generally be less than 2.5 volts.

The screw-in type neon lamp is not as readily available as it once was; however, it can still be purchased at many electrical or electronic supply houses. Some other type of neon will work OK, too; simply purchase a mating socket for it that will mount suitably. Again, a word of caution: A neon lamp must have a resistor in series with it or it will burn out almost immediately. Some neon lamps have the resistor built into the lamp itself; some sockets have the resistor built-in, and sometimes you will have to mount the resistor in the circuit externally. Be sure to check the specifications when you purchase the lamp and socket. The size of the resistor is not too critical, but it should not be less than about 22,000 ohms. Larger resistance values will work but the lamp will not be as bright.

When mounting any parts which might sometimes overheat, such as the shunts around the lamps, keep them away from any

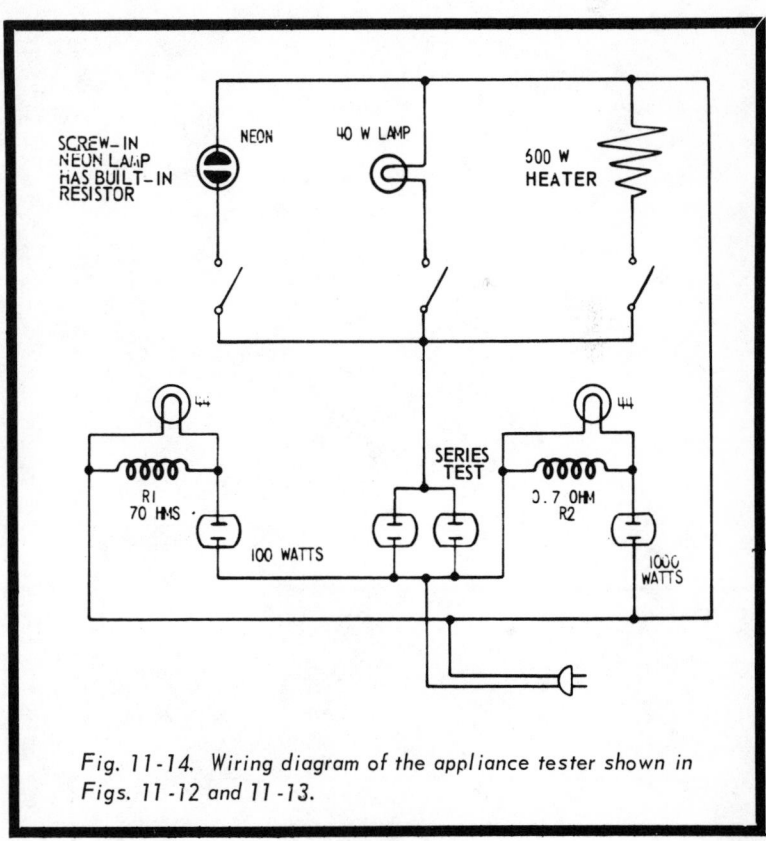

Fig. 11-14. Wiring diagram of the appliance tester shown in Figs. 11-12 and 11-13.

flammable material. Any current - carrying component will overheat if the appliance shorts while under test, in which case the lamp would burn out, but the resistor would probably be able to take the excess current for a short while. So unless you want to risk heat damage, be careful where you place heat-producing parts.

APPENDIX 1

Appliance Parts and
Accessory Supplies

APPENDIX 1

APPLIANCE PARTS AND ACCESSORY SUPPLIES

ALABAMA

Appliance Parts and Supply Co.
805 Church St.
Mobile, Ala. 36602

Jones-McLeod Appliance Service
1616-7th Ave.
Birmingham, Ala. 35203

Nolin-McInnis, Inc.
211 Commerce St.
Montgomery, Ala. 36103

Washer & Refrigerator Supply Co.
718 2nd Ave. North
Birmingham, Ala. 35201

ARIZONA

Appliance Dealer Supply Co.
Box 2017
19-21 Central
Phoenix, Ariz. 85001

Elliott Electric Appliance Service
1424 E. McDowell Rd.
Phoenix, Ariz. 85006

ARKANSAS

Bronley's Appliance Service
1217 Broadway
Little Rock, Ark. 72202

CALIFORNIA

California Electric Service Inc.
832 S. Alvarado St.
Los Angeles, Cal. 90057

Branches:

1407 E. 4th St.
Long Beach, Cal. 90812

2582 E. Colorado St.
Pasadena, Cal. 91107

697 W. 2nd St.
San Bernardino, Cal. 92410

14753 Oxnard
Van Nuys, Cal. 91401

650 S. 2nd Ave.
Covina, Cal. 91722

California Electric Service Inc.
55 Potrero
San Francisco, Cal. 94130

Branches:

1329 E. 12th
Oakland, Cal. 94606

783 The Alameda
San Jose, Cal. 95126

1821 Q. St.
Sacramento, Cal. 95814

117 S. Bristol
Santa Ana, Cal. 92703

Electrical Appliance Service Co.
1434 Howard St.
San Francisco, Cal. 84603

Western States Service
5707 Santa Monica Blvd.
Los Angeles, Cal. 90038

CONNECTICUT

Electric Appliance Parts
55 Grove St.
Waterbury, Conn. 06710

FLORIDA

Miami Appliance Parts, Inc.
6921 N.W. 7th Ave.
Miami, Fla. 33150

Moore's Appliance Parts
2907 47th Ave.
St. Petersburg, Fla. 33714

Southern Electric Co.
510 N. Parramore Ave.
Orlando, Fla. 32801

White's Inc.
405-7 Park St.
Jacksonville, Fla. 33021

GEORGIA

Harris Appliance Parts
227 W. Dougherty St.
Athens, Ga. 30601

Wodall Appliance Service Co.
1024 Monroe Dr. N.E.
Atlanta, Ga. 30306

HAWAII

Appliance Parts Co. of Hawaii
1550 Kalani St.
Honolulu, Hawaii 96814

ILLINOIS

Brand Service
2850 Belvidere,
Waukegan, Ill. 69985

Branches:

732 W. Main St.
Peoria, Ill. 61606

5618 Dempster
Morton Grove, Ill. 60053

117 W. Grand Ave.
Chicago, Ill. 60610

Brand Service (BRANCHES)

6741 W. Cermak,
Berwyn, Ill. 60402

Midwest Appliance Service Center
907 S. Western Ave.
Chicago, Ill. 60612

C.E. Sundberg Co.
615 W. 79th St.
Chicago, Ill. 60620

Trangle Electric Co.
224 E. Case
Joliet, Ill. 60432

Waage Manufacturing Co.
632 North Albany Ave.
Chicago, Ill. 60612
(Not a direct parts distributor but a
publisher of a buyer's guide of small
appliance parts used by other dis-
tributors.)

INDIANA

Aid TV Sales & Service
4145 N. College Ave.
Indianapolis, Ind. 46025

IOWA

General Parts and Supply Co.
202 4th St.
Sioux City, Iowa 51101

KANSAS

Alan Appliance Service, Inc.
339 North Main
Wichita, Kans. 67200

KENTUCKY

Beyers Appliance Repair
131 S. 3rd
Paducah, Ky. 42001

Irvin Martin Electric Co.
1280 Bardstown Rd.
Louisville, Ky. 40204

Triple A Washer Parts, Inc.
130 Indiana Ave.
Lexington, Ky. 40501

LOUISIANA

Naugle's Appliance Service
Center
Davenport, La. 52801

Royal Supply Co.
710 Baronne St.
New Orleans, La. 70110

MAINE

Portland Appliance Service
Center
252 Oxford St.
Portland, Me. 04101

MARYLAND

Electric Motor Repair
700 E. 25th St.
Baltimore, Md. 21218

MASSACHUSETTS

Appliance Service and Parts, Inc.
23 South St.
Boston, Mass. 02111

MICHIGAN

McNichols Appliance Service
13725 W. McNichols Rd.
Detroit, Mich. 48235

MINNESOTA

General Parts and Supply Co.
54-56 Glenwood Ave.
Minneapolis, Minn. 55403

General Parts & Supply Co.
593 Fairview North
St. Paul, Minn. 55104

W.A. George Appliance Parts
332 E. 4th St.
Duluth, Minn. 55810

MISSISSIPPI

May & Jackson
838 W. Capital
Jackson, Miss. 39205

MISSOURI

Kaemmerlen Electric
2728 Locust St.
St. Louis, Mo. 63103

Mar-Beck Appliance Service
1722 Oak St.
Kansas City, Mo. 64108

Marcone Appliance Parts Center
2320 Pine St.
St. Louis, Mo. 63101

MONTANA

General Appliance Co.
3107 1st Ave. North
Billings, Mont. 59101

NEBRASKA

J.L. Tucker Co.
19th and Cuning St.
Omaha, Nebr. 68102

NEVADA

Electrical Appliance Parts
611 North
Reno, Nev. 89502

NEW JERSEY

Electra-Craft Appliance Co.
250 Halsey St.
Newark, N.J. 07102

NEW YORK

Authorized Appliance Repair
Service
95 Lake Ave.
Tuckahoe, N.Y. 10707

Electra-Craft Appliance Co.
348 W. 42nd St.
New York, N.Y. 10036

Fortunato Electric Co.
808 Butternut Road
Syracuse, N.Y. 13208

NORTH CAROLINA

Authorized Appliance Service
1030 Tuckaseegee R.
Charlotte, N.C. 28208

Branches:

104 Glenwood Ave.
Raleigh, N.C. 27267

1919 Marshall St.
Winston Salem, N.C. 27105

D & L Appliance Parts
708 E. Mint St.
Charlotte, N.C. 27601

Moore & Stewart, Inc.
316 E. Franklin St.
Gastonia, N.C. 28052

NORTH DAKOTA

General Parts and Supply Co.
1706 Main Ave.
Fargo, N.D. 58102

OHIO

Layer Electric Service
431 E. 5th St.
Dayton, Ohio 45402

Marietta Radio & TV Supply, Inc.
1028 Greene St.
Marietta, Ohio 45750

W.W. Neff Co.
581 Marshall St.
Youngstown, Ohio 44502

Bruck Radio and Hobby Shop
Williams Ave.
Hamilton, Ohio 45015

Golden Rule Electric Co.
808 Elm Street
Cincinnati, Ohio 45202

OREGON

Bressie Electric Co.
902 S.W. 3rd St.
Portland, Ore. 97204

W.L. May Co., Inc.
215 N.W. Park Ave.
Portland, Ore. 97209

PENNSYLVANIA

The Arnold Company
1427 Vine St.
Philadelphia, Pa. 19102

Ferri Electric Service
7221 Church Ave.
Pittsburgh, Pa. 15102

McKeesport Appliance Parts Co.
Jenny Lind & Shaw Ave.
McKeesport, Pa. 15132

SOUTH CAROLINA

Authorized Appliance Service
1811 Taylor St.
Columbia, S.C. 29505

Authorized Appliance Service
237 W. Washington St.
Greenville, S.C. 29601

Dorchester Electric Service
3573 Dorchester Ave.
Charleston Hts., S.C. 29405

G & E Service Center, Inc.
852 S. Pine St.
Spartanburg, S.C. 29302

Harris Appliance Parts
Box 611
Anderson, S.C. 29621

Harris Appliance Parts
423 Lurens Road
Greenville, S.C. 29601

TENNESEE

Camp Electric Co.
647 Madison St. Ave.
Memphis, Tenn. 38103

Starr Company
1214 Demonbreun St.
Nashville, Tenn. 37203

TEXAS

Dawson Appliance Service
1905 Calder St.
Beaumont, Texas 77701

George R. Lee
1411 Main St.
Huston, Texas 77008

J. Luther Whatley
Box 26073
Dallas, Texas 75226

UTAH

Appliance Service Center
607 South 2nd E. St.
Salt Lake City, U. 84111

Appliance Parts and Service Co.
400 9th Ave.
Seattle, Wash. 98109

WASHINGTON

Appliance Parts and Service Co.
917 Mullen
Spokane, Wash. 99201

WEST VIRGINIA

Bluefield Distributing Co.
Appliance Serivce
250 Bluefield Ave.
Bluefield, W. Va. 14701

WISCONSIN

Power Equipment Co.
2373 S. KK Ave.
Milwaukee, Wisc. 53207

Electric Repair Co.
504 N. 9th St.
Reading, Pa. 19604

APPENDIX 2

National Appliance
Service Association

APPENDIX II

NATIONAL APPLIANCE SERVICE ASSOCIATION

Following is a list of the members of the "National Appliance Service Association" for 1969. Each company services appliances, and all stock and sell parts. For further information, contact the National Appliance Service Association, 1525 Broadway, Kansas City, Missouri 64108.

ALABAMA

Jones-McLeod Appliance Service
1616 7th Ave. N
Birmingham, Ala. 35203

Moskowitz Electric & Supply Co.
1709 N. 3rd Ave.
Birmingham, Ala. 35302

ARIZONA

Elliott Elec. Appliance Service
1424 E. McDowell Rd.
Phoenix, Ariz. 85010

CALIFORNIA

California Electric Service, Inc.
650 S. Second Ave.
Covina, Cal. 91722

California Electric Service Inc.
832 S. Alvarado
Los Angeles, Cal. 90057

California Electric Service, Inc.
1407 East 4th
Long Beach, Cal. 90812

California Electric Service, Inc.
1139 E. 12th St.
Oakland, Cal. 94606

California Electric Service, Inc.
2594 E. Colorado
Pasadena, Cal. 91107

California Electric Service, Inc.
1821 "Q" St.
Sacramento, Cal. 95814

California Electric Service, Inc.
14753 Oxnard
Van Nuys, Cal. 91401

Western States Serv. Co.
5707 Santa Monica Blvd.
Los Angeles, Cal. 90038

COLORADO

Midwest Appl. Service Center
1124-26 Santa Fe Drive
Denver, Colo. 80214

CONNECTICUT

Benco Appliance Service
281 Fairfield Ave.
Bridgeport, Conn. 06603

Utility Electric Service
10 Jefferson St.
Hartford, Conn. 06106

Hartford Element Appl. Ser. Co.
1500 Albany
Hartford, Conn. 06112

FLORIDA

Southern Elec. Co.
510 N. Pallamore
Orlando, Fla. 32801

David's Appliance Servicenter
1611 San Marco Blvd.
Jacksonville, Fla. 32204

White's Inc.
403 Park St.
Jacksonville, Fla. 32204

East Coast Appl. Service
4030 N. Miami Ave.
Miami, Fla. 33137

GEORGIA

Woodall Electric Service Co.
1024 Monroe Drive, N.E.
Atlanta, Ga. 30306

Flournoy Appl. Serv. Center
1100 15th St.
Columbus, Ga. 31901

Hagins Appl. Service Center
3 W. Victory Dr.
Savannah, Ga. 31405

HAWAII

Craft Center, Ltd.
517 Ahui St.
Honolulu, Hawaii 96813

ILLINOIS

G.W. Murphy Inc.
1200 E. State St.
Geneva, Ill. 60134

Master Electric Service
835 W. Washington Blvd.
Chicago, Ill. 60607

Midwest Elec. Appl. Serv.
907 Western Ave.
Chicago, Ill. 60612

B & M Electric
813 E. Adams
Springfield, Ill. 62701

Brand Service Center
2850 Belvidere
Waukega, Ill. 60085

IOWA

Gen. Parts & Supply Co.
800 Sixth St.
Sioux City, Iowa 51101

KANSAS

Alan Appl. Service
339 North Main
Wichita, Kans. 67202

KENTUCKY

Maury's Appliance Service
962 S. 3rd
Louisville, Ky. 40202

Irvin Martin Electric Co.
1280 Bardstown Road
Louisville, Ky. 40204

LOUISIANA

Royal Supply Co.
710 Baronne St.
New Orleans, La. 70113

MAINE

Portland Appl. Servicenter
252 Oxford St.
Portland, Maine 04101

MARYLAND

Electric Motor Repair Co.
700 E. 25th St.
Baltimore, Md. 21218

Don Reedy Appl. Service
8039 13th St.
Silver Spring, Md. 20910

MASSACHUSETTS

Appliance Serv. & Parts, Inc.
23 South St.
Boston, Mass. 02111

Boston Appl. Service Center
40-42 Middlesex St.
Lowell, Mass. 01852

Suburban Appl. Servicenter
124 Galen St.
Watertown, Mass. 02172

MICHIGAN

McNichols Elec. Service
13725 W. McNichols
Detroit, Michigan 48235

Van Howe Company
100 Ionia, S.W.
Grand Rapids, Mich. 49502

Vac. Cleaner Center
2046 S. Division
Grand Rapids, Mich. 49507

MINNESOTA

Mister Fixit's Service Center
1608 W. Superior St.
Duluth, Minn. 55806

General Parts & Supply Co.
66 Glenwood Ave. N.
Minneapolis, Minn. 55403

MISSISSIPPI

Camp Elec. Appl. Service, Inc.
431 S. West St.
Jackson, Miss. 39205

MISSOURI

Mar-Beck Appl. Serv. Co.
1722 Oak
Kansas City, Mo. 64108

Kaemmerlen Electric Co.
2728 Locust
St. Louis, Mo. 63103

MONTANA

General Appliance Co.
2045 Grand
Billings, Mont. 59102

NEBRASKA

J. L. Tucker Company
1823 Cumings
Omaha, Neb. 68102

NEW JERSEY

Electra Craft, Inc.
250 Halsey St.
Newark, N.J. 07102

Boulevard Appliance Service
25-27 Hoyt St.
Neward, N.J. 07103

Boulevard Appliance Service
57 Van Houten St.
Peterson, N.J. 07505

NEW MEXICO

Willmore Corporation
5505 Silver Ave., S.E.
Albuquerque, N.M. 87108

NEW YORK

Able Appl. Service Center
88 Livingston St.
Brooklyn, N.Y. 11201

Electra-Craft Brooklyn Corp.
150 Flatbush Ave.
Brooklyn, N.Y. 14209

Shields Bros.
1410 Main St.
Buffalo, N.Y. 14209

Electra Craft Queens Corp.
92-28 160th St.
Jamaica, N.Y. 11433

Devon Service, Inc.
870 Broadway
New York, N.Y. 10003

Electra-Craft, Inc.
348 West 42nd
New York, N.Y. 10036

General TV & Appl. Repair
333 W. Fayette
Syracuse, N.Y. 13202

NORTH CAROLINA

Authorized Appl. Serv. Center
1020 Tuckaseegee Road
Charlotte, N.C. 28208

Authorized Appliance Servicenter
2009 Chapel Hill Road
Durham, N.C. 27707

Authorized Appl. Servicecenter
315 W. Hargett St.
Raleigh, N.C. 27603

Authorized Appl. Serv. Center
952 Brookstown Ave.
Winston-Salem, N.C. 27101

OHIO

Demers Authorized Service
300 E. Long St.
Columbus, Ohio 43215

Golden Rule Electric, Inc.
808 Elm St.
Cincinnati, Ohio 45202

Electric Sweeper Service Co.
2034 Euclid Ave.
Cleveland, Ohio 44115

Layer Electric Service
431 E. 5th St.
Dayton, Ohio 45402

H.A. Dennis Co.
752 Western Avenue
Toledo, Ohio 43609

OKLAHOMA

Appliance Service Center
1714 E. 15th
Tulsa, Oklahoma 74104

OREGON

Bressie Electric Co.
902 S.W. Third Ave.
Portland, Ore. 97204

Hamilton Electric, Inc.
232 W. Fifth Ave.
Eugene, Ore. 97401

PENNSYLVANIA

Jay's Electronics
101 S. 19th St.
Harrisburg, Pa. 17104

K & D. Service Co.
528 S. Cameron St.
Harrisburg, Pa. 17104

The Arnold Company
1427 Vine St.
Philadelphia, Pa. 19102

Ferry Electric Service Co.
7221 Church Ave.
Pittsburgh, Pa. 15202

Quick Service Elec. Co.
300 Stanwix
Pittsburgh, Pa. 15222

Electric Repair Co.
504 S. 9th St.
Reading, Pa. 19604

RHODE ISLAND

Marshall Elec. Co.
681 Westminister St.
Providence, R.I. 02903

SOUTH CAROLINA

Dorchester Electric Service
3575 Dorchester
Charleston Heights, S.C. 29405

Authorized Appliance Servicecenter
1811 Taylor St.
Columbia, S.C. 29201

Authorized Appl. Servicenter
237 W. Washington St.
Greenville, S.C. 29602

TENNESSEE

Bynum Elect. Co.
716 Cherry St.
Chattanooga, Tenn. 37402

Light Electric Co.
109 E. 6th St.
Chattanooga, Tenn. 37402

Factory Service Centers
209 14th Avenue N.
Nashville, Tenn. 37203

Camp Electric Company
647 Madison Ave.
Memphis, Tenn. 38103

TEXAS

Appliance Service Co.
P.O. Box 5150
Corpus Christi, Texas 78405

Pearsol's
3127 Main St.
Dallas, Texas 75226

Arnold Electric Company
1827 W. Alabama Ave.
Houston, Texas 77006

George Lee
1411 Main Street
Houston, Texas 77002

Minter's
2135 19th St.
Lubbock, Texas 79401

UTAH

Kolby Services
57 Richards St.
Salt Lake City, Utah 84101

Appliance Service Center
615 S. 2nd East
Salt Lake City, Utah 84111

VIRGINIA

Natl. Elec. Appl. Service
2820 W. Cary
Richmond, Va. 23221

WASHINGTON

Appliance Parts & Service Co.
400 9th Ave. N.
Seattle, Wash. 98109

Spokane Appliance Repair
W. 45 2nd Ave.
Spokane, Wash. 99210

Ajax Electric Co.
747 Fawcett
Tacoma, Wash. 98402

WISCONSIN

Power Equipment Co.
2373 S. Kinnickinnic Ave.
Milwaukee, Wisc. 53207

C.W. Schneck Inc.
1333 N. 12th St.
Milwaukee, Wis. 53205

INDEX